C000110853

MY FAVOURITE CHOCOLATE COOKBOOK

My
Favourite
CHOCOLATE
COOKBOOK

Mary Norwak

CASSELL

For

Jonathan   *Andrew*   *Henry*
Matthew   *Michael*   *Bertie*
and Joseph

who are current and
future chocolate-lovers

A CASSELL BOOK
First published
1993 by Cassell
Villiers House
41/47 Strand
London
WC2N 5JE

Copyright © 1993 Mary Norwak

Designer: Richard Carr

Photographer: Laurie Evans

Jacket Photographer: Sue Atkinson

All rights reserved. No part of this book may be reproduced or
transmitted in any form or by any means, electronic or mechanical,
including photocopying, recording or any information storage and
retrieval system, without prior permission in writing from the
copyright holder and Publisher.

Distributed in the United States
by Sterling Publishing Co., Inc.
387 Park Avenue South, New York, New York 10016-8810

Distributed in Australia
by Capricorn Link (Australia) Pty Ltd
P.O. Box 665, Lane Cove, NSW 2066

British Library Cataloguing-in-Publication Data
A catalogue record for this book is available from the
British Library

ISBN 0-304-34336-6

Typeset by Litho Link Ltd, Welshpool, Powys, Wales
Printed and bound in Great Britain by Bath Press

CONTENTS

KEY TO RECIPES

★ = Easy
★★ = Fairly easy
★★★ = Needs practice

1

ALL ABOUT CHOCOLATE

WHAT IS THIS CHOCOLATE PASSION, this consuming desire for a simple food which makes strong men weak, and sensible women useless? Why do civilised human beings crave chocolate and risk their money and their weight for sensuous gratification?

Perhaps the answer is that chocolate is not as simple as we think. It is a complex mixture of flavours and textures which provides comfort and nourishment, energy and satisfaction, and that magical quality which lifts the spirit. We eat it for pleasure, tinged with a naughty guilt. We feel wicked as we crunch and munch and wrap our tongues round creamy fillings. We pamper ourselves with the sheer luxury of chocolate, reward our efforts with its comfort, and share its pleasure with our loving friends. Chocolate is handy and accessible, quick and easy to eat, and horribly addictive.

Nobody need feel alone with a chocolate addiction, for sales of chocolate continue to rise. In 1993, over £2 billion was spent on it, supporting an enormous industry employing about 70,000 people who produce the stuff we love. Confectionery is the single largest packaged food market, above milk, bread, tea and coffee, and every Briton gets through an average of 20lb (9kg) of the stuff each year.

Chocolate has come a long way since its beginnings in Central and South America. The Aztecs and Mayans used the cacao bean for a drink consumed at such ceremonial functions as weddings and funerals, and the beans were offered to the gods. In Central America the beans were used as currency, and it was probably here that Columbus discovered them and took them back to Spain where nobody showed interest. Cortés landed in Mexico in 1519, was welcomed by Montezuma the great ruler, and first encountered the royal drink of chocolate or *xocoatl*.

The drink was bitter, but highly spiced and very frothy, and much prized for its energy-giving qualities. Cortés slaughtered the Emperor and destroyed his civilisation, but his soldiers took Mexican seeds of the cocoa trees on their subsequent journey. They planted cocoa trees in Africa on their way home, setting up an industry dominated by the Spaniards as chocolate was slowly introduced to Europe. The Spaniards sweetened their chocolate drinks with sugar and flavoured them with vanilla, bringing chocolate a little nearer to today's luxury.

When the drink first came to Britain, it was introduced through the chocolate house where men gathered in London's Bishopsgate in 1657. For many years chocolate was known only as a drink, made exactly as it had been in earlier times. Lumps of chocolate were broken and soaked in a little warm water until soft. More water was added and the mixture simmered for two hours, then left to get completely cold. Fat settled on the top, which was taken off and discarded. The residual chocolate was then warmed with milk for the final drink, and it was recommended that it should be well beaten when warming so that the drink would thicken. Throughout the eighteenth and nineteenth centuries, doctors recommended chocolate as a restorative for energy and also as a soothing balm for the nerves. At the French court Madame du Barry served cups of reviving chocolate to her suitors, and it is said that Casanova preferred it to champagne.

Perhaps, surprisingly, chocolate took years to develop from a popular drink. In 1728, the first English factory was opened for processing the cocoa bean, but the first solid eating chocolate was not produced until 1847 by Messrs Fry & Sons. Development came more swiftly as the Dutch, Swiss and British worked on new ideas. The earlier and awkward chocolate 'nibs' were converted into simple cocoa liquids and powders; milk chocolate was introduced by the Swiss in 1875, who a few years later perfected the art of making very smooth eating chocolate. By 1900 chocolate was beginning to replace the earlier favourites such as toffee, formerly made in cottage kitchens. Milton Hershey developed his chocolate interests in America, saying 'chocolate is a permanent thing'. His prescience resulted in an American boom in the new confectionery, and today chocoholics gather in Hershey, Pennsylvania, for an annual chocolate festival of five days' indulgence and chocolate bingeing. In France, Switzerland and Britain new confectionery lines were developed after Jules Séchaud produced the first filled chocolate.

Curiously, nobody thought of chocolate or cocoa as a culinary ingredient. It is useless to search in nineteenth-century cookery books for recipes, because chocolate puddings and cakes simply did not exist. The confectioners and *pâtissiers* of middle Europe were the first to develop the luscious chocolate gâteaux and mousses we know today, to serve in their coffee houses with lashings of whipped cream. The taste for chocolate was given another boost as chefs began to finish meals with chocolate delicacies, later taken up by private cooks as the basic ingredients of plain chocolate and cocoa were promoted by manufacturers. Now chocolate is everywhere, easily purchased and easily used, and we may all share the sinful indulgence of the Austrian coffee house.

Chocolate is deliciously indescribable, a mouthwatering experience with a dark, melting, velvety richness. It is for the sybarite who has no wish for Puritan restraint, for the hedonist who doesn't care, for the gourmand with an all-consuming passion.

This book is not for the faint-hearted. It is for the enthusiast who cannot imagine life without chocolate. It is for the cook who always produces something chocolatey among her dinner-party puddings; for the comfort-lover who will order hot chocolate rather than coffee for that mid-morning pick-you-up; for the grown-up schoolboy who always chooses the chocolate cake; for the professed savoury-tooth who can never resist a piece of chocolate cake.

The recipes are the ultimate of their kind – the gooiest cake, the most syrupy sauce, the most sensational fudge, the almost unbelievable roulade and the deepest, fluffiest chocolate soufflé. While the recipes are seductive, they are mostly very simple to achieve. As a chocoholic, one knows that no true believer can spend hours on a complicated recipe because the most important ingredient will be eaten before it reaches the mixing bowl.

2

PRACTICAL MATTERS:
Types of Chocolate and Chocolate Preparation

W HEN PREPARING RECIPES it is important to use the best possible chocolate. If the raw material is of high quality, the resulting dish will be very special. Inferior ingredients produce inferior dishes.

There are many different types of chocolate which may be used, made from cocoa butter, chocolate liquor and sugar, and sometimes milk solids. Their value in cooking depends on the proportion of these essential constituents. In order to be called chocolate, not cake covering, the product must have a minimum of 30 per cent cocoa solids. Some chocolate contains as much as 45 per cent cocoa solids, and this may be checked by reading the packet information. European chocolate tends to be slightly more bitter than British, usually with a more brittle texture. Inevitably, good chocolate is expensive, but well worth spending money on for its depth of flavour, and the cost is usually offset by the relative cheapness of the other ingredients in a chocolate recipe.

Types of Chocolate

Plain Chocolate

This is made from cocoa butter, chocolate liquor, vegetable fats and sugar. It has a good, strong flavour and dark colour, and may be labelled 'bitter', 'fondant' or 'dessert'.

Unsweetened (Bitter) Chocolate

This chocolate is imported and very expensive, and therefore difficult to find. It is totally unsweetened, and it is necessary to adjust the sugar in a recipe to taste. It is sometimes known as 'baker's chocolate'.

Milk Chocolate

Milk chocolate contains cocoa butter, chocolate liquor, vegetable fats and sugar, with milk solids replacing some of the chocolate liquor. It is paler in colour than plain chocolate and has less chocolate flavour, so it is rarely used in recipes.

White Chocolate

Made from cocoa butter, milk and sugar, white chocolate is without colour as it contains no chocolate liquor. It is very sweet with only a light chocolate flavour, and is not easy to melt successfully. It is used in one or two recipes to give contrasting colour, but the flavour is so minimal that it is scarcely worth using.

Couverture

This chocolate for the professional cook contains a very high proportion of cocoa butter. It has a rich flavour, a high sheen and a brittle texture. It has to be tempered by repeated heating and cooling so that it melts successfully, and it is widely used by confectioners.

Chocolate Chips

Small dots of plain or milk chocolate are useful as they melt quickly, and they may be used without melting to provide the chocolate accent in biscuits, cakes and ice creams.

Cake Covering

Often described as 'cooking chocolate', these chocolate-flavoured blocks are made with less than the required minimum of cocoa solids and do not qualify as chocolate. They contain added vegetable and/or coconut oil and do not have a strong flavour. They are, however, cheaper than pure chocolate and have the advantages of melting very easily and of being easy to handle. The chocolate purist will shun a chocolate substitute, but cake covering may be used if cost is more important than flavour.

Cocoa Powder

Unsweetened cocoa powder gives a strong flavour and is useful for baking. The flavour is released by adding a little very hot liquid to the cocoa powder before it is added to a recipe. European cocoa powder has a subtly different flavour, but may be used in the same way.

Drinking Chocolate Powder

This has a subtle chocolate flavour, but it is very sweet, pale and milky and is used only occasionally in baking when other ingredients can be adjusted accordingly.

Chocolate Preparation

Chocolate is not difficult to use, but attention to detail is important as problems can occur which may make dishes unsightly. Particular care is needed in heating and setting chocolate.

Storage

Chocolate should be stored in a cool, dry place, and plain chocolate will store well for a year without loss of colour or flavour (milk chocolate is best used within six months). Chocolate may be stored in a refrigerator or freezer but should be well-wrapped as it tends to pick up other flavours. It may acquire a greyish-white film or bloom because cocoa butter or sugar crystals may rise to the surface after exposure to differing temperatures or excessive moisture. This does not affect the flavour and will disappear after melting.

Chopping and Grating

To speed melting, or to provide small pieces for recipes, chocolate may be chopped or grated. Chocolate may be chopped with a sharp knife or broken up in a food processor. A vegetable peeler or a grater may be used for grating. Be sure that the chocolate is firm and at room temperature before being prepared or it may melt in the hands and be difficult to handle.

Melting

Chocolate is very sensitive to heat and must be melted with great care. If melted on its own, it must be kept completely dry and no hotter than 110°F/44°C. Chocolate should not be melted on its own over direct heat or it will stiffen up and then cannot be reconstituted. There are three ways of melting chocolate successfully.

1. Break the chocolate into small pieces and put them into a bowl or top of a double saucepan. Bring a pan of water to the boil and put the bowl or top saucepan in place, so that the hot water does not touch the bottom of the upper container. Remove from the source of heat so that steam or water does not splash into the chocolate, which will make it seize up and discolour. Stir the chocolate as it melts so that it becomes very smooth. If necessary, reheat the water and replace the bowl or top pan to finish the melting process.

2. Break the chocolate into small pieces and warm in a very low oven (such as the warming oven of a range). The temperature should be no more than 225°F/110°C/Gas ¼.

3. Break the chocolate into small pieces and put into a microwave-proof bowl. Heat for 1–2 minutes in a microwave oven, checking with the manufacturer's instructions if possible. The chocolate will retain its shape but will become soft and smooth when stirred. Remember that foods retain heat and continue warming through after being microwaved, so be careful not to overheat the chocolate.

Do not cover a bowl in which chocolate is being heated, or condensation will form droplets of moisture which will fall back into the chocolate and ruin it.

Liquid may be mixed with chocolate before melting, so that the ingredients are heated together. 1–2 tablespoonsful of water, strong coffee or a spirit such as rum or brandy may be added in this way. If fat is to be added, butter or oil may be stirred in when the chocolate has melted.

Tempering

This is a method of melting chocolate used by professional confectioners to give a perfect finish to their work. The chocolate used has a high proportion of cocoa butter and is repeatedly heated and cooled so that it finally melts and sets perfectly. This is not necessary with the eating chocolate generally used which has a lower proportion of cocoa butter.

Setting

Chocolate sets best at a fairly cool temperature of 65°F/18°C, but will set at a room temperature of about 72°F/22°C. At this higher temperature, setting will take a little longer, but the chocolate will retain its shape and shine. Do not try to set chocolate in a refrigerator as it develops a white bloom; choose a reasonably cool, dry place instead.

Dipping

If using chocolate to coat sweets or fruit, be sure to melt it in a wide bowl for easy use. Cool the chocolate to 92–110°F/33–44°C so that it is still liquid but will adhere to the object being dipped. For a smooth, shiny finish, add 1 tablespoon vegetable oil to 6oz (175g) chocolate.

Use a cocktail stick, skewer, fondue fork or confectionery fork to dip the items concerned; allow excess chocolate to drip off, and push off the dipped object with another skewer or cocktail stick. If items are placed on foil or baking parchment, they can be easily removed.

Moulding

Chocolate may be moulded in plastic, metal or paper moulds. They should be completely dry and clean so that the chocolate will not stick and crack. Polish plastic or metal moulds with a piece of kitchen paper so that the chocolate remains very shiny, and do not handle finished chocolates with the fingers as they mark quickly.

Substitution of Chocolate

If a small quantity of chocolate is needed for a recipe and is not available, it is possible to substitute 3 tablespoons cocoa powder, ½oz (15g) butter and 1 tablespoon sugar for each 1oz (25g) chocolate.

Making Mistakes

When chocolate is overheated, or when cold liquid such as water or cream is added to hot chocolate, it will 'seize' and become cloudy, dull and lumpy. It will usually have to be discarded, but it may be possible to rectify the situation by stirring in a little vegetable oil.

3

COMPLEMENTARY FLAVOURS

THERE IS A GREAT ART in improving and enhancing a dish by complementary flavouring. Cookery experts like to keep their flavouring secrets closely guarded, because knowing 'what goes with what' lifts their cooking out of the common rut. Complementary flavourings are meant to accent a dish and give it greater depth and complexity without smothering its basic flavour. Skilful use of these flavourings improves dishes beyond all recognition, and the cook's palate needs to be finely tuned to get the combinations right and to avoid the bad restaurant disaster of hare-and-apricots-wrapped-in-spinach-in-redcurrant-sauce-served-with-a-chocolate-biscuit type. Quantities of complementary flavourings are difficult to prescribe; successful results can only be gauged by the fineness of the creator's palate, and by the people who eat the finished dish.

Chocolate is a magnificent basic ingredient, strongly flavoured and stamping its own character on any dish which includes it. Even so, a chocolate recipe can be flat, dull and cloying without a hint of liqueur, a touch of spice or a surprise of fruit. The following list gives guidance on those flavourings which are the finest complements to chocolate.

Nuts

The soft melting smoothness of chocolate is greatly enhanced by the crunch of nuts, particularly *walnuts*, *hazelnuts*, *almonds*, *pecans*, *Brazils* and *coconut*. An extra dimension is given when the nuts are lightly toasted or caramelised.

Caramel

The slightly burnt sugar flavouring of caramel is a fine foil for chocolate, probably at its best when nut praline is used in recipes.

Dried Fruit

The softness of dried fruit blends with chocolate and adds a light sweetness. Use *raisins*, *sultanas*, *candied peel* or *glacé fruit*. The texture and flavour are improved if the fruits are soaked in a little spirit, such as rum or brandy, before using in a recipe.

Spirits and Liqueurs

A few drops of liqueur lift a chocolate mousse, a cake filling or a sauce to a different plane. There is no need to drown a dish in alcohol, and this is particularly important when a dish is not heated to remove the alcoholic effect. *Rum*, *brandy* and *whisky* accent chocolate and add a light flavouring of their own. More distinctive flavouring is given by liqueurs based on *coffee*, *chocolate*, *mint*, *orange*, *raspberry*, *blackcurrant* and *cherry*.

Herbs and Spices

The combination of spice and chocolate is an old one, perhaps because they come from the same hot climate. The classics which enhance chocolate are *cinnamon*, *ginger* and *vanilla*. In a cooler climate, *peppermint* is a traditional accompaniment, giving a teasing sparkle to the heaviness of very dark chocolate. When using this flavouring, choose peppermint oil, rather than essence, which has a flat, synthetic flavour.

Fruit

The paradoxical sharp sweetness of fruit goes wonderfully with chocolate. Fresh fruit may be used in many dishes, while fruit jams make the perfect foil to chocolate cake. Use *pears*, *oranges*, *raspberries*, *strawberries*, *blackcurrants*, *apricots*, *cherries* and *pineapple*. For tremendous sophistication, try *cranberries*.

Coffee

Coffee and chocolate have an extraordinary relationship, and one which is as ancient and traditional as that of spice and chocolate, probably for the same reason that the two ingredients came from similar climates and areas of the world. The combination is usually known as *mocha*, and it will be found that a hint of coffee enhances a chocolate dish, just as a little chocolate gives depth to a coffee recipe. The flavouring may be introduced by using coffee liqueur, very strong black coffee, coffee essence or coffee powder.

Chocolate and Wine

Chocolate provides real problems for the wine-lover, and it is notoriously difficult to partner with wine at the end of a meal. One solution for the strong-hearted is to offer a small glass of *Armagnac* or *rum* which will complement the dish. Those who dislike spirits will have a greater problem in coping with the sweetness of the chocolate and its mouth-coating texture. A compromise may be a fortified wine such as *Málaga* or *port*, which contain a stiffening of brandy.

Traditional champagne and the sweet muscat dessert wines are not good partners for chocolate. General consensus seems to be in favour of simple but characterful wines, which need to be good ones to stand up to the chocolate. A good *Sauternes* or *asti spumante* seems to work well, and so surprisingly do some dry red wines. It is a good idea to experiment before offering a wine and chocolate combination, and if in doubt, leave the idea alone. Serve the cheese course with its appropriate wine before the pudding, and then serve the chocolate dish and follow up with a good cup of coffee.

4

CHOCOLATE CLASSICS

A FEW CHOCOLATE RECIPES have achieved the status of classic dishes. Mostly of French and Austrian origin, they are triumphs of the *pâtissier*'s art, which look delectable and often complicated, and which are fine examples of the skills of combining flavours and textures to produce a perfect and altogether elegant result.

Nobody need be frightened of trying to reproduce these classic dishes. All *pâtisserie* consists of a number of relatively simple recipes combined in a unique way. If a cook can make a reasonable sponge cake, meringue, shortbread, butter icing, fruit glaze and caramel, the delicious recipes in this chapter may be easily achieved. The essential ingredient is time to make each component part as perfect as possible.

Chocolate Marquise
**

This is a very light mousse but the flavour is intense and rich, since both chocolate and cocoa powder are used. Every chef has a personal recipe for Marquise, usually a closely-guarded secret.

Ingredients
FOR 6–8

7oz (200g) plain chocolate
3½oz (90g) unsalted butter
3oz (75g) caster sugar
1oz (25g) cocoa powder
3 egg yolks
2 tbs rum or brandy
½pt (300ml) double cream

Line a 1lb (450g) loaf tin with foil, smoothing down the creases carefully.

Break the chocolate into small pieces and put into a bowl over a pan of hot water. When the chocolate has melted, remove from heat and leave to cool. Whip the butter and half the sugar until very pale and creamy and work in the cocoa powder. Whisk the egg yolks and remaining sugar until almost white and very fluffy, and then whisk in the rum or brandy. Whip the cream to soft peaks.

Add the chocolate to the butter mixture and mix well. Gradually work in the egg mixture and finally fold in the cream. Pour into the prepared tin and chill for 4 hours. Turn out on to a serving dish. Serve in slices with any of the sauces on pp109–13.

Dobos Torte
★★★

This marvellous cake consists of thin layers of sponge sandwiched with chocolate cream, with the surface covered with a thick layer of caramel. It is a triumph of the Hungarian kitchen and used to be a speciality of Floris in Soho. It was always chosen for birthday celebrations by the staff of *Vogue* magazine.

Ingredients
FOR AN 8IN (20CM) CAKE

8oz (225g) unsalted butter
8oz (225g) caster sugar
4 eggs
6oz (175g) self-raising flour
½ tsp baking powder
pinch of salt

FILLING

6oz (175g) sugar
5 tbs water
2 egg yolks
6oz (175g) unsalted butter
4oz (100g) plain chocolate

CARAMEL

3oz (75g) sugar
3 tbs water

Preheat the oven to 400°F/200°C/Gas 6. Grease three 8in (20cm) sandwich tins and dust lightly with flour. Beat the butter and sugar together until very light and creamy. Separate the eggs and beat in the yolks one at a time. Sieve together the flour, baking powder and salt and fold into the mixture. Whisk the egg whites to stiff peaks and fold into the mixture.

Using half the mixture, spread thin layers in each sandwich tin and bake for 8 minutes until golden brown. Allow to cool in the tins for 2 minutes and turn on to wire racks to cool. Re-grease and flour the tins and bake the remaining mixture to make six layers in all.

To make the filling, put the sugar and water into a heavy-based pan and heat gently until the sugar has dissolved. Bring to the boil and boil to 215°F/102°C, until the syrup spins a short fine thread from a spoon. Whisk the egg yolks in a bowl until thick and creamy and gradually beat in the hot syrup until the mixture is cool and fluffy. In a separate bowl, beat the butter until soft and light and add the egg mixture a little at a time, beating until smooth and shiny. Melt the chocolate in a bowl over hot water and beat into the mixture. Refrigerate while preparing the caramel.

To make the caramel, put the sugar and water into a heavy-based pan and stir over low heat until the sugar has dissolved. Bring to the boil and boil to 345°F/174°C, when the syrup will be clear and caramel-coloured. Spread this caramel evenly over the top of one cake layer, using an oiled knife. While still soft, mark into eight triangles with a sharp knife and leave to set.

Assemble the cake layers and chocolate cream on a serving dish, making each cream layer the same depth as each cake layer. Top with the caramel-covered layer and pipe any spare chocolate cream in whorls round the edge.

COOK'S TIP
FOR MAKING BUTTERCREAM

As soon as the syrup has reached the required temperature, remove from the heat. It is best to use an electric beater so that the syrup can be poured on to the eggs while beating continues. The egg yolks must be thick and creamy and the syrup must be added in a thin trickle. The butter should be at room temperature so that it can be beaten to a soft light creaminess.

Marjolaine
★★★

A truly wonderful cake made from layers of nutty sponge with chocolate cream, coffee cream and praline cream, finished with more praline. The assembly is a little complicated but each stage of the preparation is easy, so that the cook only needs time to be successful.

Ingredients

FOR ONE 9x6IN (22.5x15CM) CAKE

8oz (225g) almonds
4oz (100g) hazelnuts
8oz (225g) caster sugar
1 tbs plain flour
1 tbs cocoa powder
8 egg whites

FILLING

8oz (225g) sugar
¼pt (150ml) water
8oz (225g) unsalted butter
3 tbs brandy
3 egg yolks
2oz (50g) plain chocolate
1 tbs strong black coffee

PRALINE

8oz (225g) almonds
4oz (100g) sugar
2 tbs water

Preheat the oven to 400°F/200°C/Gas 6. Butter and flour two 12x9in (30x22.5cm) Swiss-roll tins. Dip the almonds into boiling water and slip off their skins. Grill the hazelnuts and rub off the skins. Mix the almonds and hazelnuts and grill until golden brown. Grind in a blender until fine and stir with 7oz (200g) sugar, the flour and cocoa powder until evenly coloured. Whisk the egg whites to stiff peaks and gradually beat in the remaining sugar. Fold in the nut mixture. Spread over Swiss-roll tins and bake for 15 minutes. Cool in the tins for 5 minutes and then cool on a wire rack. Cut each cake in half.

To prepare the filling, put the sugar and water into a pan and boil to 240°F/116°C, when a little of the mixture dropped into cold water forms a soft ball. Take off the heat and cool to lukewarm. Beat the butter until very soft and light and gradually beat in the syrup, brandy and egg yolks. Divide the mixture in half and divide one half into half again. Melt the chocolate in a bowl over hot water and beat into one of the smaller portions. Flavour the other small portion with the coffee.

Prepare the praline by blanching the almonds in hot water and then grilling them until golden brown. Put the sugar and water into a heavy-based pan and simmer until it just begins to colour. Stir in the nuts until well coated and when the syrup is caramel colour, pour on to an oiled plate or marble slab. When cold, break into pieces and grind in a blender or food processor.

Fold half the praline into the large portion of filling. Put one cake on to a serving plate and spread with chocolate filling. Top with a second cake and spread with coffee filling. Top with the third cake and spread with half the praline filling. Top with the final cake and spread with remaining filling. Sprinkle with the remaining praline. Chill for 30 minutes before serving.

Bûche de Noël
***

This chocolate Swiss roll with a rich chocolate filling and icing is the traditional French Christmas cake. The centre can also be filled with chestnut purée mixed with whipped cream and flavoured with orange liqueur for something extra special.

Ingredients
FOR ONE LOG CAKE

4 eggs
4oz (100g) caster sugar
3oz (75g) self-raising flour
1oz (25g) cocoa powder

FILLING AND ICING

3oz (75g) sugar
5 tbs water
4 egg yolks
6oz (175g) unsalted butter
3oz (75g) plain chocolate
2 tbs rum
a little icing sugar

Preheat the oven to 400°F/200°C/Gas 6. Grease and base-line a 12x9in (30x22.5cm) Swiss-roll tin. Whisk the eggs and sugar together until pale, thick and creamy. Sieve together the flour and cocoa powder and fold into the egg mixture. Spread in the prepared tin and bake for 12 minutes. Turn out on to a piece of greaseproof paper sprinkled with caster sugar. Peel off the lining paper. Trim the edges of the cake and roll up firmly with the paper inside. Cover with a clean tea cloth and leave until cold.

To make the filling, put the sugar and water into a heavy-based pan and heat gently until the sugar has dissolved. Bring to the boil and boil to 215°F/102°C, until the syrup spins a short fine thread from a spoon (see Cook's Tip, p.22). Whisk the egg yolks in a bowl until thick and creamy and gradually beat in the hot syrup until the mixture is cool and fluffy. In a separate bowl, beat the butter until soft and light and add the egg mixture a little at a time, beating until smooth and shiny. Melt the chocolate in a bowl over hot water and beat into the mixture with the rum.

Unroll the cake and spread with one-third of the filling mixture. Roll up and place on a serving dish or board. Cover with the remaining mixture and mark with a fork to look like a log. Chill for 1 hour. Just before serving, sprinkle with a little icing sugar to look like snow and decorate with robins and holly.

Devil's Food
***

An American favourite which combines a dense, dark chocolate cake with a white fluffy frosting. There is also Angel Food, which by contrast is a pure white cake.

Ingredients
FOR AN 8IN (20CM) CAKE

8oz (225g) light soft brown sugar
2oz (50g) cocoa powder
¼pt (150ml) milk
4oz (100g) unsalted butter
2 eggs
8oz (225g) plain flour
1 teasp bicarbonate of soda

ICING

1lb (450g) sugar
¼pt (150ml) water
2 egg whites

Preheat the oven to 325°F/160°C/Gas 3. Grease and line an 8in (20cm) round cake tin. Put the sugar, cocoa powder and milk into a pan with the butter. Heat gently until the butter and sugar have melted and the mixture is smooth. Leave until just cold. Beat in the eggs. Sieve the flour and bicarbonate of soda and beat into the mixture. Pour into the tin and bake for 1 hour. Cool in the tin for 5 minutes and turn on to a wire rack to cool. When cold, split into three layers.

To make the icing, put the sugar and water into a heavy-based pan and stir over low heat until the sugar has dissolved. Boil to 240°F/116°C, when a little of the mixture dropped into cold water forms a soft ball. Whisk the egg whites to stiff peaks. Pour in the hot syrup gradually, whisking all the time, and continue whisking until the icing is thick and stands in soft peaks. Sandwich together the cake layers with this mixture and spread the remaining icing all over the cake. Leave to stand for 30 minutes before serving.

COOK'S TIP
FOR MAKING ICING

When making the icing, remove the syrup from the heat as soon as the correct temperature is reached. Add the syrup to the egg whites in a thin trickle, whisking all the time. Use the icing as soon as the mixture is thick and softly peaked.

Cassata
**

This Sicilian confection is a fluffy combination of cheese with fruit peel and chocolate, wrapped in sponge cake and finished with chocolate – not the often debased version, which is just a mixture of ice cream and candied peel.

Ingredients
FOR 8

1lb (450g) curd cheese
2oz (50g) caster sugar
4 tbs orange liqueur
4oz (100g) chopped mixed candied peel
2oz (50g) plain chocolate
8 trifle sponges

ICING

6oz (175g) plain chocolate
3 tbs strong black coffee
3oz (75g) unsalted butter

Line a 2pt (1.2l) pudding basin with foil. Press and smooth down the creases carefully.

Cream the cheese and sugar together until light and fluffy and work in half the liqueur. Add the peel. Chop the chocolate finely and fold into the mixture.

Split the trifle sponges in half and sprinkle the cut sides with the remaining liqueur. Line the base and sides of the basin with the sponge, cut-sides inwards, reserving a few pieces for the top. Fill with the cheese mixture and cover with remaining sponge. Cover and chill for 12 hours. Turn on to a serving dish.

To make the icing, put the chocolate and coffee into a bowl over a pan of hot water and heat gently until the chocolate has melted. Remove from heat and beat in small pieces of butter. Cool and spread over the pudding. Chill for 1 hour before serving.

Sacher Torte

***

The pride of Vienna, this rich, light chocolate sponge is glazed with apricot jam before being finished with a smooth chocolate glaze. It is often served with a mountain of whipped cream.

Ingredients
FOR A 9IN (22.5CM) CAKE

8oz (225g) plain chocolate
1 tbs rum
8oz (225g) unsalted butter
8oz (225g) caster sugar
5 eggs
6oz (175g) self-raising flour

FILLING AND ICING

4 tbs apricot jam
4oz (100g) plain chocolate
4oz (100g) caster sugar
3tbs water
2 drops olive oil

Grease and line a 9in (22.5cm) round tin. Preheat the oven to 300°F/150°C/Gas 2. Melt the chocolate with the rum in a bowl over hot water and leave to cool. Cream the butter and sugar until light and fluffy. Separate the eggs and beat in the yolks one at a time, then the melted chocolate. Sieve the flour and fold into the mixture. Whisk the egg whites to stiff peaks and fold into the chocolate mixture. Put into prepared tin and bake for 1½ hours. Leave in the tin for 15 minutes and turn on to a wire rack to cool. When cold, split into two layers. Sieve the jam and warm it slightly. With half the jam sandwich the layers together and brush the rest all over the cake.

To make the icing, melt the chocolate in a pan over hot water and leave until cool. Put the water and sugar into a heavy-based pan and simmer until the syrup is straw-coloured. Cool to lukewarm and stir into the chocolate. Add the oil and beat well. Smooth all over the cake. Leave to set for 1 hour.

Black Forest Gâteau

***

A tempting mixture of chocolate sponge, slightly sharp cherries, kirsch, cream and plain chocolate – very different from some of the versions served in a cheap restaurant meal. It is not difficult to make, but needs a little time and care.

Ingredients
FOR A 9IN (22.5CM) CAKE

5oz (125g) plain chocolate
2 tbs water
5oz (125g) unsalted butter
5oz (125g) caster sugar
4 eggs and 1 egg white
2oz (50g) self-raising flour

FILLING

1½lb (675g) canned morello cherries in syrup
1 tbs arrowroot
6 tbs kirsch
¾pt (450ml) double cream
1oz (25g) icing sugar
chocolate curls (p122)

Preheat the oven to 400°F/200°C/Gas 6. Butter a 9in (22.5cm) spring-form tin and sprinkle evenly with flour. Break the chocolate into small pieces and put into a bowl with the water. Melt over a pan of hot water and leave to cool. Cream the butter and sugar until very pale and light. Separate the eggs and beat the yolks one at a time into the butter. Beat in the flour and then the melted chocolate. Whisk the egg whites to stiff peaks and fold into the cake mixture. Put into the prepared tin and bake for 40 minutes. Turn off the oven and leave the cake in for 5 minutes. Remove from the oven and cool in the tin for 15 minutes before turning on to a wire rack to finish cooling. When cold, cut the cake in half to make two layers and put the base on to a serving dish.

Drain the cherries and mix 2 tbs of the syrup with 2 tbs kirsch. Sprinkle over the cut sides of the cake layers. Mix the arrowroot with 3 tbs cherry syrup. Heat the remaining syrup just to boiling point. Mix with the arrowroot and then reheat gently until thick. Take off the heat.

Stone the cherries and reserve 12 for decoration. Stir the rest into the sauce with half the remaining kirsch. Leave until cold. Whip the cream and icing sugar to soft peaks and fold in the remaining kirsch. Spread the bottom cake layer with the cherry mixture and one-third of the cream. Add the top cake layer. Spread the remaining cream lightly all over the cake. Decorate with the reserved cherries and plenty of chocolate curls. Chill for 1 hour before serving.

Nègre en Chemise

**

A wonderfully rich steamed chocolate pudding, which gets its name from the dark centre in a 'shirt' of white cream.

Ingredients
FOR 6

4oz (100g) white bread without crusts
¼pt (150ml) double cream
3oz (75g) plain chocolate
4oz (100g) unsalted butter
3oz (75g) caster sugar
2oz (50g) ground almonds
4 eggs
¼pt (150ml) whipping cream
½oz (15g) icing sugar

Grease a 2pt (1.2l) pudding basin. Break the bread into small pieces and put into a bowl with the cream. Leave to stand for 15 minutes and mash lightly with a fork. Break the chocolate into small pieces and put into a bowl over pan of hot water. Heat gently until melted.

Cream the butter and sugar until light and fluffy and beat in the almonds, eggs and melted chocolate. Gradually beat in the bread mixture until evenly coloured. Put into the prepared basin, cover with foil and steam for 2 hours.

Whip the whipping cream and icing sugar to soft peaks. Turn the pudding on to a serving dish. Spoon the cream over it and serve at once.

Chocolate Eclairs

**

This cunning combination of crisp light casing, sweetened cream and a dark chocolate glaze is perhaps the most indulgent of all chocolate-based cakes.

Ingredients

FOR 12 ÉCLAIRS

2½oz (65g) plain flour
pinch of salt
2oz (50g) butter
¼pt (150ml) water
2 eggs and 1 egg yolk

FILLING AND ICING

½pt (300ml) double cream
1 egg white
½oz (15g) icing sugar
6oz (175g) plain chocolate

Preheat the oven to 400°F/200°C/Gas 6. Rinse two baking sheets in cold water. Sieve the flour and salt together. Put the butter and water into a pan and bring to the boil. Tip in the flour quickly and beat hard over low heat until the mixture is smooth; cook for 1 minute until it leaves the sides of the pan cleanly. Cool to lukewarm and then beat in the eggs a little at a time until the mixture is smooth and shiny. Make sure the baking sheets are still wet, and pipe the mixture into 3in (7.5cm) lengths on to them, leaving room for expansion. Bake for 25 minutes. Slit each éclair with a sharp knife and return to the oven for 5 minutes to dry out. Cool on a wire rack.

Whip the cream to stiff peaks. Whisk the egg white to stiff peaks and then whisk in the icing sugar. Fold into the cream. Slit right along the side of each éclair and fill with cream.

Break the chocolate into small pieces and put into a bowl over a pan of hot water. Heat until melted. Dip the top of each éclair into the chocolate and leave to set. Serve freshly baked.

COOK'S TIP
FOR MAKING ÉCLAIRS

It is important to follow the recipe very carefully to achieve perfect éclairs. Be sure not to open the oven door when baking. Don't fill and ice the éclairs until just before serving so that they retain their crispness.

5

HOT PUDDINGS

A FTER A TRADITIONAL family Sunday lunch when a simple roast joint, poultry or game has been served, a hot chocolate pudding is a special treat and brings a triumphant note to the end of the meal. For those with more delicate digestions, it is best to serve such a pudding after a very simple and not very filling salad.

Many of these puddings contain their own built-in sauce, but if they do not they may be paired with one of the many delicious suggestions on pp109–13, or with cream or ice cream.

Hot Chocolate Meringue Pudding

★

A truly yummy pudding which makes a special treat for a family Sunday lunch and is easy to make.

Ingredients
FOR 4

4 oz (100g) plain chocolate
1oz (25g) butter
1oz (25g) sugar
½pt (300ml) milk
2oz (50g) fresh white breadcrumbs
2oz (50g) seedless raisins
2 eggs
4oz (100g) caster sugar

Preheat the oven to 350°F/180°C/Gas 4. Grease a 1½pt (900ml) pie dish.

Break the chocolate into small pieces and put into a pan with the butter, sugar and milk. Heat gently until the chocolate and butter have melted. Mix the breadcrumbs and raisins in a bowl and pour in the hot liquid. Mix well and leave until lukewarm. Separate the eggs and beat the yolks into the chocolate mixture. Pour into the pie dish and bake for 30 minutes. Whisk the egg whites to stiff peaks and fold in the caster sugar. Pile on top of the pudding and bake for 10 minutes. Serve at once with cream.

Chocolate Cream Pancakes

★

Thin chocolate-flavoured pancakes filled with flavoured cream and topped with rich chocolate sauce. Prepare the pancakes in advance and keep them warm and ready for quick assembly.

Ingredients
For 4

4oz (100g) plain flour
2 eggs
½pt (300ml) milk
1 tbs drinking chocolate powder
pinch of salt
1 tbs oil
lard for frying

FILLING

2oz (50g) seedless raisins
2 tbs rum
2oz (50g) walnuts
½pt (300ml) double cream

½pt (300ml) Chocolate Sauce (p109)

Put the flour into a bowl and gradually whisk in the eggs, milk, drinking chocolate powder, salt and oil. Using lard, fry 8 thin pancakes until golden on each side.

While the pancakes are being fried, leave the raisins to soak in the rum. Chop the walnuts and add to the raisins. Whip the cream to soft peaks and fold in the raisins, walnuts and rum. Just before serving, wrap each pancake round some of the cream mixture. Serve at once with Chocolate Sauce.

Chocolate Walnut Pudding

★

This very light steamed chocolate pudding studded with walnuts can be served with *Dark Chocolate Rum Sauce (p111)* or whipped cream.

Ingredients
For 6

2oz (50g) plain chocolate
3oz (75g) unsalted butter
3oz (75g) caster sugar
1 egg
4oz (100g) fresh white breadcrumbs
2oz (50g) self-raising flour
few drops of vanilla essence
5 tbs milk
2oz (50g) walnuts

Grease a 1½pt (900ml) pudding basin. Break the chocolate into a bowl over a pan of hot water and heat gently until the chocolate has melted. Cream the butter and sugar until light and fluffy. Work in the melted chocolate. Separate the egg and beat the yolk into the chocolate mixture. Stir in the breadcrumbs, flour, essence and milk. Chop the nuts roughly and add to the mixture. Whisk the egg white to stiff peaks and fold into the mixture.

Put into the pudding basin and cover with greaseproof paper and foil. Put into a pan of boiling water with the water coming half-way up the bowl. Cover and cook for 1¾ hours, adding more boiling water to the pan from time to time so that the pan does not boil dry. Unmould on to a warm serving dish and serve at once.

Saucy Mocha Pudding

＊

This chocolate-coffee baked pudding with its own sauce makes a superb finish to a Sunday lunch.

Ingredients
FOR 4

4oz (100g) self-raising flour
1oz (25g) drinking chocolate powder
4oz (100g) butter
3oz (75g) caster sugar
2 eggs

SAUCE

1 tbs drinking chocolate powder
2 teasp coffee powder
1 tbs cornflour
2 tbs light soft brown sugar
½ teasp ground cinnamon
½pt (300ml) water
1oz (25g) butter
caster sugar

Preheat the oven to 375°F/190°F/Gas 5. Grease a 2½pt (1.5l) ovenware dish. Stir the flour and drinking chocolate powder together until evenly coloured. Cream the butter and sugar together until light and fluffy, and work in the eggs alternately with the flour. Spoon into the dish and smooth the top lightly.

Mix the drinking chocolate powder, coffee powder, cornflour, soft brown sugar and cinnamon together in a heavy-based pan, and mix in the water. Bring to the boil, stirring well. Stir in the butter. Pour over the pudding mixture.

Bake for 1 hour. Leave to stand for 5 minutes and then sprinkle with caster sugar. Serve at once on its own or with whipped cream if liked.

Hot Chocolate Betty

＊

A 'Betty' is a layered pudding of bread-crumbs and fruit, and this version is a wonderful blend of delicate pears with chocolate and cinnamon.

Ingredients
FOR 4

1lb (450g) ripe eating pears
6oz (175g) white or brown breadcrumbs
3oz (75g) light soft brown sugar
½ lemon
1 teasp ground cinnamon
2oz (50g) grated plain chocolate
2 tbs golden syrup
2oz (50g) butter

Preheat the oven to 375°F/190°C/Gas 5. Grease a 2pt (1.2l) ovenware dish. Peel, core and slice the pears, and put half of them in the dish. Mix the breadcrumbs with 2oz (50g) sugar, grated lemon rind, cinnamon and chocolate. Sprinkle half the mixture on the pears. Cover with the remaining pears and top with the remaining crumb mixture. Squeeze out the lemon juice and heat gently with the syrup. Pour over the breadcrumbs and sprinkle with the remaining sugar. Cut the butter into flakes and arrange on top of the pudding. Bake for 40 minutes. Serve hot or cold with cream.

Chocolate Apricot Crumble

———————— ∗ ————————

Chocolate is a delicious enhancer of the humble crumble. Apricots make the nicest filling, but it is worth trying raspberries or black cherries.

Ingredients
FOR 4

12oz (350g) dried apricots
2oz (50g) walnuts
4oz (100g) plain flour
3oz (75g) unsalted butter
3oz (75g) light soft brown sugar
3oz (75g) chocolate chips
cream

Soak the apricots in water to cover for 2–3 hours. Simmer gently until just tender. Chop the apricots roughly and mix with the chopped walnuts. Put into a greased ovenware dish. Sieve the flour into a bowl and rub in the butter until the mixture is like fine breadcrumbs. Stir in the sugar and chocolate chips. Sprinkle over the fruit but do not press down. Bake at 350°F/180°C/Gas 4 for 45 minutes. Serve hot or cold with cream.

Chocolate Fondue

———————— ∗ ————————

An easy pudding for the chocolate addict which is good for an informal party. Be sure to have a wide variety of dipping items as some people like very sweet things, while others prefer the contrasting sharpness of fruit.

Ingredients
FOR 4–6

8oz (225g) plain chocolate
½pt (300ml) double cream
1–2 tbs rum or brandy
marshmallows, peppermint creams, pieces of fresh fruit

Break the chocolate into small pieces and put into a fondue dish or into a bowl over a pan of hot water. Add the cream and heat gently, stirring frequently until the chocolate has melted. Stir in the rum or brandy. Keep warm and use fondue forks or chopsticks for dipping in sweets and fruit.

Types of Chocolate and Decorations
Dobos Torte (p22)
Chocolate Eclairs (p28)
Hot Chocolate Soufflé (p36)

Chocolate Eggy Bread

The old nursery favourite with a special chocolate flavour is served to grown-ups with a lightly alcoholic sauce.

Ingredients
For 4–6

½pt (300ml) milk
1oz (25g) drinking chocolate powder
1 egg
6 large thick white bread slices
oil for frying
2oz (50g) caster sugar
1 teasp ground cinnamon

JAM SAUCE

8 tbs apricot jam
2 tbs rum

Put the milk and drinking chocolate powder into a pan and heat to just under boiling point, whisking to mix well. Take off the heat and cool to lukewarm. Beat in the egg. Trim the crusts from the bread and cut each piece into three rectangles. Dip each piece into the chocolate mixture and fry at once in hot shallow oil. Drain well on kitchen paper. Mix the caster sugar and cinnamon until evenly coloured and sprinkle on the fried slices.

Melt the jam, remove from heat and stir in the rum. Serve the chocolate slices very hot with the hot jam sauce.

Rum Hazelnut Pudding

This rich version of a steamed chocolate pudding is wonderful served hot with a bowl of whipped cream lightly flavoured with rum.

Ingredients
For 6

4oz (100g) plain chocolate
5oz (125g) butter
3oz (75g) caster sugar
5 eggs
2 tbs rum
3oz (75g) ground almonds
3oz (75g) ground toasted hazelnuts
3oz (75g) sultanas
3 tbs dry breadcrumbs

Grease a 2pt (1.2l) pudding basin with a little of the butter and sprinkle with a little of the sugar. Break the chocolate into a small bowl and put over a pan of hot water until melted. Cream the butter and sugar until light and fluffy. Separate the eggs and beat the yolks into the creamed mixture with the rum and melted chocolate. Stir in the almonds, hazelnuts, sultanas and breadcrumbs. Whisk the egg whites to stiff peaks and fold into the mixture.

Pour into the prepared basin and cover with a piece of greaseproof paper and a piece of foil, tying firmly with string. Put into a pan of boiling water to come half-way up the pudding basin. Cover and steam for 1½ hours, adding more boiling water to the pan if necessary. Turn on to a warm serving dish and serve at once.

Chocolate Fudge Pudding

★

A rich dark chocolate sauce forms under the cake-like top of this pudding, which is strictly for chocoholics. It is best served just warm, with cream or ice cream.

Ingredients
FOR 6

6oz (175g) granulated sugar
4oz (100g) plain flour
2 teasp baking powder
pinch of salt
1oz (25g) plain chocolate
1oz (25g) butter
¼pt (150ml) milk

TOPPING

4oz (100g) caster sugar
3oz (75g) light soft brown sugar
3 heaped tbs cocoa powder
6 tbs water

Preheat the oven to 325°F/160°C/Gas 3. Grease a 1½pt (900ml) ovenware dish. Stir together the sugar, flour, baking powder and salt. Put the chocolate, butter and milk into a small saucepan and heat until the chocolate has melted. Leave until cool and then beat into the dry ingredients. Spread in the prepared dish.

Sprinkle on top the sugars, cocoa powder and water without mixing. Bake for 1 hour. Leave to stand at room temperature for 1 hour before serving.

Chocolate Almond Pudding

★

A sophisticated steamed pudding which is very good served with whipped cream flavoured with a little rum or brandy.

Ingredients
FOR 6

4oz (100g) unsalted butter
4oz (100g) icing sugar
4oz (100g) plain chocolate
4oz (100g) ground almonds
6 eggs

Well grease a 2pt (900ml) pudding basin with butter and sprinkle with a little caster sugar. Cream the butter and icing sugar until light and fluffy. Grate the chocolate and work into the butter mixture with the almonds. Separate the eggs and beat the yolks into the mixture until it is very soft and light.

Whisk the egg whites to stiff peaks and fold into the chocolate mixture. Spoon into the prepared basin and cover with greased greaseproof paper and foil. Steam for 1 hour. Turn out on to a warm serving dish and serve at once.

Chocolate Upside-Down Pudding

*

The slight sharpness of pineapple contrasts with a rich chocolate baked pudding, served with *Chocolate Sauce (p109)*.

Ingredients
FOR 6

4oz (100g) unsalted butter
4oz (100g) caster sugar
2 eggs
2 tbs milk
5oz (125g) self-raising flour
1oz (25g) cocoa powder

TOPPING

2oz (50g) unsalted butter
2oz (50g) caster sugar
7 pineapple rings
7 glacé cherries
2oz (50g) walnuts

Preheat the oven to 350°F/180°C/Gas 4. Grease an 8in (20cm) round cake tin. Prepare the topping first by creaming the butter and sugar together and spreading over the base of the cake tin. Place the pineapple rings on top, with a glacé cherry in the centre of each. Chop the walnuts roughly and sprinkle in the tin.

Cream the butter and sugar. Beat the eggs and milk together. Sieve the flour and cocoa powder. Add the eggs and flour alternately to the creamed mixtured, beating well between each addition. Spoon over the pineapple rings. Bake for 50 minutes. Leave to stand in tin for 5 minutes and turn on to a warm serving dish. Serve at once with hot Chocolate Sauce.

White Chocolate Pudding

*

A pale golden steamed pudding with a chocolate flavour to serve with an enticing *Dark Chocolate Rum Sauce (p111)*.

Ingredients
FOR 4–6

4oz (100g) white chocolate
4oz (100g) unsalted butter
4oz (100g) caster sugar
2 eggs
4oz (100g) plain flour
pinch of salt
2 tbs milk
½ teasp vanilla essence

Break the chocolate into small pieces and put into a bowl over a pan of hot water. Heat gently until melted. Cream the butter and sugar until light and fluffy. Beat the eggs together. Sieve the flour and salt. Add the eggs and flour alternately to the creamed mixture, beating well between each addition. Fold in the melted chocolate and add the milk and essence. Put into a greased 1½pt (900ml) pudding basin. Cover with greaseproof paper and foil and steam for 2 hours. Leave to stand in the basin for 5 minutes and turn on to a hot serving dish.

Helen's Pancake Layer
★★

Pears with chocolate form a classic combination, commemorated in the ice-cream confection *Poire Belle Hélène*. This is a hot blend of the same flavours.

Ingredients
For 4–6

4oz (100g) plain flour
pinch of salt
1 egg
½pt (300ml) milk

FILLING

1½lb (675g) ripe pears
¼pt (150ml) water
1oz (25g) caster sugar
4oz (100g) plain chocolate
2 tbs lemon juice
2oz (50g) hazelnuts
vanilla ice cream
whipped cream

Prepare the pancakes first by mixing together the flour, salt, egg and milk to make a creamy batter. Fry 8 thin pancakes in lard or oil, and keep hot. While the pancakes are cooking, prepare the filling. Peel the pears and cut into neat slices. Put into a pan with the water and sugar and simmer until tender. Drain and keep the pears warm. In another bowl, melt the chocolate with the lemon juice over hot water. Chop the hazelnuts finely and stir into the chocolate.

Place a pancake on a warm serving dish, cover with pears and pour over a little chocolate sauce. Continue in layers, finishing with a pancake.

Serve at once cut in wedges, accompanied by scoops of vanilla ice cream and spoonfuls of whipped cream.

Hot Chocolate Soufflé
★

An impressive but easy soufflé, which you can partly prepare up to 8 hours beforehand.

Ingredients
For 4–6

4oz (100g) plain chocolate
2 tbs water
½pt (300ml) milk
1½oz (40g) butter
1½oz (40g) plain flour
¼ teasp vanilla essence
4 large eggs
2oz (50g) caster sugar
icing sugar

Put the chocolate into a pan with the water and 2 tbs milk. Stir over low heat until the chocolate has melted and add the remaining milk. Bring to the boil and remove from the heat. Melt the butter over low heat and stir in the flour. Cook over low heat for 1 minute. Remove from the heat and add the hot milk. Return to the heat and bring to the boil, stirring well until thick. Add the vanilla essence and leave until cool. Separate the eggs, and beat the yolks and sugar into the chocolate sauce. (At this point, the mixture may be left for up to 8 hours.)

Preheat the oven to 375°F/190°C/Gas 5 with a baking sheet inside placed in the centre of the oven. Grease a 2pt (900ml) soufflé dish well with butter and sprinkle with a little caster sugar. Whisk the egg whites to stiff but not dry peaks and fold into the chocolate mixture. Pour into the prepared dish, and run a spoon round the edge of the mixture (this makes the soufflé rise with a 'cauliflower' top). Place on the hot baking sheet and bake for 40 minutes.

Sprinkle with icing sugar and serve immediately with cream.

Steamed Chocolate Soufflé

---
*

A very rich but simple soufflé for those who are scared of making the traditional baked variety. Serve with *Chocolate Sauce (p109)* and/or cream.

Ingredients
For 6

8 medium slices white bread
6fl oz (175ml) double cream
5oz (125g) unsalted butter
7oz (200g) icing sugar
3½ oz (90g) ground almonds
4 eggs and 4 egg yolks
4oz (100g) plain chocolate
icing sugar

Grease a 2pt (1.2l) soufflé dish.

Discard the bread crusts and break the rest into crumbs. Pour on the cream and leave to soak. Break up the bread with a fork. Cream the butter and sugar until light and fluffy and then work in the almonds, eggs and egg yolks.

Break the chocolate into small pieces and melt in a bowl over a pan of hot water. Fold the chocolate into the mixture. Put into the soufflé dish and cover with grease-proof paper and foil. Steam for 2½ hours.

Sprinkle thickly with icing sugar and serve at once.

Little Chocolate Cream Soufflés

---
*

These individual soufflés are cooked until firm but still soft in the centre, and served with *Chocolate Sauce (p109)* or whipped cream.

Ingredients
For 6

4oz (100g) plain chocolate
¼pt (150ml) soured cream
few drops of vanilla essence
4 eggs
2oz (50g) caster sugar
icing sugar

Preheat the oven to 400°F/200°C/Gas 6. Grease 6 individual soufflé dishes very well with butter.

Break the chocolate into small pieces and put into a bowl over hot water. Heat gently until the chocolate has melted. Take off the heat and beat in the soured cream and vanilla essence.

Separate the eggs and beat the yolks into the chocolate one at a time. Whisk the egg whites to stiff peaks. Sprinkle in the caster sugar and continue beating until the mixture is shiny. Fold into the chocolate mixture until evenly coloured. Spoon into the dishes and place them on a baking sheet. Bake for 10 minutes. Sprinkle with icing sugar and serve at once.

6

COLD PUDDINGS

THE ADVANTAGE of a cold chocolate pudding is that it may be prepared well ahead of service. Indeed, a few hours' maturing can be a positive improvement, as flavours blend together to produce a smooth, subtle result. These cold puddings are perfect for special meals and buffet parties, and they should always be presented with flair on attractive dishes or in elegant bowls. Wine glasses make excellent receptacles for individual helpings, whether tall *flutes* or old-fashioned champagne *coupes*, placed on pretty plates or saucers, which can also hold the accompanying biscuit and spoon.

Over-decoration must be avoided with cold puddings, as a mass of piped cream and sprinkled decorations looks amateur and unappetising. Chocolate is so beautiful that it must be allowed to speak for itself, perhaps with the aid of some simple chocolate curls or other fancy bits (*see p121*). Whipped or pouring cream or an appropriate sauce may be handed separately. If a dish, such as a terrine, is obviously to be served in even-sized slices, these pieces may be presented on individual dishes in a shallow pool of sauce, perhaps decorated with a thin trail of cream, soft fruit or mint leaves.

Chocolate Rumpots
* — ✴ — *

These chocolate pots should be made in very small dishes as the mixture is wonderfully rich. Serve them with pouring cream if you like.

Ingredients
FOR 4–6

7oz (200g) plain chocolate
½pt (300ml) single cream
1 egg
1 tbs rum

Grate 1oz (25g) chocolate coarsely. Break the remaining chocolate into small pieces and put into a heavy-based pan with the cream. Heat very gently until the chocolate has melted, and bring quickly to the boil. Whisk the egg with the rum. Take the pan off the heat and beat in the egg and rum mixture. Pour into 4–6 ramekin dishes and chill in the refrigerator for 24 hours. Sprinkle with grated chocolate before serving.

Double Chocolate Fudge Flan

**

A sugary biscuit crust encloses a choco-late nut fudge filling, topped with soft chocolate.

Ingredients
FOR 6–8

4oz (100g) digestive biscuits
2oz (50g) unsalted butter
1oz (25g) demerara sugar

FILLING

10oz (300g) light soft brown sugar
¼pt (150ml) water
2oz (50g) unsalted butter
2oz (50g) plain chocolate
¼pt (150ml) double cream

TOPPING

4oz (100g) plain chocolate
1oz (25g) unsalted butter
grated plain chocolate

Crush the biscuits into crumbs. Melt the butter, remove from heat and stir in the crumbs and demerara sugar. Mix well and press into a greased 8in (20cm) flan ring placed on a serving dish.

Put the brown sugar and water into a heavy-based pan and heat gently until the sugar has dissolved. Boil for 1 minute and then simmer without stirring until the mixture is a pale fudge colour. Take off the heat and stir in the butter and chocolate broken into small pieces. Stir in the cream and bring slowly to the boil, then simmer for about 8 minutes until thickened.

Leave to cool for 10 minutes, stir well and pour into biscuit base. Put into the refrigerator for 20 minutes.

Break the chocolate into a bowl over a pan of hot water. Heat gently until melted.

Remove from heat and stir in the butter. Spread over the filling. Sprinkle thickly with grated chocolate and chill for 2 hours before serving with whipped or pouring cream.

Chocolate Mousse Cake

***

A rich ending to a simple meal, this flour-free 'cake' is sandwiched with chocolate cream.

Ingredients
FOR 6–8

9oz (250g) plain chocolate
1 teasp coffee powder
2 tbs brandy
2 tbs water
4 eggs
few drops of vanilla essence
2oz (50g) caster sugar
2 teasp cornflour
1oz (25g) cocoa powder

FILLING

¼pt (150ml) double cream
4oz (100g) plain chocolate
cocoa powder

Preheat the oven to 350°F/180°C/Gas 4. Lightly oil a 2lb (900g) loaf tin, and line the base and sides with baking parchment.

Break the chocolate into small pieces and put into a bowl with the coffee powder, brandy and water. Put over a pan of hot water and heat gently until the chocolate has melted. Remove from the heat, stir well and leave to cool.

Whisk the eggs, vanilla essence, sugar and cornflour until very thick, pale and creamy. Fold in the chocolate and cocoa powder. Put into the tin and bake for 1 hour. Leave in the tin for 5 minutes, then turn on to a piece of baking parchment on a wire rack to cool.

While the cake is cooling, prepare the filling. Put the cream into a small, heavy-based pan and bring to the boil. Break the chocolate into small pieces. Remove the cream from the heat and stir in the chocolate until melted. Return to the heat and bring to the boil again. Remove from the heat and cool. Slice the cake into four layers and sandwich together again with two-thirds of the cream mixture. Spread the remaining cream over the top and sides of the cake. Chill in the refrigerator for 20 minutes. Sprinkle with cocoa powder just before serving. The cake may be stored in the refrigerator for up to 4 days.

Chocolate Pavement
*

A French delicacy which is often served at Easter. You can vary the flavouring by using coffee powder or a little rum or liqueur instead of the orange rind.

Ingredients
FOR 6

10oz (300g) plain chocolate
6oz (175g) unsalted butter
4 egg yolks
2 teasp grated orange rind
10oz (300g) sponge fingers

Break the chocolate into small pieces and put into a bowl over a pan of hot water. Heat gently until melted and add the butter in small pieces. Stir well and remove from heat. Beat in the egg yolks, and stir in orange rind.

Count the sponge fingers and divide into three portions. Place one portion in a single layer on a serving dish. Cover with one-third of the chocolate mixture. Add a second portion of sponge fingers and a second portion of chocolate. Top with the remaining sponge fingers and spread the remaining chocolate mixture over the top and sides. Place in a refrigerator for 12 hours.

Chocolate Fruit Brulée
*

A wondrous blend of creamy chocolate with the sharpness of raspberries and crunchy caramel.

Ingredients
FOR 6

4oz (100g) raspberries
2 teasp kirsch
3 teasp caster sugar
3 egg yolks
1 teasp cornflour
½pt (300ml) single cream
4oz (100g) plain chocolate
6 teasp icing sugar

Take 6 individual ramekins and divide the raspberries between them. Sprinkle the fruit with kirsch and 1 teaspoon caster sugar. Put the remaining sugar into a bowl with the egg yolks and cornflour and mix well. Heat the cream gently to boiling point and pour into the bowl. Whisk well and return to the pan. Heat gently, stirring well until the mixture has thickened. Take off the heat and add the chocolate broken into small pieces. Stir until the chocolate has melted. Pour over the raspberries and chill in the refrigerator for 4 hours.

Place the ramekins on a baking sheet and sprinkle with icing sugar. Preheat a grill, and place the ramekins close to the grill until bubbles of dark caramel form. Cool for 30 minutes and serve.

Little Chocolate Custards

*

An Edwardian recipe with a delicate chocolate flavour which is not too rich at the end of a meal. For children, water may be used instead of brandy.

Ingredients
FOR 4–6

2oz (50g) plain chocolate
1pt (600ml) milk
2oz (50g) caster sugar
4 eggs
3 tbs brandy

Break the chocolate into small pieces and put into a heavy-based pan with the milk. Heat gently until the chocolate has melted. Whisk the sugar and eggs together and pour on the hot milk. Mix well and stir over low heat until the custard is thick and creamy. Remove from heat and cool to lukewarm. Stir in the brandy and pour into 4–6 individual glasses. If liked, serve with pouring cream.

Délice au Chocolat

*

The very best plain chocolate should be used for this recipe, which may be prepared at least 24 hours before being served.

Ingredients
FOR 8

4oz (100g) seedless raisins
4 tbs brandy
12oz (350g) plain chocolate
3 tbs strong coffee
6 eggs and 2 egg whites
10oz (300g) unsalted butter

Line a 9in (22.5cm) round cake tin with foil and brush lightly with oil. Soak the raisins in the brandy for 1 hour. Break the chocolate into small pieces and put into a bowl over a pan of hot water. Add the coffee and heat gently until melted. Take off the heat.

Separate the eggs and beat the yolks into the chocolate. Cream the butter until light and soft and gradually beat into the chocolate mixture. Whisk the egg whites to stiff peaks. Stir the raisins and brandy into the chocolate and then fold in the egg whites. Put into the prepared tin, cover with foil and chill in the refrigerator for 24 hours.

Turn on to a serving dish and mark the surface with patterns with a fork.

Chilled Chocolate Soufflé
**

A classic chocolate cream soufflé, standing high above the dish and decorated with cream and dark chocolate.

Ingredients
FOR 4–6

¾pt (450ml) milk
1½oz (40g) cocoa powder
3 eggs
3oz (75g) caster sugar
½pt (300ml) double cream
½oz (15g) gelatine
4 tbs water
2oz (50g) plain chocolate

Take a 1pt (600ml) soufflé dish and tie round it a double band of greaseproof paper to stand at least 2in (5cm) above the rim. Grease the dish and paper lightly. Put the milk and cocoa into a pan and bring to the boil, stirring well. Separate the eggs. Beat the sugar and egg yolks together in a bowl and stir in the milk. Return to the pan and heat gently, stirring all the time until the custard thickens. Cool to lukewarm. Whip half the cream and stir into the custard. Put the gelatine and water into a cup and stand it in a pan of hot water. Stir the gelatine until syrupy. Cool to the same temperture as the custard and stir it into the chocolate mixture. When it is just beginning to set, whisk the egg whites to soft peaks and fold into the mixture. Pour into the prepared dish and leave until set.

Carefully peel off the paper band. Whip the remaining cream and spread half of it round the edge of the soufflé. Grate the chocolate coarsely and press round the cream-covered sides, covering the cream completely. Pipe the remaining cream in rosettes on top of the soufflé.

Chocolate Roulade
**

A spectacular, delicious pudding which is easy to make. It must be made in advance, which is convenient for a dinner party.

Ingredients
FOR 6

6oz (175g) plain chocolate
5 eggs
6oz (175g) caster sugar
2 tbs hot water
½pt (300ml) double cream
icing sugar

Preheat the oven to 350°F/180°C/Gas 4. Oil a shallow 12x10in (30x25cm) tin and line with greaseproof paper.

Break the chocolate into small pieces and put into a bowl over a pan of hot water. Heat gently until melted. Separate the eggs and add the sugar to the yolks. Whisk until thick and pale. Cool the chocolate slightly and stir into the egg mixture. Stir in the hot water. Whisk the egg whites to stiff peaks and fold into the chocolate. Spread the mixture in the prepared tin and bake for 20 minutes. Cover with a piece of greaseproof paper and a cloth and leave overnight.

Put a piece of greaseproof paper on a flat surface and dust lightly with sieved icing sugar. Turn out the chocolate cake and remove paper. Whip the cream to soft peaks and spread lightly but evenly over the surface. Roll up like a Swiss roll (the surface may crack a little). Chill for 3 hours, and dust with sieved icing sugar.

Chocolate Hazelnut Gâteau

★★★

Nut meringue discs, layered with rich chocolate filling, for a gâteau which may be prepared the day before it is to be eaten.

Ingredients

FOR 8

2oz (50g) hazelnuts
4 egg whites
8oz (225g) light soft brown sugar
6oz (175g) unsalted butter
6oz (175g) granulated sugar
¼pt (150ml) water
3 egg yolks
4 oz (100g) plain chocolate
icing sugar

Spread the hazelnuts on a baking sheet and toast under a hot grill for a few minutes until the skins can be easily rubbed off in a cloth. Keep 12 nuts on one side and grind the rest in a blender.

Cover two baking sheets with parchment and mark two 6in (15cm) circles on each piece of baking parchment. Whisk the egg whites to stiff peaks and whisk in the sugar gradually until the mixture is stiff and shiny. Fold in the ground hazelnuts. Spread the mixture over the four circles. Bake at 275°F/140°C/Gas 1 for 1½ hours. Cool on the baking sheets and peel off the baking parchment.

To make the filling, soften the butter and beat until light and creamy. Put the sugar and water into a heavy-based pan and heat gently until the sugar has dissolved. Boil rapidly without stirring for about 10 minutes until the syrup will form long threads. Beat the egg yolks into a bowl and gradually pour the syrup over them, beating all the time (see Cook's Tip, p22). Blend in the butter and whip to a soft

cream. Break the chocolate into small pieces and put into a bowl over hot water. When just melted, stir well and add to the buttercream. Leave in a cold place (for about 5 hours) until thick.

Sandwich together the meringue discs with the chocolate cream, saving enough for decoration. Sprinkle icing sugar over the surface. Put the remaining buttercream into a piping bag with a star nozzle and pipe a ring of stars all round the top edge of the cake. Arrange the reserved hazelnuts on the piped stars. Keep in a cold place before serving.

> **COOK'S TIP**
>
> If liked, a little coffee essence or rum may be added to the chocolate cream.

Mocha Icebox Cake

★

A very rich and delicious pudding, which requires no cooking.

Ingredients

FOR 4

5oz (125g) plain chocolate
5oz (125g) unsalted butter
5oz (125g) caster sugar
2 egg yolks
24 sponge finger biscuits
4fl oz (100ml) very strong black coffee
½pt (300ml) whipping cream

Put the chocolate into a small bowl and melt over hot water. Cream the butter and sugar until light and fluffy and work in the melted chocolate and the egg yolks. Dip 8 sponge fingers in coffee and arrange next to each other on a flat dish. Spread on one-third of the chocolate mixture. Dip 8 sponge fingers in the coffee and arrange on top with the biscuits facing the other way. Cover with one-third of the chocolate mixture. Dip the remaining sponge fingers in coffee and arrange on top in the same way as the first layer. Top with the remaining mixture. Cover loosely with foil and chill in the refrigerator for at least 6 hours. Whip the cream to soft peaks and cover the pudding just before serving.

Chocolate Chestnut Loaf

A very rich pudding which is most easily made with canned chestnut purée. Serve it in thin slices with whipped cream.

Ingredients
For 8

1lb (450g) unsweetened chestnut purée
6oz (175g) unsalted butter
4oz (100g) caster sugar
8oz (225g) plain chocolate
1 tbs brandy or coffee liqueur

Grease and line a 2lb (900g) loaf tin. Put the chestnut purée into a bowl. Soften the butter slightly and add to the purée with the sugar. Beat well until creamy and smooth. Break the chocolate into pieces and put into a bowl over a pan of hot water. Heat gently until just melted. Stir into the creamed mixture until evenly coloured and add the brandy or coffee liqueur. Put into the prepared tin and

smooth the surface. Chill in the refrigerator for 8 hours. Turn on to a serving dish and serve at once.

Chocolate Cream Sophie

A pudding which is wildly popular with chocolate addicts, but which is little more than an assembly job. The ingredients may be multiplied easily and it makes a cheap but effective pudding for large numbers.

Ingredients
For 6

4oz (100g) fresh brown breadcrumbs
4oz (100g) demerara sugar
8 teasp cocoa powder
4 teasp instant coffee powder
1/2pt (300ml) double cream
1/4pt (150ml) single cream
grated plain chocolate (optional)

Stir together the breadcrumbs, sugar, cocoa powder and coffee powder until evenly coloured. Put the creams into a bowl and whip to soft peaks (it is most important that the cream is not whipped too stiffly or it will be impossible to assemble the pudding neatly).

Arrange in layers in a glass bowl, starting with crumbs and finishing with cream, and using three layers of crumbs and three layers of cream. Cover with foil and leave in the refrigerator for at least 4 hours before serving. If liked, sprinkle the surface with some grated plain chocolate at the last minute.

Julia's Chocolate Dinner Cake

★★

A soft-textured, light, nutty pudding-cake. Serve it freshly baked with a bowl of sweetened whipped cream.

Ingredients
FOR 6–8

6oz (175g) unsalted butter
6oz (175g) caster sugar
3oz (75g) plain chocolate
4 eggs
4oz (100g) walnut kernels
3oz (75g) fine white breadcrumbs

TOPPING

4 tbs apricot jam
3oz (75g) plain chocolate
1½ oz (40g) unsalted butter

Preheat the oven to 475°F/240°C/Gas 9. Grease and base-line a 9in (22.5cm) round cake tin. Put the butter, sugar and chocolate into a bowl over hot water and heat until the chocolate has melted. Stir well together and leave until cool. Separate the eggs and beat in the egg yolks, one at a time. Grind the walnuts in a blender or food processor, and mix with the breadcrumbs. Whisk the egg whites to stiff peaks. Fold the crumb mixture and egg whites alternately into the chocolate. Put into the tin and place in the oven. Reduce the heat to 350°F/180°C/Gas 4 at once, and bake the cake for 50 minutes. Cool in the tin for 5 minutes and turn on to a wire rack to cool.

Lift on to a serving dish and spread the surface with apricot jam. Melt the chocolate and butter together in a bowl over hot water. Pour over the cake and leave until cold.

Wicked Chocolate Roll

★★

Unspeakably rich and totally delicious, this pudding makes a spectacular finish to a dinner party, but needs a little last-minute attention. The faint-hearted may simply pour over the chocolate and cream and keep the cake flat, serving it in squares.

Ingredients
FOR 6–8

6 large eggs
8oz (225g) caster sugar
2oz (50g) cocoa powder
12oz (350g) plain chocolate
3 tbs water or black coffee
¾pt (450ml) double cream

Preheat the oven to 350°F/180°C/Gas 4. Grease and base-line a 12x8in (30x20cm) shallow tin. Separate the eggs and whisk the yolks until thick. Add the sugar and continue whisking until thick and pale lemon-coloured. Fold in the cocoa. Whisk the egg whites until stiff but not dry, and fold into the mixture. Spread lightly in the tin. Bake for 20 minutes until set but still slightly moist. Leave in the tin until cool and then turn on to a clean sheet of greaseproof paper on a flat dish. Melt chocolate with the water or black coffee on a bowl over hot water. Cool but keep liquid. Whip the cream.

Just before serving, pour the chocolate over the cake and top with cream. Roll up quickly and serve at once – the soft chocolate and cream will ooze from the sides, but will look very enticing.

Mocha Charlotte
**

This sumptuous pudding needs a little time to prepare, but the result is absolutely delicious.

Ingredients
FOR 6–8

4oz (100g) soft margarine
4oz (100g) caster sugar
4oz (100g) self-raising flour
1 tbs cocoa powder
2 eggs
1 tbs milk

FILLING

9oz (250g) plain chocolate
5 tbs strong black coffee
6 egg whites
3oz (75g) caster sugar

ASSEMBLY

½pt (300ml) strong black coffee
18–24 sponge fingers
plain chocolate
icing sugar

Preheat the oven to 350°F/180°C/Gas 4. Grease and base-line a 7in (17.5cm) round cake tin. Put the margarine, sugar, flour, cocoa powder, eggs and milk into a bowl and beat hard until light and creamy. Put into the prepared tin and bake for 35 minutes. Turn out and cool on a wire rack.

Break the chocolate into a heavy-based pan and add the coffee. Heat gently until the chocolate has melted. Remove from heat and leave to cool. Whisk the egg whites to stiff peaks and fold in the sugar. Add a little of the mixture to the chocolate and then gradually fold in all the egg mixture until the mousse is smooth and evenly coloured.

Take a 7in (17.5cm) cake tin and remove the base. Stand the metal ring on a serving plate. Split the chocolate cake into three layers. Put one layer on the plate and sprinkle with coffee. Carefully put the sponge fingers in a wall round the inside of the tin and outside the sponge base. Spoon in one-third of the chocolate mousse mixture. Cover with a second piece of sponge and sprinkle with coffee. Top with one-half of the remaining mousse, then with remaining sponge. Sprinkle with coffee and spoon in the remaining mousse. Grate some plain chocolate coarsely and sprinkle thickly on the surface. Refrigerate for 3 hours. Sprinkle with a light dusting of icing sugar. Carefully remove the cake tin just before serving.

Mocha Rum Creams
*

A wonderful balance of chocolate and complementary flavourings combine in this easy recipe. The slight sharpness of yoghurt offsets the richness of chocolate and cream, spiced with a hint of coffee and mellowed by rum and brown sugar.

Ingredients
FOR 6–8

½pt (300ml) whipping cream
½pt (300ml) natural yoghurt
3oz (75g) plain chocolate
3 tbs water
1 tbs instant coffee powder
2 tbs rum
2 tbs dark soft brown sugar

Whip the cream to soft peaks and fold in the yoghurt.

Put the chocolate, water and coffee powder into a bowl over a pan of hot water. When the chocolate has melted, remove from the heat and stir in the rum and sugar. Leave until cool and fold into the cream. Spoon into 6–8 individual pots and chill before serving.

Devil's Mountain
**

A mound of soft rum-soaked chocolate cake covered with cream and chocolate curls. It must be prepared 24 hours before serving.

Ingredients
FOR 6–8

5oz (125g) plain flour
1oz (25g) cocoa powder
2 teasp baking powder
pinch of salt
5oz (125g) light soft brown sugar
6 tbs corn oil
6 tbs milk
2 eggs

SYRUP

4oz (100g) granulated sugar
1/4pt (150ml) water
4 tbs rum

COVERING

1/2pt (300ml) whipping cream
3oz (75g) plain chocolate

Preheat the oven to 350°F/180°C/Gas 4. Grease a 2pt (1.2l) pudding basin. Sieve the flour, cocoa powder, baking powder and salt into a bowl. Stir in the sugar until evenly coloured. Mix together the oil and

milk. Separate the eggs and beat the yolks into the oil. Add to the dry ingredients and beat hard to a smooth batter. Whisk the egg whites to stiff peaks and fold into the mixture. Spoon into the basin and bake for 55 minutes until well-risen. Turn on to a wire rack to cool.

To make the syrup, put the sugar and water into a heavy-based pan and heat gently until the sugar has dissolved. Simmer for 5 minutes. Take off the heat and stir in the rum. Return the cold cake to the basin and prick all over the surface with a skewer. Pour over the hot syrup, cover and leave overnight. Just before serving, carefully turn the cake on to a serving dish. Whip the cream to soft peaks and spoon over the cake to cover it completely. Using a potato peeler, peel long curls of chocolate and sprinkle over the cake.

Chocolate Syllabub
*

In this mouthwatering modern version of a seventeenth-century dish, chocolate takes the place of the original fruit juices.

Ingredients
FOR 6

7 tbs boiling water
1 tbs cocoa powder
2oz (50g) caster sugar
2 tbs orange liqueur
1/2pt (300ml) double cream

Mix the water and cocoa and leave until cold. Add the sugar, liqueur and cream and whisk to soft peaks (the mixture splashes a lot, so use a large bowl). Pile into 6 glasses and chill before serving with sponge fingers or small sweet biscuits.

Profiteroles

**

Little puffs of choux pastry are filled with cream and topped with *Chocolate Sauce* (*p109*). As a sumptuous alternative, fill the puffs with vanilla or coffee ice cream instead of whipped cream.

Ingredients

FOR 6

2oz (50g) butter
1/4pt (150ml) water
2½oz (65g) plain flour
pinch of salt
2 eggs
½pt (300ml) double cream

Preheat the oven to 425°F/220°C/Gas 7. Rinse two baking sheets in cold water and leave wet (do not grease). Put the butter into a heavy-based pan. Add the water and bring to the boil. Sieve the flour and salt and tip into the liquid. Beat hard over low heat until the mixture is smooth and leaves the sides of the pan.

Remove from the heat and cool for 5 minutes. Add the eggs gradually, beating hard until the mixture is smooth and glossy. Make sure the baking sheets are still wet, and either pipe or spoon out with a teaspoon 18 small balls on to them, leaving plenty of room between them. Bake for 20 minutes without opening the oven. Take out of the oven and slit each bun with a sharp knife along one side. Leave until cold. Just before serving, fill with whipped cream or ice cream and pile in a pyramid on a serving dish. Serve with hot Chocolate Sauce.

Hungarian Mocha Gâteau

**

This very special cake with a truffle filling and rich, fudge-like icing is best served after a simple meal.

Ingredients

FOR 8–10

3oz (75g) plain chocolate
6oz (175g) unsalted butter
4oz (100g) caster sugar
4 eggs
4oz (100g) plain flour
pinch of salt
1 teasp vanilla essence

FILLING

10oz (300g) plain chocolate
¾pt (450ml) whipping cream
2 tbs Tia Maria

ICING

4oz (100g) sugar
7 tbs strong black coffee
6oz (175g) plain chocolate
2 tbs golden syrup
1oz (25g) unsalted butter
2 tbs Tia Maria

Preheat the oven to 375°F/190°C/Gas 5. Grease and base-line two 9in (22.5cm) sponge sandwich tins. Put the chocolate into a bowl over a pan of hot water and heat until melted. Take off the heat and stir in the butter and sugar. Separate the eggs and stir the yolks into the chocolate mixture. Whisk the egg whites to stiff peaks and fold into the mixture. Sieve the flour and salt and fold into the chocolate, with the essence. Spoon into the prepared tins and bake for about 25 minutes until firm. Turn on to a wire rack to cool.

Make the filling by melting half the chocolate in a bowl over hot water. Whisk in the cream to make a light cream. Grate the remaining chocolate. Remove the cream mixture from the heat and stir in the grated chocolate and liqueur.

Put one of the cakes on a serving dish and spoon on the cream filling. Chill for 1 hour.

Make the icing by mixing the sugar with hot coffee and then boiling until a little of the mixture dropped into a cup of cold water forms a soft ball. Remove from the heat. Melt the chocolate in a bowl over hot water, cool and then stir in the coffee syrup. Add the golden syrup, butter and Tia Maria. Mix very well and pour over the top of the second cake. Leave until completely cold and firm and then place this cake layer on top of the chocolate cream. Chill for 1 hour before serving.

Fudge Pots
*

Little pots of soft chocolate fudge are wonderful served with whipped cream.

Ingredients
FOR 6

8oz (225g) plain chocolate
4 eggs
4oz (100g) unsalted butter
2 teasp caster sugar

Break the chocolate into small pieces and put into a bowl over hot water. Heat gently until melted. Separate the eggs and beat the yolks into the hot chocolate. Cut the butter into small pieces and add gradually to the chocolate, stirring well until

evenly blended. Remove from the heat and cool for 6 minutes. Whisk the egg whites to stiff peaks and whisk in the sugar. Fold into the chocolate mixture until evenly coloured. Divide among 6 individual ramekins or glasses. Chill for 24 hours. Serve with whipped cream.

Chocolate Truffle
**

This blissful pudding, much loved by chocolate fans, needs a little care when preparing the chocolate cream mixture.

Ingredients
FOR 8–10

4oz (100g) soft margarine
4oz (100g) caster sugar
4oz (100g) self-raising flour
1oz (25g) cocoa powder
2 eggs
1 tbs milk

SYRUP

2oz (50g) caster sugar
4 tbs water
2 tbs rum or orange liqueur

CHOCOLATE CREAM

³/4pt (450ml) whipping cream
12oz (350g) plain chocolate
cocoa powder

Preheat the oven to 350°F/180°C/Gas 4. Grease and base-line a 9in (22.5cm) round cake tin.

Put the margarine, sugar, flour, cocoa powder, eggs and milk into a bowl and beat hard until light and creamy. Put into the prepared tin and bake for 25–30 minutes until firm. Turn on to a wire rack to cool. Prepare the syrup by putting the sugar and water into a small, heavy-based pan and heating gently until melted. Boil for 2 minutes, take off heat and stir in the rum or orange liqueur.

Place the cake on a serving dish. Cool the syrup and sprinkle all over the cake.

Whip the cream to soft peaks. Melt the chocolate in a bowl over hot water. Cool until still running easily but not hot. Pour on to the cream, mixing well until evenly coloured. Spoon over the cake. Refrigerate for 2–3 hours and sprinkle well with cocoa powder.

COOK'S TIP
FOR CHOCOLATE CREAM

Watch the temperature of the chocolate – if it is too hot it will cook and curdle the cream, but if it is too cool it will not blend easily into the cream. The texture should be like smooth whipped chocolate cream.

Chocolate Crackling Flan

**

A crunchy flan case contrasts with a creamy chocolate filling and meringue topping.

Ingredients
FOR 6

6oz (175g) ground almonds
2oz (50g) caster sugar
1 teasp rum
1 egg white

FILLING AND TOPPING

8oz (225g) plain chocolate
8fl oz (225ml) double cream
1 egg yolk
1 tbs icing sugar
1 tbs rum
4 egg whites
4oz (100g) caster sugar
1oz (25g) flaked almonds

Butter an 8in (20cm) flan tin.

Stir together the almonds, sugar and rum until evenly coloured. Whisk the egg white to soft peaks and stir into the dry ingredients. Form into a ball, wrap in film and chill for 30 minutes. Preheat the oven to 350°F/180°C/Gas 4.

Roll out the dough on a lightly floured board and press into the prepared tin, patching the delicate dough if necessary. Cut a strip of foil to fit round the inside edge of the dough and press lightly to keep the dough firm. Bake for 25 minutes. Leave until cold and carefully remove the foil and the tin. Place the case on an ovenware serving plate.

To make the filling and topping, break the chocolate into small pieces and put into a bowl with the cream. Put over a pan of hot water and heat gently, stirring well until the mixture is smooth and thick. Take off the heat and leave to stand for 5 minutes. Stir in the egg yolk, icing sugar and rum and beat until light and fluffy. Pour into the flan case.

Whisk the egg whites to stiff peaks. Gradually beat in the sugar until firm and glossy. Spread over the chocolate filling to cover completely. Sprinkle with the flaked almonds. Bake at 450°F/230°C/Gas 8 for 5 minutes. Serve freshly baked.

Saint Emilion au Chocolate

*

St Emilion is known for its wine, but it is also the centre of a macaroon-baking industry. This local speciality combines chocolate with rum and the texture and flavour of almond macaroons.

Ingredients
FOR 6

12 almond macaroons
4 tbs rum
4oz (100g) unsalted butter
4oz (100g) caster sugar
¼pt (150ml) milk
1 egg
8oz (225g) plain chocolate

Put the macaroons in a single layer on a dish and sprinkle with the rum. Put the butter and sugar into a bowl and beat together until light and creamy. Bring the milk to the boil, take off the heat and leave to stand for 10 minutes before beating in the egg. Break the chocolate into small pieces and put into a bowl over a pan of hot water. Heat gently until the chocolate has melted and then leave over the heat while beating in the milk and the creamed butter mixture. Beat until very smooth.

Put 4 macaroons in the bottom of a serving bowl. Pour over half the chocolate mixture. Put 4 macaroons on top and cover with the remaining chocolate mixture. Top with the remaining macaroons. Cover with film and chill for 12 hours.

COOK'S TIP

Be sure to use real almond macaroons, not the cheaper coconut substitutes.

Floating Islands in a Chocolate Sea

**

A classic French pudding looks very dramatic when the sweet custard is replaced by a chocolate version,

Ingredients
FOR 4–6

6 eggs
13oz (375g) caster sugar
1pt (600ml) milk
2oz (50g) plain chocolate
cocoa powder or grated plain chocolate

Separate the eggs and whisk the whites to stiff peaks. Gradually add 9oz (250g) sugar to the egg whites, beating well between each addition. Put the milk and 2oz (50g) sugar into a heavy-based wide and shallow pan and bring just to boiling point. Using a tablespoon, take up a spoonful of the egg mixture and slide it gently on to the milk. Add more spoonfuls of egg mixture and poach for 3 minutes until firm, turning them once. Lift out with a slotted spoon and drain well. Continue until all the egg mixture has been used.

Strain the milk into a bowl. Whisk the egg yolks and remaining sugar until pale and creamy. Stir in the milk and put into a heavy-based pan. Heat gently, stirring well and gradually adding the broken chocolate. When the sauce coats the back of a spoon, pour into a glass bowl. Cool slightly and place poached meringues on the surface. Just before serving, sprinkle the meringues with cocoa powder or a little grated chocolate. Serve cold.

White Chocolate Terrine

**

A moulded white chocolate mousse which is particularly delicious served with fresh summer fruit such as strawberries or raspberries.

Ingredients
FOR 6

1 teasp gelatine
7 tbs water
2 tbs clear honey
10oz (300g) white chocolate
pinch of salt
3 egg yolks
12fl oz (350ml) whipping cream

Rinse a 1lb (450g) loaf tin in cold water and keep on one side. Put the gelatine and 2 tbs water into a cup and stand in a pan of hot water. Heat gently until the gelatine is syrupy. Put the honey into a heavy-based pan and add the remaining water. Bring to the boil and take off the heat. Break the chocolate into small pieces and stir into the honey. Add the gelatine and salt and stir until smooth. Stir in the egg yolks. Whip the cream to soft peaks and fold into the chocolate mixture. Spoon into the prepared tin and chill for 24 hours. Turn on to a serving dish and slice thickly to serve with fruit or with Chocolate Sauce (*p109*).

Chocolate Pavlova

**

Pavlova is an Australian version of meringue cake, with a crisp surface and marshmallow-like centre. Filled with chocolate cream, it is delicious served with fresh strawberries or raspberries.

Ingredients
FOR 6

3 egg whites
8oz (225g) caster sugar
1oz (25g) cocoa powder
1oz (25g) cornflour
1 teasp white vinegar
½pt (300ml) whipping cream
2oz (50g) plain chocolate
few drops of vanilla essence
8oz (225g) fresh strawberries or raspberries
icing sugar

Preheat the oven to 225°F/110°C/Gas ¼. Line a baking sheet with baking parchment and draw an 8in (20cm) circle in the centre.

Whisk the egg whites to stiff peaks and gradually whisk in half the sugar until stiff and glossy. Sieve the cocoa powder and cornflour together and fold into the meringue with the remaining sugar and the vinegar.

Spoon the meringue on to the circle and slightly scoop the centre of the meringue with the back of a spoon to form a slight well. Bake for 3 hours, turn off the oven and leave until cold. Carefully remove the meringue from baking parchment and place on a serving dish.

Just before serving, whip the cream to soft peaks. Grate the chocolate finely. Fold into the cream with the essence and spoon into the centre of the meringue. Top with a layer of fruit and sprinkle lightly with icing sugar.

Baked Chocolate Cheesecake

**

A creamy baked cheesecake on a nutty pastry base. Make it the day before serving so that the flavour matures.

Ingredients
For 6–8

2½oz (65g) plain flour
1oz (25g) ground hazelnuts or walnuts
1oz (25g) caster sugar
pinch of salt
1oz (25g) unsalted butter
2 teasp water

FILLING

1lb (450g) full fat soft cheese
5oz (125g) caster sugar
2 tbs plain flour
3 eggs
4oz (100g) plain chocolate
6 tbs double cream
grated plain chocolate and icing sugar

Stir together the flour, nuts, sugar and salt. Rub in the butter and add the water to make a dough. Gather into a ball, wrap in film and chill for 1 hour.

Preheat the oven to 400°F/200°C/Gas 6. Butter an 8 in (20cm) round cake tin with spring-form sides. Press the dough firmly into the base and bake for 15 minutes. Leave until cold.

To make the filling, beat the cheese until light and fluffy and work in the sugar and flour. Separate the eggs and beat in the yolks one at a time. Melt the chocolate in a bowl over hot water and gradually beat into the cheese mixture with the cream. Whisk the egg whites to soft peaks and fold into the chocolate.

Pour into the tin and bake at 325°F/160°C/Gas 3 for 1 hour. Turn off the oven and leave the cheesecake in for another 20 minutes. Remove from the oven and leave to stand until cold. Remove the sides of the tin, and place the cheesecake on a serving dish. Chill overnight. Sprinkle the surface thickly with grated plain chocolate and icing sugar.

Chilled Chocolate Cheesecake

**

A richly simple, gelatine-set cheesecake with a crunchy, chocolatey base.

Ingredients
For 8

1½oz (40g) butter
4oz (100g) plain chocolate digestive biscuits
2oz (50g) walnuts

FILLING

8oz (225g) full fat soft cheese
4oz (100g) caster sugar
1 tbs mint liqueur
4oz (100g) plain chocolate
½oz (15g) gelatine
8fl oz (225ml) water
¼pt (150ml) double cream
whipped cream, chocolate curls and walnuts

Preheat the oven to 350°F/180°C/Gas 4. Grease a 7in (17.5cm) cake tin with a removable base. Put the butter into a small pan and heat until melted. Crush the biscuits into crumbs and chop the walnuts finely. Stir into the butter and press on to the base of the prepared tin. Bake for 10 minutes. Leave until cold.

To make the filling, cream the cheese until smooth and gradually beat in the sugar and liqueur. Put the chocolate into a bowl over hot water and heat until melted. Gradually beat the chocolate into the cheese mixture. Put the gelatine and water into a cup and stand in a pan of hot water. Heat gently until the gelatine is syrupy and then beat into the cheese mixture. Whip the cream to soft peaks and fold into the mixture. Spoon over the biscuit base and chill until firm. Remove from the tin and decorate as liked with whipped cream, chocolate curls and walnut halves.

Chocolate Zabaglione

A classic Italian mixture of eggs, sugar and Marsala is flavoured with chocolate. Serve it freshly made and warm with sponge finger biscuits.

Ingredients
FOR 4

4 egg yolks
4oz (100g) caster sugar
4fl oz (100ml) Marsala
3 teasp cocoa powder

Put the egg yolks and sugar into a bowl over a pan of simmering water. Use a rotary or electric beater and whisk until thick and creamy. Gradually beat in the Marsala and cocoa powder, beating for about 5 minutes until the mixture is again thick and creamy and frothing well. Pour into 4 serving glasses and serve at once.

Mont Blanc

This very light chocolate sponge crowned with a peak of rum-flavoured cream looks and tastes spectacular.

Ingredients
FOR 6

8oz (225g) plain chocolate
2 tbs rum
1 tbs strong black coffee
4 oz (100g) unsalted butter
4 eggs
4oz (100g) caster sugar
3oz (75g) plain flour
½pt (300ml) double cream
1 tbs icing sugar

Preheat the oven to 350°F/180°C/Gas 4. Butter and lightly flour a Kugelhopf mould (if this is not available, use an ovenware pudding basin). Break the chocolate into small pieces and put into a bowl with half the rum and the coffee over a pan of hot water. Heat gently until the chocolate has melted. Take off the heat and add small pieces of butter, stirring until melted.

Separate the eggs and beat the yolks into the chocolate, one at a time. Stir in the sugar and flour until well mixed. Whisk the egg whites to stiff peaks and fold into the mixture. Pour into the prepared mould and bake for 45 minutes. Cool in the tin for 10 minutes and turn on to a serving dish.

Whip the cream and icing sugar to soft peaks and fold in the remaining rum. When the pudding is cold, spoon the cream into the centre and over the sides.

Chocolate Chestnut Gâteau

— ** —

A cake with a mousse-like texture is layered with whipped cream and served with *Chocolate Sauce (p109)*.

Ingredients
FOR 6

4oz (100g) plain chocolate
4 eggs
7oz (200g) caster sugar
8oz (225g) unsweetened chestnut purée
pinch of salt
few drops of vanilla essence
½pt (300ml) double cream
cocoa powder
Chocolate Sauce

Preheat the oven to 350°F/180°F/Gas 4. Grease and base-line a Swiss-roll tin, approximately 12x9in (30x22.5cm).
  Break the chocolate into small pieces and put into a bowl over a pan of hot water. Heat gently until melted. Whisk the eggs and sugar in a bowl over a pan of hot water until very pale and light. Whisk in the melted chocolate. Fold into the chestnut purée with the salt and essence. Spread in the prepared tin and bake for 20 minutes. Turn on to a piece of lightly sugared greaseproof paper to cool.
  Cut the cake into three equal-sized rectangles and place one on a serving dish. Whip the cream to soft peaks and spoon half over the cake. Top with a second piece of cake, remaining cream and the remaining cake. Sprinkle lightly with cocoa powder. Serve at once with Chocolate Sauce.

Chocolate Mousse

— * —

This classic chocolate mousse may be flavoured with grated orange peel, rum, brandy or orange liqueur, and is best prepared the day before serving.

Ingredients
FOR 4–6

6oz (175g) plain chocolate
1 tbs water or black coffee
3 eggs
few drops of vanilla essence

Break the chocolate into small pieces and put into a bowl with water or coffee. Put over a pan of hot water and heat until the chocolate has melted. Separate the eggs and whisk the whites to stiff peaks. Remove the chocolate from the heat and cool for 5 minutes. Beat in the eggs and essence or any other flavouring. Fold in the egg whites until evenly coloured and pour into individual ramekins or glasses. Chill before serving with small sweet biscuits.

Mars Bar Mousse

— * —

A light-textured mousse with the magical flavour of Mars Bars and a toffee-like deposit at the base of each dish.

Ingredients
FOR 4–6

4oz (100g) Mars Bars
2oz (50g) plain chocolate
2 teasp water
3 eggs

Slice the Mars Bars thinly and put into a bowl with the broken chocolate and water. Put over a pan of hot water and heat gently until melted, stirring well. Separate the eggs and whisk the whites to stiff peaks. Remove the chocolate mixture from the heat and leave to cool for 6 minutes. Beat in the egg yolks and then fold in the egg whites. Divide between individual ramekins or glasses and chill before serving. Serve with cigarette biscuits or cat's tongues to dip into the toffee deposit.

Brandy Cream Mousse
*

This very rich mousse makes a perfect ending for a special party. You can also use crème de menthe or Grand Marnier instead of brandy, as exotic variations.

Ingredients
For 8

4oz (100g) plain chocolate
2 tbs water
5 eggs
2 tbs brandy
½pt (300ml) double cream
pinch of salt

Break the chocolate into pieces and put into a bowl with the water over a pan of hot but not boiling water. Separate the eggs and beat the yolks with the brandy. Beat into the chocolate and remove from the heat. Whip the cream to soft peaks and fold into the chocolate. Whisk the egg whites and salt to soft peaks and fold into the chocolate mixture. Spoon into 8 glasses. Chill for 12 hours before serving.

Double Chocolate Mousse
★★

Glasses of dark chocolate mousse laced with an orange liqueur are topped with a white chocolate mousse spiked with brandy, and the contrast is delicious.

Ingredients
For 8

12oz (350g) plain chocolate
6 tbs water
1oz (25g) unsalted butter
1 tbs orange-flavoured liqueur
6 eggs
12oz (350g) white chocolate
1 tbs brandy
grated plain chocolate

Break the plain chocolate into a bowl over a pan of hot water. Add 3 tbs of the water to the bowl. Heat gently until melted and then stir in the butter and orange-flavoured liqueur. Remove from the heat. Separate the eggs and beat 3 yolks into the chocolate. Whisk 3 egg whites to stiff peaks and fold into the mixture. Divide between 8 glasses and chill for 2 hours.

Break the white chocolate into a bowl and add the remaining 3 tbs of water. Put over a pan of hot water and heat gently until melted. Stir in the brandy and take off the heat. Beat in the remaining egg yolks. Whisk the remaining egg whites to stiff peaks and fold into the mixture. Pour over the dark mousse and chill until set. Sprinkle with grated chocolate and serve.

White Chocolate Mousse

**

Rum-flavoured white chocolate mousse to serve with a topping of grated plain chocolate or a few spoonfuls of *Chocolate Sauce (p109)*.

Ingredients

FOR 4–6

4oz (100g) white chocolate
2 tbs white rum
2 tbs water
¼pt (150ml) double cream
2 eggs
1 tbs milk
1 teasp gelatine
*plain chocolate or **Chocolate Sauce***

Break the chocolate into small pieces and put into a bowl with the rum and water. Place over a bowl of hot water and heat until the chocolate has melted. Whip the cream to soft peaks. Separate the eggs and fold the yolks and chocolate into the cream. Put the milk into a cup and sprinkle in the gelatine. Stand the cup in a small pan of hot water and heat until the gelatine is syrupy. Stir into the chocolate mixture.

Cool until the mixture is beginning to set. Whisk the egg whites to stiff peaks and fold into the chocolate mixture. Spoon into individual ramekins and leave until set. Either sprinkle with grated chocolate or top with a spoonful of Chocolate Sauce.

7

ICES

A HOME-MADE ICE is the most delicious finish to a meal, and an even better refreshment between meals on a sunny morning or afternoon. Ices are not difficult to prepare, even with unsophisticated equipment. First-class ingredients are essential, carefully blended so that they withstand the freezing process. An emulsifying agent such as cream, custard, egg or gelatine gives smoothness; whisked egg whites give a light texture. Too much sweetening and too much alcohol inhibit freezing, so that mixtures of ingredients must be carefully balanced as in the following recipes.

Some recipes which are rich in emulsifying agents do not need beating during freezing, but others (such as sorbets) will need two or three beatings. This is most easily done by putting the half-frozen mixture into a food processor and blending until smooth before freezing again, and the process may be repeated two or three times. The ice may be frozen in a covered freezer box or metal container in the freezer or in the ice-making compartment of the refrigerator at lowest setting. All ices will taste better if taken from the freezer about twenty minutes before service, so that they soften slightly and the flavours recover from the intense cold.

For perfect ices, a *sorbetière* which freezes and churns is the answer, although expensive. A simpler version is a container which can be placed in the freezer and which has paddles which move constantly as the ice freezes. The result in both cases is a very smooth ice.

Like other cold puddings, an ice needs attractive presentation in a glass or metal container. A scoop dipped in hot water ensures beautifully domed portions, which may be arranged in containers and returned to the freezer before service (if the container is freezer-proof). A matching or contrasting sauce will make an ice a feast, and all sorts of flavoured ices, sauces and decorations may be combined to make attractive sundaes and *coupes*.

Chocolate Granita

An ice which has the texture of frozen snow, and which looks exciting served in tall glasses topped with whipped cream.

Ingredients
FOR 4

8oz (225g) sugar
½pt (300ml) water
4oz (100g) plain chocolate

Put the sugar and half the water into a heavy-based pan and heat gently until the sugar has dissolved. Bring to the boil without stirring and simmer for about 5 minutes to make a syrup. Add the remaining water and the chocolate broken into small pieces and stir until the chocolate has melted. Leave for 1½ hours until cold and pour into a freezing tray. Freeze to a firm mush, stirring once or twice. To serve, spoon into tall glasses and top with whipped cream.

White Chocolate Ice Cream

For those who like a sweet chocolate flavour, this ice cream is good served with *Dark Chocolate Rum Sauce (p111)* or *Raspberry Liqueur Sauce (p113)*.

Ingredients
FOR 6

½pt (300ml) single cream
4oz (100g) white chocolate
2oz (50g) caster sugar
6 egg yolks

Put the cream into a heavy-based pan with the chocolate and sugar. Heat gently until the chocolate has melted. Whisk the egg yolks in a bowl. Slowly pour on the chocolate and whisk until well blended. Return to the pan and heat gently until smooth and thick, but do not boil. Leave until cold and freeze for 3 hours, stirring twice during freezing.

Chocolate Rum Sorbet

For the smoothest texture, this sorbet is best made in an ice-cream machine, but it may be half-frozen and then whirled in a food processor to break up crystals.

Ingredients
FOR 6

1lb (450g) sugar
2pt (1.2l) water
8oz (225g) plain chocolate
2 teasp coffee powder
½ teasp ground cinnamon
pinch of salt
4 tbs rum

Put the sugar, water, broken chocolate, coffee powder, cinnamon and salt into a heavy-based pan. Bring slowly to the boil, stirring until the sugar has dissolved. Boil for about 5 minutes, stirring occasionally, to make a chocolate syrup. Remove from the heat and cool to lukewarm. Stir in the rum. Either freeze in an ice-cream machine, or put into the freezer for 1½ hours until half-frozen, before whirling with a food processor and then freezing until firm. Serve in scoops, with whipped cream if liked, and with small sweet biscuits.

Rum Bumble Ice

★★

Rich rum-flavoured ice cream filled with soft raisins and walnuts.

Ingredients

For 4–6

5 tbs rum
2oz (50g) seedless raisins
2oz (50g) walnuts
1¹/₂oz (40g) cocoa powder
2 tbs boiling water
3oz (75g) plain chocolate
4 eggs
4oz (100g) caster sugar
¹/₂pt (300ml) double cream

Put the rum into a bowl with the raisins. Chop the walnuts roughly and add to the bowl. Leave to stand for 1 hour. In another bowl, mix the cocoa powder and water and add the chocolate broken into small pieces. Put over a pan of hot water and heat gently until the chocolate has melted. Separate the eggs and stir the yolks together until well mixed. Whisk the egg whites to stiff peaks and gradually whisk in the sugar. Whip the cream to soft peaks. Work the chocolate mixture into the egg yolks and stir in the raisins, nuts and rum. Fold in the egg whites and the cream. Put into a covered container and freeze for 3–4 hours until firm. Before serving, leave at room temperature for 5–10 minutes.

Rum Parfait

★

A light, creamy ice spiked with rum and enhanced by *Chocolate Sauce (p109)*.

Ingredients

For 6

2oz (50g) caster sugar
4 tbs water
4oz (100g) plain chocolate
3 egg yolks
2 tbs rum
¹/₂pt (300ml) double cream
3 tbs Chocolate Sauce

Put the sugar and water into a small, heavy-based pan. Heat gently until the sugar has dissolved and then boil to make 4 tbs syrup. Break the chocolate into small pieces and place in a liquidiser. Pour in the hot syrup and blend enough to break up the chocolate. Add the yolks and rum and blend until smooth.

Whip the cream to soft peaks. Pour on the chocolate mixture and whisk until well mixed. Spoon into 6 individual ramekins. Place on a baking sheet, cover and freeze for 3 hours. To serve, remove from freezer and leave at room temperature for 5 minutes. Spoon Chocolate Sauce over each serving to cover the surface. Serve at once with small sweet biscuits.

Mocha Ice Cream

*

The unbeatable combination of chocolate and coffee makes a sophisticated ice cream. For added luxury, serve each portion with a spoonful of rum or Tia Maria.

Ingredients
FOR 6

4oz (100g) light soft brown sugar
2oz (50g) unsalted butter
2oz (50g) cocoa powder
1oz (25g) coffee powder
5 tbs water
¾pt (450ml) whipping cream

Put the sugar, butter, cocoa powder, coffee powder and water into a small, heavy-based pan. Heat gently, stirring until the butter has melted. Bring to the boil, remove from the heat and leave until cool. Whip the cream to soft peaks, and then gradually whisk in the chocolate mixture. Freeze for 1½ hours until half-frozen and then beat very well until smooth. Return to the freezer until firm. Allow 20 minutes out of the freezer before serving.

Double Chocolate Ice Cream

*

Creamy chocolate ice cream dotted with tiny chunks of plain chocolate. For the addict, serve it with *Chocolate Fudge Sauce (p112)* or *Mint Cream (p112)*.

Ingredients
FOR 6

8oz (225g) plain chocolate
½pt (300ml) milk
3 egg yolks
3oz (75g) caster sugar
½pt (300ml) double cream

Break half the chocolate into pieces and put into a heavy-based pan with the milk. Heat gently until the chocolate has melted, and stir until smooth. Whisk the egg yolks and sugar together until the mixture is very pale and thick. Gradually whisk in the chocolate milk. Return to the pan and cook very gently until the mixture thickens. Leave until cold, stirring occasionally. Whip the cream to soft peaks and fold into the chocolate custard.

Freeze for 1½ hours until half-frozen, and then beat well. Chop the remaining chocolate finely and fold into the ice cream. Continue freezing for 1½ hours, beating twice more.

Chocolate Fudge Ice Cream

*

A lightly flavoured chocolate ice cream given a special flavour and texture with small pieces of chocolate fudge. If possible use a good home-made fudge, such as one of the recipes on pp102-3.

Ingredients
For 6

4oz (100g) light soft brown sugar
¼pt (150ml) water
4 egg yolks
1 tbs cocoa powder
¾pt (450ml) double cream
8oz (225g) chocolate fudge

Put the sugar and water into a small, heavy-based pan. Heat gently until the sugar has dissolved, and then boil for 5 minutes. Whisk the egg yolks and cocoa powder together and gradually pour in the hot syrup, beating well all the time. Continue beating until cool. Whip the cream to soft peaks and fold in the egg mixture. Freeze for 1½ hours until half-frozen and then beat well until creamy. Continue freezing for 1 hour, beating once more.

Chop the fudge roughly. Beat the ice cream and fold in the fudge pieces. Continue freezing for 30 minutes. To serve, leave in the refrigerator for 15 minutes before scooping so that the fudge softens slightly.

Brown Bread Chocolate Ice Cream

*

Brown bread ice cream was a Victorian favourite and its unusual texture is enhanced by small pieces of chocolate. For added bliss, serve the ice cream with *Dark Chocolate Rum Sauce (p111)*.

Ingredients
For 6

½pt (300ml) double cream
¼pt (150ml) single cream
2 eggs
3oz (75g) icing sugar
3oz (75g) plain chocolate
4oz (100g) wholemeal bread

The breadcrumbs should not be too fine but should retain a crumbly texture. Put the double cream and single cream into a bowl and whip to soft peaks. Separate the eggs and beat the yolks and sugar until pale and thick. Chop the chocolate very finely. Mix the breadcrumbs and chocolate into the egg yolk mixture and fold into the whipped cream. Whisk the egg whites to stiff peaks and fold into the mixture. Freeze for 3 hours until firm.

Frozen Chocolate Soufflé

**

A spectacular-looking and very light ice, which may be served with a sauce (*pp109-13*) and small sweet biscuits.

Ingredients
FOR 6

3 eggs
2oz (50g) caster sugar
4oz (100g) plain chocolate
³⁄₄pt (450ml) double cream
plain chocolate and icing sugar

Prepare a 1pt (600ml) soufflé dish by tying a double piece of greaseproof paper round the dish to stand 2in (5cm) above the rim.

Separate the eggs and put the yolks and sugar into a bowl over a pan of hot water. Whisk until the sugar has dissolved and the mixture forms thick ribbons. Melt the chocolate in a bowl over hot water and then whisk into the egg mixture until cool. Whip the cream to soft peaks and fold into the chocolate mixture. Whisk the egg whites to stiff peaks and fold into the mixture until evenly coloured. Spoon into the prepared dish and freeze for 4 hours.

To serve, remove the paper. Grate some plain chocolate coarsely and sprinkle over the top surface, then dust lightly with icing sugar.

Peppermint Cream Ice

*

Chocolate and peppermint combine in an ice cream with a slightly crunchy texture. Serve each portion decorated with a thin peppermint cream.

Ingredients
FOR 6

4 egg yolks
6oz (175g) caster sugar
¹⁄₂pt (300ml) milk
4oz (100g) plain chocolate
2 tbs crème de menthe
3oz (75g) chocolate mint crisps
¹⁄₂pt (300ml) double cream

Whisk the egg yolks and sugar together until very pale and creamy. Heat the milk and chocolate in a heavy-based pan until just boiling. Gently pour on to the egg mixture, whisking all the time. Return to the pan and cook over gentle heat until thick and creamy. Remove from the heat and leave until cold. Stir in crème de menthe. Grate the chocolate mint crisps and.fold into the chocolate mixture.

Whip the cream to soft peaks and fold into the chocolate custard. Freeze for 1½ hours until half-frozen. Beat well and return to the freezer for 1½ hours, beating once more during freezing.

Chocolate Roulade (p43)
White Chocolate Terrine (p53)
White Chocolate and Dark Chocolate
Ice Creams (p60 & 67)
Coffee Truffle Bombe with
Mocha Cream Sauce (p67)

Nutty Chocolate Terrine

*

A rich chocolate ice studded with three kinds of nuts and made in a loaf shape for easy slicing. Serve with *Crème Anglaise (p113)* or *Dark Chocolate Rum Sauce (p111)*.

Ingredients
FOR 8

8oz (225g) caster sugar
6 egg yolks
8oz (225g) plain chocolate
1pt (600ml) whipping cream
3oz (75g) walnuts
3oz (75g) hazelnuts
3oz (75g) flaked almonds

Whisk the sugar and egg yolks together until very pale and creamy. Break the chocolate into small pieces and melt in a bowl over a pan of hot water. Cool slightly and fold into the whisked mixture. Whip the cream to soft peaks and fold into the chocolate. Chop the walnuts and hazelnuts and add all the nuts to the mixture. Line a 2lb (900g) loaf tin with foil and spoon in the mixture. Cover and freeze for 6 hours. To serve, leave to stand in the refrigerator for 30 minutes, turn out and peel off the foil. Cut into slices and place each serving on a pool of the chosen sauce.

Frozen Mocha Mousse

*

A very light iced mousse which may be prepared up to 10 days in advance.

Ingredients
FOR 6

4oz (100g) plain chocolate
1 tbs cocoa powder
1 teasp coffee powder
2 tbs boiling water
6 egg whites
3oz (75g) caster sugar
grated plain chocolate

Break the chocolate into pieces and put into a bowl over a pan of hot water. Heat gently until melted. Mix the cocoa powder, coffee powder and water to a paste and stir into the chocolate, mixing well until thick and creamy.

Whisk the egg whites to stiff peaks. Gradually add the sugar, whisking all the time until the mixture is glossy. Fold in the chocolate mixture until thoroughly blended. Spoon into 6 ramekins. Place on a metal tray, and cover with freezer film. Freeze for 2 hours until firm. Store in the freezer for up to 10 days. Serve frozen with a sprinkling of grated chocolate.

Chocolate Fruit Bombe

*

An impressive frozen pudding which may be made 24 hours before serving.

Ingredients
For 6

4oz (100g) plain chocolate
¾pt (450ml) double cream
1lb (450g) can apricots
2 tbs bitter orange marmalade
2 teasp brandy
grated plain chocolate

Brush a 1½pt (900ml) metal bowl with flavourless oil. Break the chocolate into small pieces and put into a bowl over hot water. Heat gently until melted. Remove from the heat. Whip the cream to soft peaks, and put one-third into another bowl. Stir the larger portion of cream into the chocolate. Line the prepared bowl with the chocolate mixture. Cover and freeze until firm.

Drain the apricots and put into a blender or food processor with the marmalade and brandy. Blend and pour the mixture into the chocolate case. Cover and freeze for 6 hours until firm. To serve, put into a refrigerator for 1 hour before turning out on to a serving plate. Decorate with the remaining whipped cream and sprinkle with grated chocolate.

Chocolate Brandy Terrine

**

A light chocolate ice layered with sweet prunes soaked in brandy, to be served with *Creme Anglaise (p113)* or *Chocolate Sauce (p109)*.

Ingredients
For 8

8oz (225g) large prunes
6 tbs brandy or Armagnac
6 eggs
4oz (100g) caster sugar
8oz (225g) plain chocolate
1pt (600ml) whipping cream

Cut the prunes in half and discard the stones. Put into a bowl and cover with the brandy or Armagnac. Leave to stand while preparing the ice cream.

Separate the eggs and whisk the yolks with the sugar until very pale and creamy. Break the chocolate into small pieces and melt in a bowl over a pan of hot water. Cool slightly and fold into the whisked mixture. Whisk the egg whites to stiff peaks. Whip the cream to soft peaks. Fold the egg whites and cream into the chocolate mixture. Drain the prunes and fold in any liquid.

Line a 2lb (900g) loaf tin with foil and spoon in half the mixture. Cover with the prunes and top with the remaining chocolate mixture. Cover and freeze for 6 hours.

To serve, leave to stand in the refrigerator for 30 minutes, turn out and peel off the foil. Cut into slices and serve with chosen sauce.

Coffee Truffle Bombe with Mocha Cream Sauce

**

A rich coffee ice cream stuffed with chocolate truffles and served with a mocha cream sauce.

Ingredients
FOR 6–8

1 tbs coffee powder
1 tbs boiling water
3 eggs
4oz (100g) caster sugar
1pt (600ml) double cream
2 tbs coffee liqueur

TRUFFLE FILLING

4oz (100g) plain chocolate
2oz (50g) unsalted butter
2 tbs double cream
2 tbs icing sugar

SAUCE

4oz (100g) plain chocolate
¼pt (150ml) double cream
1 tbs coffee liqueur

Dissolve the coffee in boiling water and leave until cold. Whisk the eggs and sugar in a bowl over hot water until thick, white and creamy. Leave until cold. Whip the cream, coffee and liqueur to stiff peaks and fold in the egg mixture. Pour into a freezer tray, cover and freeze for 3 hours until firm.

While the ice cream is freezing, prepare the truffles. Melt the chocolate and butter together in a bowl over a pan of hot water. Remove from the heat and stir in the cream and icing sugar. Mix well and chill until firm. Roll into balls and refrigerate until the ice cream is ready.

Beat the ice cream with an electric mixer or food processor until soft and smooth. Put a layer of ice cream into a 2pt (1.2l) pudding basin and arrange some truffles on top. Add another layer of ice cream and remaining truffles, and top with ice cream. Cover and freeze for 3 hours until firm.

Just before serving, prepare the sauce. Melt the chocolate in a bowl over a pan of hot water. Remove from heat and stir in the cream and liqueur. Unmould the iced bombe on to a serving dish, and serve each portion with some of the sauce.

Dark Chocolate Ice Cream

*

A deeply flavoured ice which is delicious on its own, or used as a base for a sundae with sauce, nuts and whipped cream.

Ingredients
FOR 6

1pt (600ml) creamy milk
5oz (125g) caster sugar
4oz (100g) plain chocolate
3oz (75g) cocoa powder
½pt (300ml) double cream

Put the milk and sugar into a heavy-based pan and just bring to the boil. Take off the heat and add the chocolate broken into small pieces. Stir until well mixed. Whisk in the cocoa powder and return to heat for 2 minutes. Leave until cold, stirring occasionally. Whip the cream to soft peaks and fold in the chocolate mixture. Freeze for 1½ hours until half-frozen and beat well until smooth. Freeze again for 1 hour, beat again, and freeze until firm.

8
CAKES AND BISCUITS

ALL CHOCOHOLICS LOVE CHOCOLATE CAKE. There is never any doubt which will be the most popular cake on the table or biscuit in the tin, but there are dozens of ways of producing the most perfect confection. There is, of course, the simple chocolate sponge, layered with buttercream and topped with icing, or there may be the more sophisticated fudgy-chocolate cake filled with a slightly sharp fruit jam and covered with a soft chocolate glaze. There may be truffle cakes and meringues, chewy brownies and wicked combinations of shortbread, toffee and plain chocolate. There may be biscuits dipped in soft chocolate, or layered with coffee cream, and tray-baked squares dripping with chocolate icing. This chapter contains just about everyone's favourite chocolate cake or biscuit.

There is no magic in producing a good result, but there must be attention to detail. As with all chocolate cookery, it is important to use the best ingredients – nothing tired or stale, or cheap-tasting. It is then important to measure them accurately, and to combine them in the way described in a recipe. It is also important to use the correct sized tin for baking, or the area of the mixture will be altered, which can result in an undercooked or over-baked cake. Finally, it is important to set the oven at the correct temperature, and to be sure that it has reached that temperature before use. Many chocolate mixtures are fragile, and it is usually best to allow cakes to set in their tins for a few minutes before turning them out for final cooling. In other words, follow each recipe exactly for perfect results.

As with puddings, don't be tempted to over-decorate cakes. The rich chocolate finish speaks for itself, only needing a simple chocolate decoration to make it luxurious.

Chocolate Bran Cake

* * *

The bran gives a lovely texture to this simple cake, finished with orange-hinted chocolate icing.

Ingredients
MAKES 8IN (20CM) CAKE

1oz (25g) All Bran cereal
4 tbs milk
2oz (50g) butter
2oz (50g) dark soft brown sugar
1 egg
1½oz (40g) plain chocolate
2oz (50g) self-raising flour

ICING

2oz (50g) plain chocolate
1oz (25g) butter
1 tbs milk
2oz (50g) icing sugar
½ teasp grated orange rind

Preheat the oven to 350°F/180°C/Gas 4. Grease and base-line an 8in (20cm) round cake tin. Put the cereal and milk into a small bowl and leave until the milk has been absorbed. Cream the butter and sugar until light and fluffy. Beat the egg lightly. Melt the chocolate. Beat the cereal mixture, egg and flour into the creamed mixture and finally stir in the melted chocolate. Put into the tin and make a slight hollow in the surface. Bake for 40 minutes and turn on to a wire rack to cool.

To make the icing, put the chocolate, butter and milk into a bowl over a pan of hot water, and stir until the chocolate has melted. Take off the heat and gradually stir in the icing sugar and orange rind. The mixture should be a thick pouring consistency, but if not, leave to cool slightly before using. Pour over the cake and leave until cold.

Chocolate Ginger Cake

* * *

An unusual combination of chocolate and ginger, with a light gingerbread paired with whipped cream and a dark chocolate icing.

Ingredients
FOR AN 8IN (20CM) CAKE

6oz (175g) butter or soft margarine
5oz (125g) dark soft brown sugar
3 eggs
6oz (175g) self-raising flour
3 teasp ground ginger

FILLING

¼pt (150ml) whipping cream

ICING

3oz (75g) plain chocolate
2 tbs water
1oz (25g) butter or margarine
8oz (225g) icing sugar
2oz (50g) crystallised ginger

Preheat the oven to 350°F/180°C/Gas 4. Grease and base-line two 8in (20cm) sandwich tins. Cream the fat and sugar until light and fluffy. Beat the eggs lightly. Sieve the flour and ginger together. Add eggs and flour alternately to the creamed mixture, beating well between each addition. Divide between the two tins and bake for 30 minutes. Turn on to a wire rack to cool.

Whip the cream to soft peaks and use to sandwich the cakes together. Put the chocolate, water and fat into a bowl over a pan of hot water and stir until the chocolate melts. Remove from the heat and beat in the sugar gradually. Spread over the top of the cake and decorate with the crystallised ginger.

Chocolate Parkin

The rich gingerbread which is traditionally eaten on Guy Fawkes' Day tastes very special when combined with chocolate.

Ingredients
FOR A 6IN (15CM) SQUARE CAKE

4oz (100g) butter
4oz (100g) black treacle
4oz (100g) dark soft brown sugar
½ teasp bicarbonate of soda
6 tbs milk
4oz (100g) plain flour
4oz (100g) fine oatmeal
1 teasp ground ginger
1 teasp ground mixed spice
pinch of salt
1 egg
4oz (100g) plain chocolate

Preheat the oven to 325°F/160°C/Gas 3. Grease and base-line a 6in (15cm) square cake tin. Put the butter, treacle and sugar into a pan and heat gently until the fat has melted. Leave to cool. Stir the bicarbonate of soda into the milk. Stir the flour, oatmeal, ginger, spice and salt together. Beat in the butter mixture, milk and egg. Chop the chocolate finely and stir into the cake mixture. Put into the prepared tin and bake for 1 hour. Cool in the tin for 5 minutes and turn on to a wire rack to finish cooling. Store in a tin for 3 days before using.

Chocolate Marble Cake

An old-fashioned nursery cake which is simple to make but looks spectacular.

Ingredients
FOR A 7IN (17.5CM) CAKE

8oz (225g) soft margarine
8oz (225g) caster sugar
few drops of vanilla essence
3 large eggs
10oz (300g) self-raising flour
3oz (75g) plain chocolate

Preheat the oven to 350°F/180°C/Gas 4. Grease and base-line a 7in (17.5cm) round cake tin. Cream the fat, sugar and essence until light and fluffy. Beat the eggs lightly together. Sieve the flour. Add the eggs and flour alternately to the creamed mixture.

Put half the mixture into another bowl. Melt the chocolate in a bowl over hot water and beat into half the mixture. Put alternate spoonfuls of plain and chocolate mixture into the prepared tin. Bake for 45 minutes. Cool in the tin for 2–3 minutes and turn on to a wire rack to cool.

Chocolate Caramel Cake

*

Everyone loves chocolate caramels, so it is worth combining the two distinctive flavours for a popular cake.

Ingredients
FOR A 7IN (17.5CM) CAKE

4oz (100g) soft margarine
4oz (100g) caster sugar
4oz (100g) self-raising flour
1oz (25g) cocoa powder
2 eggs
2 tbs milk

TOPPING

3oz (75g) sugar
2 tbs double cream
1 tbs plain flour
2oz (50g) whole blanched almonds
1oz (25g) grated plain chocolate

Preheat the oven to 375°F/190°C/Gas 5. Grease and base-line a 7in (17.5cm) round cake tin.

Put the margarine, sugar, flour, cocoa and eggs into a bowl with the milk and beat hard with a wooden spoon until light and soft. Put into the prepared tin and bake for 25 minutes.

Put the sugar in a small pan and heat gently until melted. Stir in the cream, flour and almonds. Pour over the cake and continue baking for 10 minutes. Leave in the tin for 2 minutes and turn on to a wire rack to cool, with caramel side upwards. After 10 minutes, sprinkle the surface with grated chocolate.

Chocolate Rum Cake

**

Chocolate and rum are natural partners, and they are combined here in a rich, dark cake for a special occasion.

Ingredients
FOR A 8IN (20CM) CAKE

6oz (175g) butter or soft margarine
6oz (175g) caster sugar
6 tbs black treacle
2 eggs
6oz (175g) self-raising flour
1oz (25g) cocoa powder
1oz (25g) cornflour
5 tbs milk

FILLING AND ICING

8oz (225g) unsalted butter
12oz (350g) icing sugar
2 tbs black treacle
6 tbs milk
2 tbs rum
4 tbs boiling water

Preheat the oven to 350°F/180°C/Gas 4. Grease and base-line two 8 in (20cm) sandwich tins.

Cream the fat, sugar and treacle until light and fluffy. Beat the eggs lightly. Sieve the flour, cocoa powder and cornflour together. Add to the creamed mixture alternately with the milk, and the eggs, beating well between each addition. Divide between the two tins and bake for 30 minutes. Turn on to a wire rack to cool. When cold, split each cake into two layers.

To make the icing, cream the butter, sugar and treacle together. Work in the milk and rum slowly and finally whisk in the boiling water, a little at a time. Sandwich the layers together and use any surplus icing for the top of the cake.

Rich Dark Chocolate Cake

The unusual addition of Guinness results in a chocolate cake which is very dark but light-textured.

Ingredients

FOR AN 8IN (20CM) CAKE

4oz (100g) soft margarine
6oz (175g) dark soft brown sugar
2 eggs
6oz (175g) plain flour
1 teasp baking powder
½ teasp bicarbonate of soda
¼pt (150ml) Guinness
2oz (50g) cocoa powder

FILLING AND ICING

4oz (100g) plain chocolate
1 tbs milk
4oz (100g) soft margarine
8oz (225g) icing sugar
walnut halves

Preheat the oven to 350°F/180°C/Gas 4. Grease and base-line two 8in (20cm) sandwich tins.

Cream the fat and sugar until light and fluffy. Beat the eggs lightly. Sieve the flour, baking powder and soda. Add the eggs and flour alternately to the creamed mixture, beating well between each addition. Mix the Guinness and cocoa powder together to make a thick paste. Stir into the cake mixture and beat just enough to mix. Divide between the tins and bake for 30 minutes. Cool on a wire rack.

To make the icing, put the chocolate and milk into a bowl over a pan of hot water. When the chocolate has melted, remove from the heat and cool to lukewarm. Cream the fat and sugar together and beat in the chocolate until evenly coloured. Use one-third of the icing to put the two cake halves together. Swirl the remaining icing on top and decorate with walnut halves.

Brazilian Chocolate Cake

Nuts, dates and cherries combine with chocolate chips in a cut-and-come-again cake which needs no decoration.

Ingredients

FOR A 2LB (900G) LOAF CAKE

4oz (100g) dates
8oz (225g) Brazil nuts
2oz (50g) glacé cherries
4oz (100g) chocolate chips
4oz (100g) plain flour
½ teasp baking powder
pinch of salt
5½oz (150g) sugar
3 eggs

Preheat the oven to 375°F/190°C/Gas 5. Grease and base-line a 2lb (900g) loaf tin.

Reserve 6 dates and 6 nuts and chop the rest roughly. Put into a bowl. Cut the cherries in half and add to the bowl with the chocolate chips. Sieve the flour, baking powder and salt and add to the bowl with the sugar. Stir well. Separate the eggs and whisk the whites until frothy. Stir in the yolks and add to the bowl. Mix well and put into the prepared tin. Arrange reserved dates and nuts on top. Bake for 1½ hours. Turn on to a wire rack to cool.

Chocolate Fudge Layer Cake

**

A dark, dense chocolate cake with creamy fudge filling and topping – lovely for tea, or as a pudding.

Ingredients
FOR AN 8IN (20CM) CAKE

4oz (100g) plain chocolate
3 tbs boiling water
7oz (200g) self-raising flour
1oz (25g) cocoa powder
6oz (175g) unsalted butter
6oz (175g) caster sugar
1 teasp vanilla essence
4 eggs
2 tbs milk

FILLING AND TOPPING

7oz (200g) plain chocolate
6fl oz (175ml) evaporated milk
8oz (225g) icing sugar

Preheat the oven to 350°F/180°C/Gas 4. Grease and base-line two 8in (20cm) sandwich tins.

Break the chocolate into small pieces and put into a bowl with the water over hot water. Heat gently until melted. Sieve the flour and cocoa together. Cream the butter and sugar until soft and fluffy. Add the essence and chocolate. Separate the eggs and beat the yolks into the chocolate mixture. Fold in the flour mixture and milk. Whisk the egg whites to stiff peaks and fold into the mixture. Divide between the tins and bake for 30 minutes. Turn out on to a wire rack to cool.

To make the filling, melt the chocolate in a bowl over a pan of hot water. Add the evaporated milk and beat over the heat until light and creamy. Remove from the heat and leave to cool for 5 minutes,

stirring often. Sieve the icing sugar and work into the chocolate mixture. When thick and smooth, sandwich the cakes together with one-third of the icing. Spread the rest over the surface of the cake.

Chocolate Teabread

*

This chocolate-flavoured fruit loaf may be eaten plain, or is even more delicious spread with unsalted butter.

Ingredients
FOR A 2LB (900G) LOAF CAKE

9oz (250g) self-raising flour
4oz (100g) butter or hard margarine
4oz (100g) caster sugar
2oz (50g) seedless raisins
2oz (50g) currants
1oz (25g) chopped mixed peel
2 eggs
2oz (50g) plain chocolate
3–4 tbs milk

Preheat the oven to 350°F/180°C/Gas 4. Grease and base-line a 2lb (900g) loaf tin. Sieve the flour into a bowl. Rub in the fat until the mixture is like fine breadcrumbs. Stir in the sugar, raisins, currants and peel. Beat the eggs lightly and stir into the mixture. Melt the chocolate in a pan over hot water and add to the mixture. Beat well, adding enough milk to make a soft dropping consistency. Put into the prepared tin and bake for 1 hour. Cool in the tin for 3 minutes and turn on to a wire rack to cool.

Austrian Chocolate Cake

*

Austrian cooks have a way with rich chocolate cakes. This one has a particularly light texture and is very rich.

Ingredients
FOR A 8IN (20CM) CAKE

8oz (225g) plain chocolate
8oz (225g) unsalted butter
8oz (225g) dark soft brown sugar
6 eggs
8oz (225g) ground almonds
8oz (225g) fresh white breadcrumbs
2 teasp coffee powder

FILLING

4 tbs apricot jam

ICING

5oz (125g) plain chocolate
1 tbs caster sugar
3 tbs water

Preheat the oven to 375°F/190°F/Gas 5. Grease and base-line two 8in (20cm) sandwich tins. Put the chocolate into a bowl over a pan of hot water and heat gently until melted. Leave to cool. Cream the butter and sugar until light and fluffy, and gradually beat in the eggs one at a time. Whisk in the melted chocolate and gradually add the almonds. Stir in the breadcrumbs and coffee powder. Spoon into the tins and bake for 25 minutes. Leave to cool in the tins and then turn one cake on to a serving plate.

Spread lightly with the apricot jam. Cover with the second cake. To make the icing, put the chocolate, sugar and 2 tbs water into a pan and heat very gently until melted. Take off the heat and stir in the remaining water. Beat well and cool slightly before pouring over the cake.

Chocolate Whisky Cake

★★

A wonderful blending of flavours make this a very rich and completely irresistible cake, which may be eaten at the end of a meal.

Ingredients
FOR AN 8IN (20CM) CAKE

2oz (50g) seedless raisins
4 tbs whisky
7oz (200g) plain chocolate
2 tbs water
4oz (100g) unsalted butter
3 eggs
5oz (125g) light soft brown sugar
2oz (50g) plain flour
3oz (75g) ground almonds
pinch of salt

ICING

6oz (175g) plain chocolate
6fl oz (175ml) double cream

Put the raisins into a bowl with the whisky and leave to soak overnight. Preheat the oven to 350°F/180°F/Gas 4. Grease and line a loose-bottomed 8in (20cm) round tin. Break the chocolate into small pieces and put into a bowl with the water. Heat gently until melted. Cut the butter into small pieces, and add gradually to the chocolate, stirring until smooth. Remove from the heat.

Separate the eggs and beat the yolks and sugar until pale and fluffy. Slowly pour in the chocolate mixture, stirring well until evenly coloured. Stir in the flour, almonds, raisins and whisky. Whisk the egg whites and salt to stiff peaks and fold into the chocolate mixture. Place in the tin and bake for 35 minutes. Leave in the tin for 5 minutes, and remove the sides of the tin. Gently slide the cake from its base on to a wire rack to cool. When cold, carefully peel off the lining paper and put the cake on to a serving plate.

To make the icing, break the chocolate into a bowl and add the cream. Heat gently over a pan of hot water until just melted. Stir until smooth, cool slightly and pour over the cake.

Chocolate Baba
**

A glorious confection for a special teatime, or for the end of a meal. This cake looks spectacular on a buffet table, but needs to be prepared the day before.

Ingredients
FOR 8–10

4oz (100g) seedless raisins
2oz (50g) chopped mixed peel
2oz (50g) glacé cherries
4 tbs rum
8oz (225g) plain flour
1oz (25g) cocoa powder
2 teasp baking powder
½ teasp salt
5oz (125g) light soft brown sugar
2 eggs
6 tbs corn oil
6 tbs milk
½ teasp vanilla essence

SYRUP AND TOPPING

4oz (100g) sugar
¼pt (150ml) water
4 tbs rum
½pt (300ml) whipping cream
chocolate shapes

Put the raisins and peel into a bowl. Chop the cherries and mix with the other fruit. Stir in the rum and leave to soak. Preheat the oven to 350°F/180°C/Gas 4. Grease a 2½pt (1.5l) ring tin. Sieve the flour, cocoa powder, baking powder and salt into a bowl and stir in the sugar until evenly coloured. Separate the eggs, and put the yolks into a bowl with the oil, milk and essence and mix well. Add to the dry ingredients and beat well to a creamy batter. Whisk the egg whites to stiff peaks and fold into the mixture. Lightly stir in the raisins, peel, cherries and rum. Put into the tin and bake for 55 minutes. Leave in the tin for 5 minutes and turn on to a wire rack to cool.

Put the sugar and water into a heavy-based pan and bring them slowly to the boil. Simmer for 5 minutes and then take off the heat and stir in the rum. When the cake is cold, return it to the tin and spoon over the hot syrup. Cover and leave overnight.

Just before serving, whip the cream to soft peaks. Turn out the cake on to a serving dish. Pipe the cream in lines and decorate with chocolate shapes. Serve at once.

Never-fail Chocolate Cake

*

A very easy cake prepared in two layers which may be filled with chocolate or coffee butter icing, but is just as good if layered with apricot or raspberry jam and topped with melted plain chocolate.

Ingredients
FOR A 7IN (17.5CM) ROUND CAKE

6oz (175g) soft margarine
6oz (175g) caster sugar
6oz (175g) self-raising flour
1 teasp baking powder
1oz (25g) cocoa powder
3 eggs
2 tbs milk

ICING

4oz (100g) soft margarine
6oz (175g) icing sugar
1oz (25g) cocoa powder
2 tbs boiling water

Preheat the oven to 350°F/180°C/Gas 4. Grease and base-line two 7in (17.5cm) sponge sandwich tins.

Put the margarine, sugar, flour, baking powder, cocoa powder, eggs and milk into a bowl and beat hard until very light and creamy. Divide between the two tins and bake for 30 minutes. Turn on to a wire rack to cool.

To make the icing, put the margarine and sugar into a bowl and beat until creamy. Mix the cocoa powder with boiling water and gradually beat into the creamed mixture. Leave until cold before sandwiching the cake layers together and spreading the remaining icing on the top of the cake.

Chocolate Chip Orange Cake

**

Chocolate and orange provide a sophisticated flavour combination for a delicious but simple cake with a soft icing.

Ingredients
FOR A 7IN (17.5CM) ROUND CAKE

6oz (175g) butter
8oz (225g) caster sugar
4 eggs
10oz (300g) plain flour
1 teasp baking powder
grated rind of 1 orange
2oz (50g) plain chocolate

ICING

4oz (100g) plain chocolate
3 tbs water
1 teasp salad oil
1 oz (25g) caster sugar
9 crystallised orange slices

Preheat the oven to 350°F/180°C/Gas 4. Grease and base-line a 7in (17.5cm) round cake tin.

Cream together the butter and sugar until light and fluffy. Beat the eggs lightly. Sieve together the flour and baking powder. Add the eggs and flour alternately to the creamed mixture, beating well between each addition. Chop the chocolate into small pieces, and fold the orange rind and chocolate into the cake mixture. Put into the prepared tin and bake for 1¼ hours. Turn on to a wire rack to cool.

To prepare the icing, break the chocolate into small pieces and put into a heavy-based pan with the water, oil and sugar. Heat gently, stirring until the chocolate has melted and the mixture is smooth. Cool for 5 minutes, stir well and pour over the cake. Arrange orange slices on top.

Panforte
**

A rich, chewy confection from Siena, which has many varieties. This chocolate-flavoured version is rich with honey, nuts and glacé fruit.

Ingredients
FOR A 10IN (25CM) CAKE

6oz (175g) hazelnuts
6oz (175g) blanched split almonds
3oz (75g) glacé pineapple
3oz (75g) glacé apricots
2oz (50g) glacé cherries
2oz (50g) chopped mixed candied peel
3oz (75g) plain flour
1¹/₂oz (40g) cocoa powder
3 teasp ground cinnamon
12oz (350g) honey
5oz (125g) sugar

Preheat the oven to 325°F/160°C/Gas 3. Grease a 10in (25cm) round cake tin and line the base with baking parchment.

Put the hazelnuts on to a baking sheet and toast in the oven until the skins blister. Rub off the skins with a clean cloth. Put the almonds on to a baking sheet and toast in the oven until golden. Chop the hazelnuts and almonds coarsely. Chop the pineapple, apricots, cherries and peel and mix with the nuts. Stir in the flour, cocoa powder and cinnamon until evenly coloured. Put the honey and sugar into a heavy-based pan and bring to the boil. Boil until the mixture reaches 237°F/114°C (or until a little of the mixture dropped into a cup of cold water forms a soft ball). Pour over the mixture and stir well. Pour into the prepared tin and press down evenly. Bake for 30 minutes and then cool in the tin for 10 minutes. Turn on to a wire rack and peel off the baking parchment. Cool completely. Wrap in foil and store for 7 days before serving.

Chocolate Hazelnut Cake
**

This moist-textured, rich chocolate nut cake, topped by a chocolate cream icing, may be served as a cake or pudding with cream.

Ingredients
FOR A 7IN (17.5CM) CAKE

4oz (100g) unsalted butter
4oz (100g) caster sugar
3 eggs
4oz (100g) plain chocolate
5oz (125g) ground hazelnuts
1oz (25g) plain flour

ICING

¹/₄pt (150ml) double cream
5oz (125g) plain chocolate
8 Liqueur Truffles (p98)

Preheat the oven to 350°F/180°F/Gas 4. Grease and base-line a 7in (17.5cm) spring-form tin. Butter the base paper and dust lightly with flour. Cream the butter and sugar until very light and fluffy. Separate the eggs and beat in the yolks one at a time. Melt the chocolate in a bowl over hot water and stir into the creamed mixture. Mix the nuts and flour until evenly coloured and fold into the chocolate. Whisk the egg whites to stiff peaks and fold into the mixture. Place in the prepared tin and bake for 1 hour. Leave in the tin for 5 minutes and turn on to a wire rack to cool.

To make the icing, put the cream into a heavy-based pan and heat to just under boiling point. Add the chocolate and stir until thick and smooth. Take off the heat, and stir well until very creamy. Put the cake on to a serving plate and pour over the icing. When set (after about 1 hour), decorate with Liqueur Truffles.

Triple Cake
★★

Three ways of using plain chocolate in a rich cake, with a sponge layered with smooth chocolate buttercream and topped with mocha cream icing.

Ingredients
FOR A 6IN (15CM) CAKE

3 eggs
3oz (75g) caster sugar
2oz (50g) plain chocolate
3oz (75g) plain flour

FILLING

2oz (50g) caster sugar
4 tbs water
2 egg yolks
5oz (125g) unsalted butter
1¹/₂oz (40g) plain chocolate

ICING

4 tbs double cream
1 tbs strong black coffee
2¹/₂oz (65g) plain chocolate

Preheat the oven to 350°F/180°C/Gas 4. Grease and line a 6in (15cm) round cake tin. Grease the lining paper and dust lightly with flour. Separate the eggs and whisk the yolks and sugar until very pale and thick. Melt the chocolate in a bowl over a pan of hot water. Fold into the egg mixture. Whisk the egg whites to stiff peaks and fold into the mixture alternately with the flour. Put into the prepared tin and bake for 35 minutes. Cool in the tin for 5 minutes and turn on to a wire rack to cool.

Prepare the buttercream by putting the sugar and water into a heavy-based pan. Dissolve the sugar over low heat and cook over medium heat to 215°F/102°C or until a little of the mixture forms a thin thread from the spoon (see Cook's Tip, p.22). Whisk the egg yolks until thick and creamy and gradually whisk in the hot syrup until the mixture is fluffy and cool. Beat the butter in another bowl until light and creamy and gradually beat in the egg mixture until thick and shiny. Melt the chocolate in a bowl over hot water, cool and stir into the buttercream.

Split the cake into three layers and reassemble with the buttercream between each layer. Put the cream and coffee into a heavy-based pan and bring just to the boil. Break the chocolate into small pieces and stir into the cream until melted. Remove from the heat and continue stirring until cool and smooth. Pour over the cake and leave to stand for 15 minutes.

Truffle Roll
★★

A chocolate Swiss roll with a rum truffle filling is rolled in grated chocolate and garnished with truffle sweets.

Ingredients
FOR 1 CAKE

4 eggs
4oz (100g) caster sugar
2oz (50g) plain flour
1¹/₂oz (40g) cocoa powder

FILLING AND TOPPING

6 fl oz (175ml) double cream
1 tbs rum
5oz (125g) plain chocolate
3oz (75g) grated plain chocolate
8 chocolate truffles

Preheat the oven to 450°F/230°C/Gas 8. Grease and base-line a 12x9in (30x22.5cm) Swiss-roll tin, and lightly grease and flour the paper.

Separate the eggs and whisk the egg yolks and sugar until very pale and thick. Sieve the flour and cocoa powder together. Whisk the egg whites to stiff peaks and fold into the egg mixture alternately with the flour. Fill the tin and bake for 12 minutes. Put a clean tea towel on to a flat surface and cover with a piece of greaseproof paper lightly dusted with caster sugar. Turn the cooked cake on to this and peel off the lining paper. Trim the crisp edges from the cake. Put a piece of greaseproof paper on top of the cake and roll up carefully. Cover with a damp tea towel and leave until cold.

Prepare the filling by putting the cream and rum into a heavy-based pan and bringing just to the boil. Break the chocolate into small pieces and stir into the pan. When the chocolate has melted, remove from heat and stir well until thick and smooth. Chill for 1 hour and then whisk until light and fluffy.

Unroll the cake and spread lightly with half the filling mixture. Roll up gently. Spread the remaining mixture lightly over the surface of the cake, including the ends. Coat completely with grated chocolate. Put on to a serving dish and arrange a line of chocolate truffles down the centre. Serve each slice of cake with a chocolate truffle.

Chocolate Ginger Cup Cakes
———— ⋆ ————

Small light sponge cakes are delicious freshly baked, and make a good emergency pudding served warm with ice cream.

Ingredients
FOR 18 CAKES

4oz (100g) butter
4oz (100g) caster sugar
2 eggs
4oz (100g) self-raising flour
1 teasp ground ginger
2oz (50g) chocolate chips

Preheat the oven to 350°F/180°C/Gas 4. Place paper baking cases in tartlet tins so that they keep their shape.

Cream the butter and sugar until light and fluffy. Beat the eggs. Sieve the flour with the ginger. Add eggs and flour alternately to the creamed mixture, and beat well. Spoon the mixture into baking cases. Sprinkle chocolate chips on each one. Bake for 20 minutes. Cool on a wire rack.

Assorted Truffles (pp98-101)
Chocolate Baba (p76)
Chocolate Marble Cake (p71)
Chocolate Liègeois (p119)

Cup Cakes
**

Nursery favourites with a deep chocolate flavour and soft, smooth icing.

Ingredients
FOR 30 CAKES

1oz (25g) cocoa powder
2 tbs boiling water
4oz (100g) soft margarine
6oz (175g) caster sugar
6oz (175g) self-raising flour
1 teasp baking powder
2 eggs
4 tbs milk

ICING

4oz (100g) plain chocolate
4 tbs water
1oz (25g) unsalted butter
6oz (175g) icing sugar

Preheat the oven to 350°F/180°C/Gas 4. Put 30 paper cake cases into patty tins.

Put the cocoa into a large bowl and add the boiling water. Mix well and leave to stand for 5 minutes. Add the margarine, sugar, flour, baking powder, eggs and milk. Beat hard until well mixed and creamy. Divide between the paper cases and bake for 15 minutes. Leave to cool in the tins.

To make the icing, break the chocolate into small pieces and put into a bowl over hot water. Add the water and butter and melt gently. Take off the heat and beat in the icing sugar. Cool slightly and pour on top of each cake. Leave until cold and set before removing cakes from tins.

Chocolate Fruit Celebration Cake
*

Those who are addicted to chocolate on all occasions might like to serve this as a Christmas cake or even a wedding cake.

Ingredients
FOR AN 8 IN (20CM) SQUARE CAKE

350g (12oz) sultanas
6oz (175g) glacé cherries
6oz (175g) glacé apricots
6oz (175g) plain chocolate
7oz (200g) unsalted butter
5oz (125g) light soft brown sugar
8fl oz (225ml) sweet sherry
4 eggs
6oz (175g) chocolate chips
7oz (200g) plain flour
1oz (25g) self-raising flour
½ teasp bicarbonate of soda

Preheat the oven to 300°F/150°C/Gas 2. Grease and line the base and sides of an 8in (20cm) square cake tin.

Put the sultanas, halved cherries and chopped apricots into a heavy-based pan. Add the chocolate broken into small pieces with the butter and sugar. Reserve 2 tbs sherry and put the rest into the pan. Heat gently until the chocolate and butter have melted. Bring to the boil, and then simmer for 10 minutes. Turn into a large bowl and leave until lukewarm.

Beat the eggs into the fruit mixture and then beat in the chocolate chips, flours and soda. Spread in the tin and bake for 2½ hours. Brush with reserved sherry, cover with foil and cool in the tin. Turn out when cold.

Sicilian Chocolate Squares

**

This incredibly light chocolate cake sandwiched with a luscious cream cheese filling can only be eaten in very small portions.

Ingredients
FOR 16 SQUARES

3 eggs
3 tbs caster sugar
2 tbs cocoa powder
few drops of vanilla essence

FILLING

3oz (75g) cream cheese
3 tbs icing sugar
2 tbs orange liqueur
2 tbs chopped mixed candied peel
1½oz (40g) plain chocolate
cocoa powder

Preheat the oven to 350°F/180°C/Gas 4. Grease a 12x8in (30x20cm) Swiss-roll tin and line the base with greaseproof paper. Grease the paper and sprinkle lightly with flour. Shake off excess flour.

Separate the eggs and beat the yolks with sugar until light and fluffy. Fold in the cocoa powder and vanilla essence. Whisk the egg whites to stiff peaks and fold into the mixture. Spread lightly to cover the base of the tin. Bake for 12 minutes. Cool in the tin for 10 minutes. Turn out on to a piece of greaseproof paper, and peel the paper from the base.

Beat the cream cheese until very light. Stir in the sugar and liqueur. Chop the peel very finely, and grate the chocolate finely. Add to the cheese mixture. Trim the hard edges from the sheet of cake, and cut the cake in half. Spread the filling over one piece of cake and top with the other half, pressing lightly together. Sift cocoa powder lightly over the top. Chill in the refrigerator for 2 hours and cut into squares. Store covered in the refrigerator for up to 48 hours.

Truffle Cakes

*

Richly-flavoured gooey balls of chocolate cake which are very addictive, but incredibly easy to make.

Ingredients
FOR 12–15 CAKES

1lb (450g) stale cake
syrup from canned fruit (or weak orange squash)
1oz (25g) cocoa powder (optional)
2–3oz (50–75g) seedless raisins (optional)
2–3 tbs rum
4oz (100g) apricot jam
3 tbs water
8oz (225g) chocolate vermicelli

Any type of cake may be used, or a mixture of cakes such as chocolate, sponge cake and fruit cake. If there is plenty of chocolate cake, no cocoa powder will be needed; if there is plenty of fruit cake, the raisins may be omitted. Break the cake into crumbs and put into a large bowl with the cocoa and raisins, if used. Sprinkle with some syrup from canned fruit, or some weak orange squash to moisten the crumbs, but not to make them soggy. Leave in a cool place for 30 minutes. Stir in the rum. Mix well and form the damp crumbs into round, firm balls.

Put the apricot jam and water into a heavy-based pan and bring to the boil, stirring well. Leave to stand for 5 minutes.

Meanwhile, spread the chocolate vermicelli on a plate. Using two spoons, dip each cake ball into the apricot jam until completely coated. Drain well and toss in vermicelli until completely coated. Put cakes in a single layer on a tray and leave for 2 hours until firm. Put into paper cake cases to serve.

Chocolate Meringues
*

These meringues should not be filled with cream as they are already rich enough. They make good sweetmeats for wedding receptions and similar parties.

Ingredients
For 24–30 meringues

2 egg whites
pinch of cream of tartar
pinch of salt
6oz ((175g) caster sugar
6oz (175g) plain chocolate chips

Preheat the oven to 300°F/150°C/Gas 2. Base-line two baking sheets with baking parchment. Whisk the egg whites, cream of tartar and salt to stiff peaks. Gradually add the sugar, whisking all the time, until the mixture stands in stiff peaks and is thick and shiny. Fold in the chocolate chips. Drop the mixture in large rounded teaspoonfuls on to the baking sheets, and bake for 30 minutes.

Carefully lift off the meringues and return them to the baking sheets with the flat bases upwards. Bake for 15 minutes. Turn off the oven and leave in the meringues for 30 minutes. Remove from the tins and leave on a wire rack until cold. Store in an airtight tin.

Crunch Brownies
*

Plain chocolate cake with a rich, soft texture contrasts with a sugared nut topping.

Ingredients
For 16 squares

8oz (225g) self-raising flour
1 teasp ground cinnamon
pinch of salt
4oz (100g) soft margarine
4oz (100g) dark soft brown sugar
3oz (75g) plain chocolate
5oz (125g) golden syrup
1 teasp bicarbonate of soda
2 tbs milk

TOPPING

4oz (100g) plain flour
2oz (50g) butter
1oz (25g) demerara sugar
2oz (50g) chopped walnuts

Preheat the oven to 375°F/190°C/Gas 5. Grease and base-line a deep 11x7in (27.5x17.5cm) tin.

Sieve the flour, cinnamon and salt together. Cream the fat and sugar until light and fluffy. Melt the chocolate and golden syrup together. Stir in the bicarbonate of soda and milk, and add alternately to the creamed mixture with the flour. Beat well and put into the tin.

Make the topping by rubbing the butter into the flour, and stirring in the sugar and walnuts. Sprinkle over the cake. Bake for 45 minutes. Cool in the tin and cut into squares.

Syrup Brownies
**

Another version of this popular American cookie which has a particularly fudge-like consistency.

Ingredients
FOR 12 SQUARES

4oz (100g) sugar
¼pt (150ml) water
1oz (25g) cocoa powder
4oz (100g) unsalted butter
8oz (225g) light soft brown sugar
2 egg yolks
6oz (175g) plain flour
¼ teasp bicarbonate of soda
pinch of salt
3oz (75g) walnuts

Put the sugar and water into a heavy-based pan and stir over low heat until the sugar has dissolved. Bring to the boil and boil gently to 215°F/102°C (or until a little of the mixture dropped into a cup of cold water forms fine threads). Take off the heat and stir in the cocoa. Stir over low heat for 2 minutes and leave to cool.

Preheat the oven to 350°F/180°C/Gas 4. Grease an 11x7in (27.5x17.5cm) tin. Cream the butter and sugar together until light and fluffy. Beat in the egg yolks one at a time, and stir in the chocolate syrup. Sieve the flour, soda and salt together and fold into the chocolate mixture. Chop the walnuts finely and stir into the mixture. Put into the tin and bake for 40 minutes. Leave in the tin for 5 minutes and turn on to a wire rack to cool. Cut into squares.

Chocolate Fudge Squares
*

Careful timing is needed for baking these biscuits to achieve the perfect texture.

Ingredients
FOR 24 BISCUITS

4oz (100g) soft margarine
2oz (50g) dark soft brown sugar
4oz (100g) self-raising flour
2oz (50g) porridge oats
3 teasp cocoa powder

ICING

4oz (100g) icing sugar
3 teasp cocoa powder
5 teasp lukewarm water

Preheat the oven to 325°F/160°C/Gas 3. Grease an 11x7in (27.5x17.5cm) shallow tin. Put the margarine and sugar into a bowl and cream them until soft and well mixed. Work in the flour, oats and cocoa and mix well until evenly coloured. Press into the tin, using a fork to spread the mixture evenly. Bake for exactly 30 minutes (no longer, or the biscuits become hard and unpalatable).

Mix the icing ingredients until smooth and evenly coloured. As soon as the tin is removed from the oven, leave to cool for exactly 5 minutes, then pour over the icing. Leave in the tin until completely cold and set. Cut into squares or fingers and store in an airtight tin.

Chocolate Macaroons

*

Delicious chocolate almond morsels for teatime, or to serve with creamy puddings.

Ingredients
FOR 12 MACAROONS

2 egg whites
8oz (225g) caster sugar
4¹/₂oz (115g) ground almonds
1¹/₂oz (40g) drinking chocolate powder
edible rice paper
blanched almonds

Preheat the oven to 350°F/180°C/Gas 4. Cover two baking sheets with rice paper. Whisk the egg whites to stiff peaks. Stir the sugar, almonds and chocolate powder together until evenly coloured. Fold into the egg whites. Place in small spoonfuls on the rice paper, leaving room for spreading.

Place an almond on each biscuit. Bake for 20 minutes. Lift carefully on to a wire rack to cool. When cold, trim off surplus rice paper round the edge of each macaroon. Store in an airtight tin.

Chocolate Flapjacks

*

Simple family favourites become irresistible when chocolate is added.

Ingredients
FOR 12 FLAPJACKS

4oz (100g) butter
1oz (25g) light soft brown sugar
2 tbs golden syrup
8oz (225g) porridge oats
3oz (75g) plain chocolate

Preheat the oven to 350°F/180°C/Gas 4. Put the butter, sugar and syrup into a pan and heat gently until the fat has melted. Remove from the heat and stir in the oats. Chop the chocolate finely and stir into the mixture. Press into a greased 11x7in (27.5x17.5cm) tin. Bake for 25 minutes. Cool and mark into squares. When nearly cold, cut firmly and lift on to a wire rack to cool.

One-pot Brownies

*

One of the easiest recipes for these popular cookies, but one of the best. They are very addictive, but especially good for tucking into a lunchbox or picnic hamper.

Ingredients
FOR 24 BROWNIES

3oz (75g) butter or hard margarine
8oz (225g) granulated sugar
2 eggs
¹/₂ teasp vanilla essence
3 heaped tbs cocoa powder
2oz (50g) plain flour
1 teasp baking powder
4oz (100g) chopped walnuts
4oz (100g) seedless raisins

Preheat the oven to 350°F/180°C/Gas 4. Line an 11x7in (27.5x17.5cm) tin with foil and grease it lightly.

Melt the fat in a large pan. Cool to lukewarm and beat in all the other ingredients. Spread in the tin and bake for 30 minutes. Leave in the tin for 15 minutes. Mark into squares or fingers and remove from the tin. Leave to cool on a wire rack.

Picnic Bars

—— * ——

Crunchy bars with a chocolate and cherry topping are perfect for packed meals but just as good with a glass of milk or cup of coffee.

Ingredients
FOR 16 BARS

2oz (50g) butter
2oz (50g) white vegetable fat
10oz (300g) light soft brown sugar
5½oz (150g) plain flour
2 eggs
1 teasp baking powder
pinch of salt
4oz (100g) chocolate chips
4oz (100g) glacé cherries

Preheat the oven to 350°F/180°C/Gas 4. Grease an 11x7in (27.5x17.5cm) tin. Cream together the butter, white fat and 3oz (75g) sugar. Stir in 4oz (100g) flour and mix well. Press into the prepared tin and bake for 10 minutes. Beat together lightly the eggs and remaining sugar and stir in the remaining flour, baking powder and salt. Stir in the chocolate chips. Chop the cherries roughly and add to the mixture.

Spread over the partly cooked base and continue baking for 30 minutes. Cool in the tin. Cut into 16 bars and put on to a wire rack to finish cooling.

Chocolate Marshmallow Shortbread

—— ** ——

An addictive mixture of rich shortbread, a soft filling studded with nuts and glacé fruit, and a plain chocolate topping.

Ingredients
FOR 30 PIECES

4oz (100g) plain flour
pinch of salt
3oz (75g) unsalted butter
2 tbs icing sugar
1 egg yolk

FILLING

1 tbs double cream
7oz (200g) marshmallows
3oz (75g) walnuts
2oz (50g) glacé cherries
1oz (25g) angelica

TOPPING

4oz (100g) plain chocolate
1oz (25g) unsalted butter

Preheat the oven to 350°F/180°C/Gas 4. Grease an 11x7in (27.5x17.5cm) tin. Sieve flour and salt into a bowl and rub in butter lightly until the mixture is like coarse breadcrumbs. Stir in the icing sugar and egg yolk. Mix well and press into the tin in an even layer. Prick well with a fork and chill for 20 minutes. Bake for 20 minutes and leave to cool in the tin.

Put the cream in a small pan with the marshmallows and heat gently until melted. Chop the walnuts, cherries and angelica. Stir into the pan, remove from heat and spread over the shortbread. Leave until cold and set.

Put the chocolate and butter into a bowl

over a pan of hot water and heat gently until the chocolate has melted. Stir well and spread quickly over the marshmallow layer. Leave until set. Cut into small pieces. For storage, wrap the tin and store in the refrigerator for up to 7 days.

No-bake Chocolate Squares

A good way of using leftover biscuits to make a rich teatime treat.

Ingredients
FOR 16 SQUARES

6oz (175g) mixed sweet biscuits
2oz (50g) hazelnuts
2oz (50g) seedless raisins
3oz (75g) unsalted butter
2 tbs golden syrup
6 oz (150g) plain chocolate

Grease an 8in (20cm) square tin.

Crush the biscuits, but not too finely. Chop the nuts and mix with the biscuit crumbs and raisins. Put the butter and syrup into a small pan and add 2oz (50g) chocolate. Heat gently until melted and stir into the crumb mixture. Mix well and press into the tin in an even layer. Leave until cold and hard. Put the remaining chocolate into a bowl over hot water and heat gently until melted. Pour over the biscuit mixture and leave to harden. Cut into squares and remove from the tin.

Turtles
★★

Shortbread with a thick caramel topping, completed by a coating of plain chocolate and crunchy nuts.

Ingredients
FOR 15 SQUARES

4oz (100g) soft margarine
2oz (50g) caster sugar
6oz (175g) plain flour

TOPPING

4oz (100g) hard margarine
3oz (75g) caster sugar
2 tbs golden syrup
7oz (200g) can sweetened condensed milk

COATING

4oz (100g) plain chocolate
2oz (50g) hazelnuts or walnuts

Preheat the oven to 350°F/180°C/Gas 4. Grease an 11x7in (27.5x17.5cm) tin.

Work the soft margarine, sugar and flour together to make a firm dough. Press into the tin to give an even layer and prick with a fork. Bake for 25 minutes.

While the base is cooking, prepare the topping. Put the margarine, sugar, syrup and condensed milk into a heavy-based pan and heat gently until melted. Boil for 7–8 minutes until the mixture is caramel coloured, stirring well so that the mixture does not burn. Remove from heat and cool to lukewarm.

Remove the shortbread from the oven and leave to cool in the tin for 5 minutes. Pour over the topping and leave until cold.

Melt the chocolate in a bowl over a pan of hot water. Pour over the caramel and mark in lines with a fork. Sprinkle with finely chopped nuts. Leave until cold before cutting.

Hungarian Mocha Cookies

**

A subtle blend of chocolate and coffee makes these lovely filled biscuits suitable for a special tea party. The filling is nicest when it is not too sweet.

Ingredients

FOR 20 COOKIES

8oz (225g) unsalted butter
4oz (100g) caster sugar
8oz (225g) self-raising flour
2oz (50g) cocoa powder

FILLING

2oz (50g) cocoa powder
¼pt (150ml) strong black coffee
2oz (50g) unsalted butter
caster sugar to taste

Preheat the oven to 350°F/180°C/Gas 4. Grease two baking sheets.

Cream the butter and sugar until light and fluffy. Stir the flour and cocoa together until evenly coloured, and then work into the creamed mixture. With the hands, form the mixture into balls the size of a large walnut. Place the pieces on the baking sheets, leaving a little space between them. Dip a fork into cold water and press the biscuits down lightly. Bake for 12 minutes and lift carefully on to a wire rack to cool.

To make the filling, put the cocoa into a small pan with the coffee. Heat gently, stirring well, until the mixture is a thick cream. Take off the heat and beat in the butter. Add sugar to taste, but do not oversweeten. When the mixture is cold, sandwich the biscuits together in pairs. If liked, the tops may be dusted with sieved icing sugar just before serving.

Chocolate Chip Walnut Cookies

*

An unbeatable combination of plain chocolate and walnut pieces in a crisp biscuit casing. These are especially good with a glass of milk or cup of coffee.

Ingredients

FOR 40–50 BISCUITS

3oz (75g) butter
3oz (75g) dark soft brown sugar
3oz (75g) granulated sugar
½ teasp vanilla essence
6oz (175g) self-raising flour
pinch of salt
1 egg
4oz (100g) plain chocolate chips
2oz (50g) chopped walnuts

Preheat the oven to 350°F/180°C/Gas 4. Grease two baking sheets.

Cream the butter and sugars until light and fluffy, and work in the essence. Mix the flour and salt and work into the creamed mixture with the beaten egg. Stir in the chocolate chips and walnuts until evenly mixed. Drop teaspoonfuls of the mixture on to the baking sheets, leaving room for the biscuits to spread. Bake for 10 minutes. Lift carefully on to a wire rack to cool. Store in an airtight tin.

Viennese Chocolate Shells

————— ** —————

Biscuits with a very short texture and a simple filling which enhances the chocolate flavour.

Ingredients
FOR 12 BISCUITS

5oz (125g) unsalted butter
3oz (75g) caster sugar
7oz (200g) self-raising flour
1oz (25g) cornflour
3oz (75g) plain chocolate
2oz (50g) apricot jam
icing sugar

Preheat the oven to 375°F/190°C/Gas 5. Grease two baking sheets.

Cream the butter and sugar until light and fluffy. Sieve the flour and cornflour together and work into the creamed mixture. Melt the chocolate in a bowl over hot water. Cool slightly and work into the mixture.

Put into a piping bag fitted with a large star nozzle, and pipe out shell shapes on the baking sheets. Bake for 15 minutes. Cool on a wire rack.

Sandwich the biscuits together in pairs with the jam and sprinkle the top surfaces with sieved icing sugar.

Hazelnut Crisps

————— * —————

These chocolate nut biscuits are very good with ice cream.

Ingredients
FOR 40 BISCUITS

4oz (100g) butter or margarine
4oz (100g) caster sugar
6oz (175g) plain flour
2oz (50g) ground hazelnuts
2oz (50g) plain chocolate
1 egg white
1½ oz (40g) shelled hazelnuts

Preheat the oven to 375°F/190°C/Gas 5. Grease two baking sheets.

Cream the fat and sugar together until light and fluffy. Work in the flour and ground hazelnuts. Chop the chocolate finely and work into the mixture, with a little egg white if necessary to bind to a firm paste.

Roll out and cut into rounds or other shapes. Whisk the egg white and brush over the biscuits. Arrange shelled nuts on each one. Bake for 20 minutes, and lift on to a wire rack to cool.

Chocolate Lemon Bourbons

*

The traditional Bourbon biscuit is given extra flavour with ground almonds and a hint of lemon rind.

Ingredients
FOR 12 BISCUITS

3oz (75g) butter
3oz (75g) caster sugar
3oz (75g) plain flour
3oz (75g) ground almonds
grated rind of 1 lemon
2oz (50g) plain chocolate

FILLING

2oz (50g) butter
4oz (100g) icing sugar
½oz (15g) cocoa powder

icing sugar

Preheat the oven to 375°F/190°C/Gas 5. Grease two baking sheets.

Cream the butter and sugar until light and fluffy. Work in the flour, ground almonds and lemon rind. Melt the chocolate in a bowl over hot water. Cool slightly and work into the mixture. Roll out and cut into rectangles. Place on the baking sheets and prick each biscuit three or four times with a fork. Bake for 20 minutes. Cool on a wire rack.

To make the filling, cream the butter, icing sugar and cocoa powder together until smooth and light. Sandwich the biscuits together in pairs and sprinkle the top surfaces with sieved icing sugar.

Chocolate Rings

*

Rich chocolate biscuits dipped in plain chocolate are the perfect accompaniment to milk or coffee, or they may be used as a base for serving ice creams or sorbets.

Ingredients
FOR 36 BISCUITS

4oz (100g) unsalted butter
4oz (100g) caster sugar
1 egg
few drops of vanilla essence
8oz (225g) plain flour
1oz (25g) cocoa powder
6oz (175g) plain chocolate

Preheat the oven to 375°F/190°C/Gas 5. Grease two baking sheets.

Cream the butter and sugar until light and fluffy. Beat in the egg and essence. Work in the flour and cocoa. Chill for 30 minutes, and roll out. Cut into 2½in (6.25cm) rounds. Remove centres with a small round cutter and re-roll until all dough is used. Bake for 15 minutes, and cool on a wire rack.

Put the chocolate into a bowl over hot water, and heat gently until melted. Dip each biscuit into the chocolate until coated, and place on a sheet of baking parchment until cold and set.

Florentines

★★

Crisp fruit and nut biscuits contrast with smooth dark chocolate. They are perfect for a wedding reception or special party.

Ingredients
FOR 20 BISCUITS

3oz (75g) blanched almonds
1¹/₂oz (40g) glacé cherries
2oz (50g) unsalted butter
3oz (75g) caster sugar
1oz (25g) flaked almonds
2oz (50g) chopped mixed peel
2 tbs double cream
4oz (100g) plain chocolate

Preheat the oven to 350°F/180°C/Gas 4. Line 2 baking sheets with baking parchment. Chop the blanched almonds and quarter the cherries. Put the butter into a pan and stir in the sugar. Bring slowly to the boil. Remove the butter from the heat and stir in the chopped and flaked almonds, peel, cherries and cream.

Put teaspoonfuls far apart on the baking sheets. Bake for 8–10 minutes until golden-brown. Neaten the edges with a knife to form circles. Cool slightly and lift on to a wire rack to cool.

Melt the chocolate in a bowl over a pan of hot water. Spread on the smooth side of the biscuits and mark with a fork in wavy lines. Leave for 15 minutes to set.

Chocolate Chip Raisin Cookies

★

Tempting cookies which are particularly good eaten freshly baked and still slightly warm.

Ingredients
FOR 15 COOKIES

4oz (100g) butter
4oz (100g) light soft brown sugar
2oz (50g) caster sugar
1 egg
few drops of vanilla essence
6oz (175g) plain flour
¹/₂ teasp salt
¹/₂ teasp bicarbonate of soda
4oz (100g) plain chocolate chips
4oz (100g) seedless raisins

Preheat the oven to 325°F/160°C/Gas 3. Grease two baking sheets.

Cream together the butter, brown sugar and caster sugar until light and fluffy. Beat in the egg and vanilla essence. Sieve the flour with salt and soda and work into the creamed mixture. Fold in the chocolate chips and raisins. Form into 15 balls and place at intervals on the baking sheets, allowing room for spreading. Press down lightly with a fork dipped in cold water. Bake for 18 minutes. Cool for 2 minutes and lift on to a wire rack to finish cooling.

Chocolate Chip Shortbread

*

Traditional shortbread with contrasting pieces of chocolate and flaked almonds.

Ingredients

For a 6in (15cm) shortbread round

4oz (100g) unsalted butter
2oz (50g) caster sugar
6oz (175g) plain flour
2oz (50g) rice flour or cornflour
4oz (100g) chocolate chips
1oz (25g) flaked almonds
icing sugar

Preheat the oven to 300°F/150°C/Gas 2. Butter and flour a flan ring and place on a greased baking sheet.

Rub together the butter, sugar, flour and rice flour or cornflour to make a smooth, firm paste. Work in the chocolate chips. Press into the flan ring and press down lightly with a fork. Sprinkle with flaked almonds. Bake for 40 minutes until very pale gold in colour. Leave to stand until cold. Lift on to a serving plate and dust lightly with icing sugar. For convenience of serving, the shortbread may be marked lightly into triangles before it cools.

Chocolate Coconut Bars

*

Useful cookies to have in the tin for emergencies, with the slightly crunchy base contrasting with smooth chocolate.

Ingredients

For 12–16 bars

4oz (100g) unsalted butter
6oz (150g) caster sugar
2 eggs
4oz (100g) ground rice
4oz (100g) desiccated coconut
4oz (100g) sultanas
4oz (100g) glacé cherries
6oz (175g) plain chocolate

Preheat the oven to 325°F/160°C/Gas 3. Grease and base-line an 11x7in (27.5x 17.5cm) tin.

Cream the butter and sugar together until light and soft. Beat in the eggs and then stir in the ground rice, coconut, sultanas and chopped cherries. Put into the prepared tin and bake for 30 minutes. Leave to cool in the tin.

Break the chocolate into small pieces and put into a bowl over a pan of hot water. When the chocolate has melted, pour over the base. Leave until cold and firm before cutting into bars and removing from the tin.

White Chocolate Fruit Bars

*

An incredible confection of dried fruit and mixed nuts held together by white chocolate and honey, which is good with after-dinner coffee.

Ingredients
FOR 24 SQUARES

4oz (100g) flaked almonds
8oz (225g) chopped walnuts
8oz (225g) desiccated coconut
4oz (100g) currants
4oz (100g) chopped dried apricots
1oz (25g) plain flour
8oz (225g) white chocolate
6oz (175g) clear honey
6oz (175g) apricot jam
2 tbs icing sugar

Preheat the oven to 325°F/160°C/Gas 3. Grease and base-line an 8x12in (20x30cm) tin and grease the lining paper.

Put the almonds, walnuts, coconut, currants, apricots and flour into a large bowl and stir well together. Break the chocolate into small pieces and put into another bowl over hot water. Heat until melted, and then mix with the honey and jam. Stir into the dry ingredients and spread evenly in the prepared tin. Bake for 50 minutes. Cool in the tin and then sprinkle with icing sugar. Cut into small squares and remove from the tin. Store in the refrigerator.

Chocolate Maple Bars

**

A simple chocolate cake stuffed with raisins and topped with an unusual chocolate and maple syrup icing.

Ingredients
FOR 16 BARS

5oz (125g) unsalted butter
4¹/₂oz (115g) light soft brown sugar
2 eggs
2oz (50g) plain flour
1oz (25g) self-raising flour
1oz (25g) cocoa powder
¼ teasp bicarbonate of soda
4oz (100g) seedless raisins
½ teasp vanilla essence

ICING

4oz (100g) plain or milk chocolate
3 tbs maple syrup

Preheat the oven to 350°F/180°C/Gas 4. Grease and base-line an 8x12in (20x30cm) tin and grease the lining paper.

Cream the butter and sugar until light and fluffy. Beat the eggs lightly. Sieve together the flours and cocoa. Add the eggs and flour mixture alternately to the creamed mixture, beating well. Beat in the soda and raisins with the vanilla essence. Spread in the prepared tin and bake for 25 minutes. Leave to stand for 5 minutes.

For the icing, break the chocolate into small pieces in a heavy-based pan with the maple syrup. Heat gently until the chocolate has melted. Stir well and pour over the warm cake. Leave until cold before cutting into bars.

Rum Raisin Toffee Bars

**

A chocolate shortbread base is topped with rum-flavoured toffee spiked with raisins and coconut and finished with soft chocolate icing.

Ingredients
FOR 16 BARS

5oz (125g) unsalted butter
4oz (100g) caster sugar
4oz (100g) plain flour
1oz (25g) cocoa powder

TOFFEE LAYER

14oz (400g) can sweetened condensed milk
1oz (25g) unsalted butter
1 tbs rum
4oz (100g) seedless raisins
3oz (75g) desiccated coconut

TOPPING

5oz (125g) plain chocolate
1oz (25g) unsalted butter

Preheat the oven to 350°F/180°C/Gas 4. Grease and base-line an 8x12in (20x30cm) tin and grease the lining paper.

Cream the butter and sugar until light and fluffy. Sieve the flour and cocoa powder together and fold into the mixture. Press evenly into the prepared tin and bake for 20 minutes. Cool in tin for 10 minutes.

To make the toffee layer, put the condensed milk and butter into a heavy-based pan and bring to the boil, stirring all the time and then continue cooking for 10 minutes until the mixture is golden brown. Take off the heat and stir in the rum, raisins and coconut. Cool to lukewarm and spread on the cooked base.

To make the icing, put the chocolate and butter into a bowl over a pan of hot water and heat gently until melted. Remove from the heat, stir well and spread on the cool filling. Leave until cold and set before cutting into bars.

Peanut Brownies

*

Children's favourites, which are nourishing (and non-sticky) for the lunchbox or a mid-morning snack.

Ingredients
FOR 16 SQUARES

5oz (125g) unsalted butter
4½oz (115g) dark soft brown sugar
2oz (50g) plain chocolate
2 tbs peanut butter
2 eggs
4oz (100g) unsalted roasted peanuts
3oz (75g) self-raising flour
1 tbs icing sugar

Preheat the oven to 350°F/180°C/Gas 4. Grease and base-line an 8in (20cm) square tin, and grease the lining paper.

Put the butter, sugar and chocolate into a heavy-based pan and heat gently until the chocolate has melted. Cool to lukewarm. Beat the peanut butter and eggs in a bowl and add the chopped peanuts. Stir in the chocolate mixture and the flour. Pour into the prepared tin and bake for 30 minutes.

Leave in the tin for 5 minutes and turn on to a wire rack to cool. When cold, sprinkle with icing sugar and cut into squares.

Chocolate Croissants
**

A special treat for French children is equally appreciated by adults for a leisurely breakfast with good cup of coffee.

Ingredients
FOR 8–10 CROISSANTS

6fl oz (175ml) milk
*½oz (15g) fresh yeast **or** ¼oz (7g) dried yeast*
1 teasp caster sugar
10oz (300g) bread flour
5oz (125g) butter
4oz (100g) plain chocolate
beaten egg for glazing

Warm the milk to lukewarm and mix with the yeast and sugar. Leave to stand until bubbling strongly. Sieve the flour into a warm mixing bowl and add the milk and 1oz (25g) melted butter. Mix to a soft dough and knead lightly until smooth. Place in a lightly oiled bowl, cover with a cloth and leave in a warm place for about 30 minutes until doubled in size. Knead again and roll lightly into a rectangle three times as long as wide.

Soften, but do not melt, the remaining butter, and divide into three portions. Dot one portion over the top two-thirds of the dough. Fold the bottom third up and the top third down over the butter. Seal the edges and turn so that the folded edges are at the sides. Roll into a rectangle again and repeat the process twice more. Cover the dough and leave in a cool place for 15 minutes. Roll out thinly and cut into triangles with 9in (22.5cm) long sides and 6in (15cm) base. Cut the chocolate into as many short thick bars as there are triangles.

Place a piece of chocolate at the base of each triangle and roll up loosely from the base. Curl the ends round to form a crescent. Place on baking trays and leave in a warm place for 20 minutes until well risen. Brush with beaten egg and bake at 450°F/230°C/Gas 8 for 10–15 minutes until golden brown. Eat freshly made.

9

Sweetmeats and Petits Fours

CHOCOLATE IS BOOMING. Everywhere there are chocolate shops together with grocers and gift shops with speciality chocolate departments. It is easy to buy luxury chocolates as presents or as self-indulgence, and after-dinner coffee is rarely served without some delectable sweetmeat. The traditional chocolate square allowed to children after a meal has been transformed into the adult truffle, liqueur cream or smooth fudge.

Sweet-making is a delicate art, but it is not difficult to acquire. For a few confections such as fudge, a sugar thermometer is useful, though not essential. Most sweetmeats rely on careful melting of the chocolate, a combination of the most delicious complementary flavours and long setting in a cool place. It is important not to over-handle chocolate sweetmeats as they quickly lose their shine and their charm, and they are best placed in paper or foil sweet cases as soon as they are prepared. Those who want to make very professional-looking sweets can now buy moulds and dipping tools in kitchen shops, so that little handling is required.

These sweetmeats are not designed to last a long time, and they are so good that they will get little chance to do so. Use the best possible chocolate, fresh cream, unsalted butter and good flavourings, and make only a small batch which will be eaten quickly.

Fresh Cream Truffles
★★

A light hand and scrupulous attention to detail will produce delectable truffles which must be eaten quickly.

Ingredients
FOR 1¼LB (550G) TRUFFLES (ABOUT 24)

¼pt (150ml) double cream
1 vanilla pod
1 egg yolk
1oz (25g) caster sugar
1lb (450g) plain chocolate
1oz (25g) unsalted butter
1 teasp oil

Put the cream and vanilla pod into a small, heavy-based pan and bring to the boil. Remove from the heat, cover and leave to stand for 20 minutes. Take out the vanilla pod (which may be washed, dried and used again). Put the egg yolk and caster sugar into a bowl and whisk until pale and thick. Whisk in the cream and return to the pan. Heat very gently for 3 minutes until the mixture begins to thicken, but do not boil. Break 5oz (125g) plain chocolate into small pieces. Take the cream off the heat and stir in the chocolate until melted. Chill in the refrigerator for 1 hour. Soften the butter and whisk into the mixture. Scoop out small spoonfuls of the mixture in rough truffle shapes and place on a piece of baking parchment. Freeze for 1 hour until very firm.

Break the remaining chocolate into a bowl over a pan of hot water and heat gently until melted. Stir in the oil. Remove from the heat and cool to lukewarm. Spoon a thin layer of chocolate over each truffle. When the chocolate has set firmly, turn the truffles over. Melt and cool any remaining chocolate and spoon over the base of each truffle to coat completely. Chill in the refrigerator and eat freshly made.

COOK'S TIP

For speed, or if a lighter Fresh Cream Truffle is preferred, only use 5oz (125g) chocolate from the ingredients. When the prepared mixture has been shaped and frozen, simply toss lightly in cocoa powder just before serving.

Liqueur Truffles
★★

Rich cream truffles flavoured with any favourite liqueur should be served freshly made.

Ingredients
FOR 24 TRUFFLES

8 tbs whipping cream
12oz (350g) plain chocolate
1oz (25g) unsalted butter
2 tbs liqueur

Put the cream into a heavy-based pan and heat gently to just below boiling point. Remove from the heat. Break half the chocolate into small pieces and stir into the cream with the butter. Beat well until smooth and thick. Cool to lukewarm and stir in the liqueur. Beat thoroughly and chill until firm. Shape the mixture into balls and chill again.

Break the remaining chocolate into small pieces and put into a bowl over hot water. Put a cocktail stick into each truffle. Remove the chocolate from heat and dip in each truffle. Drain well and fit sticks into a large potato or grapefruit. Leave until set and remove the cocktail sticks.

Double Truffles

**

These truffles are a little fiddly to make but the contrast between the dark coating and creamy white interior is worth the trouble taken.

Ingredients

FOR 18 TRUFFLES

2 teasp liquid glucose
4 tbs double cream
5oz (125g) white chocolate

COATING

7oz (200g) plain chocolate
2oz (50g) unsalted butter
3 tbs double cream
2 tbs rum or Grand Marnier
cocoa powder

Put the glucose and cream into a small pan and bring to the boil. Take off the heat and stir in the white chocolate broken into small pieces. Stir until the chocolate has melted and then chill in the refrigerator until firm. Form into 18 small balls and chill until very firm.

To make the coating, put the chocolate and butter into a bowl over a pan of hot water and heat gently until the chocolate has melted. Take off the heat and stir well. Add the cream and rum or Grand Marnier. Chill until just firm. Form the mixture into 18 balls and flatten each ball into a round disc. Place a white chocolate ball in the centre of each one and wrap the dark coating round it. Roll lightly in cocoa powder, and chill for 3 hours until firm. Store in the refrigerator.

White Chocolate Truffles

**

The sweet blandness of white chocolate is contrasted with kirsch and a mixture of fruit and nuts.

Ingredients

FOR 6OZ (175G) TRUFFLES (ABOUT 15)

4oz (100g) white chocolate
3 tbs double cream
2 tbs chopped mixed glacé fruit
1oz (25g) blanched split almonds
1 tbs kirsch
icing sugar

Chop the chocolate into small pieces. Put the cream and chocolate into a bowl over hot water and heat gently until the chocolate has melted. Meanwhile, chop the glacé fruit very finely. Spread the almonds on a baking sheet and toast under a medium grill until just golden. Chop the almonds finely and mix with the fruit. Stir into the chocolate and add the kirsch. Chill in the refrigerator for about 3 hours until firm. Roll into small balls with the hands, and roll lightly in icing sugar. Store in the refrigerator.

Parisian Truffles

*

Rich little truffles which are easily made for a dinner party.

Ingredients
FOR 8OZ (225G) TRUFFLES (ABOUT 20)

4oz (100g) plain chocolate
4oz (100g) unsalted butter
2oz (50g) icing sugar
2 egg yolks
cocoa powder

Break the chocolate into small pieces and put into a bowl over a pan of hot water. Add the butter and heat gently until melted. Beat in the sugar and egg yolks, and continue cooking until thick. Cool and leave in a cold place overnight. Roll into small balls with the hands and roll lightly in cocoa powder. Store in the refrigerator.

Walnut Truffles

*

Slightly crunchy truffles which seem to melt in the mouth. Follow the method carefully or the sweets will be too sticky to roll successfully.

Ingredients
FOR 12OZ (350G) TRUFFLES (ABOUT 30)

8oz (225g) plain chocolate
2oz (50g) unsalted butter
4 tbs double cream
2oz (50g) walnuts
2–3 tbs drinking chocolate powder

Break the chocolate into small pieces and put into a bowl over a pan of hot water.

Heat gently until just melted. Remove from the heat and stir in the butter and cream. Grind the walnuts in a blender and stir into the mixture. Leave until completely cold.

Scoop out teaspoonfuls of the mixture and form into balls with the hands. Place in a single layer on a sheet of baking parchment. Chill in the refrigerator and then roll the truffles lightly in drinking chocolate powder. Store in the refrigerator.

Chocolate Orange Truffles

**

Rich but delicate creamy truffles wrapped in dark chocolate.

Ingredients
FOR 12OZ (350G) TRUFFLES (ABOUT 24)

4oz (100g) ground almonds
4oz (100g) icing sugar
1 tbs Cointreau or Grand Marnier
2 tbs double cream
6oz (150g) plain chocolate

Put the almonds into a bowl. Sieve in the icing sugar, and stir well until evenly coloured. Add the liqueur and cream and mix to a firm paste. Chill in the refrigerator for 20 minutes. Form into small balls. Break the chocolate into small pieces and put into a bowl over a pan of hot water. Heat gently until just melted. Use a teaspoon to dip the little balls until they are coated. Drain well and place on a sheet of baking parchment until cold and set. Place in paper sweet cases.

Rum and Almond Truffles

Quickly made truffles which are perfect with coffee after dinner.

Ingredients
FOR 18 TRUFFLES

4oz (100g) plain chocolate
4oz (100g) ground almonds
1oz (25g) caster sugar
2 tbs rum
2oz (50g) blanched almonds

Break the chocolate into small pieces and put into a bowl over a pan of hot water. Heat gently until the chocolate has melted. Stir in the almonds, sugar and rum. Remove from the heat and cool for 10 minutes. Roll into small balls. Chop the blanched almonds finely, and roll each truffle in the nuts. Chill for 30 minutes and put into sweet cases.

Rum Truffles

The flavouring may be varied by using brandy or an orange- or cherry-flavoured liqueur instead of rum.

Ingredients
FOR 12OZ (350G) TRUFFLES (ABOUT 24)

8oz (225g) plain chocolate
2oz (50g) unsalted butter
1 tbs caster sugar
1 tbs rum
1 tbs double cream
1 egg yolk
cocoa or chocolate vermicelli

Break the chocolate into small pieces and put into a bowl over a pan of hot water. Heat gently until just melted. Take off the heat and stir in the butter, sugar, rum, cream and egg yolk. Beat until thick and cool. Put into the refrigerator for 20–30 minutes until firm but not hard. Shape into small balls and roll in cocoa or chocolate vermicelli. Place in paper sweet cases.

Rich Orange Truffles

Oranges and dark chocolate are natural companions, and in this recipe the truffles are richly flavoured with an orange liqueur, fresh orange rind and candied peel.

Ingredients
FOR 12OZ (350G) TRUFFLES (ABOUT 30)

2oz (50g) unsalted butter
5 tbs double cream
7oz (200g) plain chocolate
1 egg yolk
2 tbs chopped mixed candied peel
2 tbs Grand Marnier or Cointreau
1 teasp grated orange rind
cocoa powder

Cut the butter into small pieces and put into a small, heavy-based pan with the cream. Heat gently until the butter has melted and the cream is bubbling. Take off heat and add the chocolate broken into small pieces. Leave until the chocolate has melted and stir well. Mix in the egg yolk. Chop the peel very finely and stir into the mixture with the liqueur and orange rind. Chill in the refrigerator for about 3 hours until firm. Roll into small balls with the hands. Roll lightly in cocoa powder and chill before serving. Store in the refrigerator.

Chocolate Fudge
**

Chocolate fudge is always delicious, but extra flavour may be added with nuts, dried fruit or a little rum.

Ingredients
FOR 1½LB (675G) FUDGE

1lb (450g) sugar
6fl oz (175ml) milk
2oz (50g) plain chocolate
2oz (50g) unsalted butter
few drops of vanilla essence

Put the sugar and milk into a thick-based pan. Chop the chocolate finely and add to the milk. Stir over a low heat until the chocolate and sugar have melted. Boil gently to 237°F/114°C (or until a little of the mixture dropped into a cup of cold water forms a soft ball), stirring occasionally to prevent burning.

Take off the heat and add the butter. Cool for 5 minutes and beat hard with a wooden spoon until the mixture loses its gloss. Pour quickly into an oiled 11x7in (27.5x17.5cm) tin. Mark into squares while still slightly soft. Leave until cold before cutting and removing from the tin.

Chocolate Cinnamon Fudge
**

A rich fudge in which the chocolate is spiked with cinnamon to make a very sophisticated sweetmeat.

Ingredients
FOR 2LB (900G) FUDGE

1½lb (675g) sugar
½pt (300ml) milk
6oz (175g) plain chocolate
4½oz (115g) unsalted butter
1½ teasp ground cinnamon

Put the sugar and milk into a heavy-based pan. Break the chocolate into small pieces and add to the pan with the butter. Heat gently until the sugar has dissolved, stirring well. Boil gently to 237°F/114°C (or until a little of the mixture dropped into a cup of cold water forms a soft ball), stirring occasionally to prevent burning.

Take off the heat and cool for 5 minutes. Add the cinnamon and beat hard with a wooden spoon until the mixture loses its gloss. Pour quickly into an oiled 11x7in (27.5x17.5cm) tin. Mark into squares while still slightly soft. Leave until set before cutting and removing from the tin.

Uncooked Chocolate Fudge

★

A fudge for fainthearts who are worried about boiling sugar. This fudge stores well in a freezer and is useful for holiday periods.

Ingredients
FOR 2LB (900G) FUDGE

8oz (225g) plain chocolate
4oz (100g) unsalted butter
1 egg
1lb (450g) icing sugar
4 tbs sweetened condensed milk or double cream

Break the chocolate into small pieces and put into a bowl with the butter over a pan of hot water. Heat gently until melted. Beat the egg lightly in a bowl. Sieve the icing sugar and add gradually to the egg with the milk or cream and the chocolate mixture. Beat well and put into a lightly buttered 11x7in (27.5x17.5cm) tin. Chill in the refrigerator for 3 hours until firm and cut into squares. Store in the refrigerator or freezer.

For ease of freezer storage, pour the mixture into rigid non-metal containers and do not mark into squares. Cover with foil or a freezer bag for storage up to 3 months.

If liked, chopped nuts, dried fruit or grated orange rind may be added to the fudge.

Chocolate Orange Creams

★★

Squares of creamy orange chocolate are easily made and are very good with coffee after dinner.

Ingredients
FOR 1¼LB (550G) SQUARES (ABOUT 40)

3oz (75g) caster sugar
2 egg yolks
2oz (50g) unsalted butter
4 tbs double cream
juice of ½ orange
1 teasp grated orange rind
1lb (450g) plain chocolate
2oz (50g) candied orange peel

Put the sugar and egg yolks into a bowl and whisk together until light and creamy. Put over a pan of hot water and stir in the butter, cream, orange juice and rind. Stir over heat until thick, but do not let the mixture boil. Break 8oz (225g) chocolate into small pieces and stir into the mixture. When the chocolate has melted, stir in the finely chopped candied peel. Line an 8x10in (20x25cm) tin with baking parchment. Pour the mixture into the tin and leave until cold and set. Turn out on to a clean sheet of baking parchment and peel off the lining paper.

Break the remaining chocolate into small pieces and put into a bowl over hot water. Heat until just melted. Leave to cool for 5 minutes and then spread over the chocolate cream. Leave until set and mark into small squares. When completely cold and firm, cut into squares and place in paper sweet cases.

Praline Log

**

A mocha truffle mixture is formed into a log and then rolled in crushed almond praline before being cut into tempting slices.

Ingredients

FOR 1LB (450G) SWEETS

6oz (175g) plain chocolate
3oz (75g) unsalted butter
1oz (25g) caster sugar
1 tbs strong black coffee
1 tbs brandy
1 egg and 1 egg yolk

PRALINE

3oz (75g) blanched almonds
4oz (100g) sugar
4 tbs water

Break the chocolate into small pieces and put into a bowl with the butter, sugar, coffee and brandy. Put the bowl over a pan of hot water and heat gently until the chocolate has melted. Take off the heat and cool for 5 minutes. Separate the egg and beat the two yolks into the chocolate mixture. Beat the egg white to stiff peaks and fold in. Cool and then chill for 3 hours. Shape into a log 2in (5cm) in diameter and chill again.

While the mixture is chilling, prepare the praline. Put the nuts on to a baking sheet and bake at 350°F/180°C/Gas 4 for 5 minutes. Put the sugar and water into a heavy-based pan and heat gently until the sugar has dissolved. Bring to the boil and cool to a light caramel colour. Stir in the nuts. Butter a 10in (25cm) tin or a marble slab. Pour the mixture into the tin or on to the slab. Leave until cold and break into pieces. Crush in a food processor or with a rolling pin, but do not reduce to powder.

Roll the chilled log in the praline to make a thick coating, and chill again until needed. Slice into about 30 pieces.

Chocolate Torrone

**

A fudge-like sweetmeat containing crisp little nuggets of biscuit.

Ingredients

FOR 12OZ (350G) TORRONE

4oz (100g) plain chocolate
4oz (100g) unsalted butter
2 tbs icing sugar
2 tbs rum
2 eggs
2oz (50g) ground almonds
4 tbs broken Petit Beurre biscuits

Line a 1lb (450g) loaf tin with foil, and brush lightly with oil.

Break the chocolate into a bowl over a pan of hot water and heat gently until melted. Remove from the heat and leave to cool to lukewarm. Cream the butter and sugar until light and fluffy and work in the rum. Separate the eggs and beat the yolks into the mixture. Stir in the ground almonds, and gradually beat in the chocolate.

Whisk the egg whites to stiff peaks and fold into the mixture. Break the biscuits into pieces about the size of a pea and stir into the mixture. Put into the prepared tin and smooth the surface. Cover and chill in the refrigerator for 6 hours. Turn out on to a flat surface and cut into slices, then cut each slice in half. Store in the refrigerator.

Colettes

**

Classic chocolate creams to serve with coffee. They will store in the refrigerator for up to 7 days.

Ingredients

FOR 24 COLETTES

1lb (450g) plain chocolate
¼pt (150ml) double cream
2 tbs rum or brandy
2oz (50g) unsalted butter
24 hazelnuts

Take 48 paper sweet cases and put them together in pairs to make 24 thicker containers. Take 6oz (175g) chocolate and put into a bowl over a pan of hot water. When the chocolate has melted, stir well and remove from the heat. Spread chocolate on the base and sides of the paper cases to form an interior chocolate case. Place on a tray and chill in the refrigerator until set. Put the cream into a bowl over a pan of hot water. When the cream is almost boiling, add the remaining chocolate broken into small pieces. Stir until the chocolate has melted. Add the rum or brandy and butter, and continue stirring over hot water until the mixture is thick and smooth. Take off heat and leave until cool. Put into a piping bag fitted with a large star nozzle and pipe a whorl of chocolate cream into each case. Place a hazelnut on each one. Store in the refrigerator.

Chocolate Snaps

**

Tiny chocolate biscuit cones filled with chocolate liqueur cream are an exciting addition to the *petits fours* selection. If cream horn moulds are not available, roll the mixture round oiled wooden spoon handles like brandy snaps.

Ingredients

FOR 15 SNAPS

1oz (25g) plain chocolate
1oz (25g) unsalted butter
2 tbs light soft brown sugar
1½ tbs clear honey
1oz (25g) plain flour

FILLING

¼pt (150ml) double cream
1 tbs orange liqueur
1 tbs icing sugar
2oz (50g) plain chocolate

Preheat the oven to 350°F/180°C/Gas 4. Cover two baking sheets with baking-parchment. Put the chocolate, butter, sugar and honey into a small, heavy-based pan and heat gently until melted. Take off the heat and work in the flour. Drop teaspoonfuls of mixture on to the baking parchment, leaving room for spreading (for ease of working, bake only 2–3 snaps on each sheet at a time). Bake for 5 minutes until just setting round edges. Leave on the tray for 30 seconds, lift off with a palette knife and wrap at once around the base of cream horn tins. When cold and crisp, slip off the moulds. If liked, the snaps may be stored in an airtight tin for 24 hours before filling.

To make the filling, whip the cream, liqueur and icing sugar to soft peaks. Melt the chocolate in a bowl over hot water, cool and stir into the cream. Just before serving, pipe the chocolate cream into the biscuit cases.

Chocolate Almond Crunch

**

Rich coffee-flavoured toffee packed with toasted almonds is covered with chocolate and more nuts.

Ingredients
FOR 1½LB (675G) TOFFEE

6oz (175g) blanched split almonds
8oz (225g) caster sugar
6oz (175g) unsalted butter
1 tbs coffee powder
1 tbs boiling water
4oz (100g) plain chocolate

Place the almonds in a thin layer on a baking sheet and toast under a medium grill until just tinged with gold. Chop 2oz (50g) almonds and keep on one side. Put the sugar and butter into a thick-based pan. Dissolve the coffee in the water and add to the pan. Heat gently, stirring all the time until the sugar has dissolved. Boil gently to 280°F/138°C (or until a little of the mixture dropped into a cup of cold water separates into threads which are hard but not brittle).

Take off the heat and stir in the split almonds. Pour into an oiled baking tin and leave until cold. Put the chocolate into a bowl over a pan of hot water and heat until melted. Spread the chocolate over the toffee and sprinkle with chopped almonds. Leave until set and break the toffee into pieces.

Chocolate Cherry Creams

**

These *petits fours* take a little care and time to make, but the results are delicious.

Ingredients
FOR 24 CHOCOLATES

24 maraschino cherries
4 tbs brandy
8oz (225g) plain chocolate
2oz (50g) sugar
2 tbs water
2oz (50g) unsalted butter
2oz (50g) icing sugar

Put the cherries into a bowl and cover with the brandy. Leave to stand for 8 hours. Take 48 paper sweet cases and put them together in pairs to make 24 firmer cases. Break the chocolate into small pieces and put half of it into a bowl over a pan of hot water. Heat gently until just melted. Brush the chocolate fairly thickly inside the sweet cases to cover the sides and bases completely. Leave until cold and set.

Drain the cherries and place one in each chocolate case. Put the sugar and water into a thick-based pan and boil to a thick syrup. Add half the drained brandy, stir well and cool. Cover the cherries with this syrup. Cream the butter and icing sugar and remaining brandy, and pipe this mixture over the cherries. Chill in the refrigerator until cold and firm.

Grate 1oz (25g) chocolate and keep on one side. Melt the remaining chocolate over hot water, leave until almost cold, and pour over the sweets. Sprinkle with grated chocolate. Leave until cold and set before removing from the paper cases.

Crazy Pavement

Quickly made and delicious, this sweet-meat provides a contrast of flavours and textures as well as colours.

Ingredients
FOR 1¼LB (550G) SWEETS

1lb (450g) plain chocolate
12 pink and white marshmallows
3oz (75g) walnuts
3oz (75g) seedless raisins

Break the chocolate into small pieces and put into a bowl over a pan of hot water. Heat gently until just melted. Chop the marshmallows with kitchen scissors. Chop the walnuts roughly.

Line a baking tray with baking parchment. Remove the chocolate from the heat and stir in the marshmallows, raisins and walnuts until well coated. Pour into the tin and smooth evenly. Leave until cold and hard, and break into pieces.

Chocolate Pralines

Creamy nutty little chocolates which are an attractive addition to a dish of *petits fours*.

Ingredients
FOR 18 PRALINES

4oz (100g) plain chocolate
2oz (50g) unsalted butter
3oz (75g) icing sugar
1oz (25g) ground hazelnuts
1 teasp rum or coffee liqueur
18 crystallised violets

Break the chocolate into small pieces and put into a bowl with the butter. Place over a pan of hot water and heat gently until just melted. Remove from the heat and stir in the sugar, nuts and liqueur. Beat well and then put the mixture into a piping bag fitted with a star nozzle. Place 18 paper sweet cases on a plate and pipe the mixture in a whorl into each case. Top with a crystallised violet. Chill in the refrigerator for 30 minutes and serve freshly made.

Chocolate Strawberries

A colourful way of combining the sharpness of fruit with the smooth richness of chocolate makes *petits fours* for the end of a summer meal or a wedding reception.

Ingredients
FOR 1LB (450G) *petits fours*

6oz (175g) plain chocolate
1½oz (40g) unsalted butter
6 tbs double cream
1lb (450g) strawberries

Use fresh, ripe, firm strawberries and make sure that they are very clean and dry; leave the green tops in place. Put the chocolate into a bowl with the butter over a pan of hot water. Heat gently until the chocolate has melted. Take off the heat and stir in the cream. Leave until cool and just beginning to thicken.

Place a piece of baking parchment on a flat surface. Hold each strawberry by its stalk and dip into the chocolate until two-thirds covered. Place on the baking parchment. Leave until completely cold and firm. Lift off the paper and arrange on a serving dish.

Orange Thins

Flavoured chocolate morsels to serve with after-dinner coffee.

Ingredients
FOR 10OZ (300G) SWEETS

8oz (225g) plain chocolate
2oz (50g) unsalted butter
1 teasp grated orange rind
2 tbs orange liqueur

Line an 8in (20cm) square cake tin with foil and brush the foil lightly with flavourless oil. Put the chocolate and butter into a bowl over a pan of hot water and heat gently until just melted. Remove from the heat and stir in the orange rind and liqueur. Pour into the lined tin. Cover and chill until set. Turn out of the pan and cut into squares or triangles. Keep in the refrigerator before serving.

Coffee Thins Substitute 1 teasp instant coffee powder and 2 tbs coffee liqueur for the orange rind and liqueur.

Chocolate Coconut Ice

Coconut ice is a very old-fashioned sweetmeat but is rather unusual when flavoured with chocolate.

Ingredients
MAKES 1¼LB (550G) COCONUT ICE

1lb (450g) granulated sugar
¼pt (150ml) milk
2 tbs cocoa powder
4oz (100g) desiccated coconut

Put the sugar, milk and cocoa powder into a heavy saucepan. Stir well and boil for 5 minutes. Take off the heat and stir in the coconut. Beat hard for 1 minute and pour into a tin rinsed in cold water. Leave until cold before cutting into squares or bars.

Chocolate Crunchies

Quickly-made little sweets which store well in a tin.

Ingredients
FOR 1LB (450G) SWEETS (ABOUT 20)

8oz (225g) plain chocolate
2oz (50g) glacé cherries
2oz (50g) angelica
2oz (50g) sultanas
2oz (50g) seedless raisins
2oz (50g) walnuts

Break the chocolate into small pieces and put into a bowl over a pan of hot water. Heat gently until just melted. Chop all the other ingredients roughly. Remove the chocolate from the heat and stir in the fruit and nuts. Drop spoonfuls into paper sweet cases and leave until set.

10

SAUCES

A SMOOTH SAUCE provides a professional finish to a dish, producing a flavour which intensifies or enhances a pudding, a texture which adds richness and a colour which improves appearances. Even simple custard or flavoured cream can provide the perfect partner for a chocolate pudding. On the other hand a very dark and syrupy chocolate sauce, coffee sauce or a contrasting fruit sauce will provide a most sophisticated blending of flavours, colours and textures. Try a sauce with almost any hot or cold pudding or ice – even mousses and soufflés benefit from the contrast. Chocolate addicts may care to make up a large quantity of chocolate sauce and store it in the refrigerator or freezer to use with everything.

Chocolate Sauce

A quickly made sauce which is richly flavoured and glossy. It will thicken as it cools, and should be stirred occasionally. Serve it hot or cold, or store in the freezer for emergencies.

Ingredients
FOR 4–6

¼pt (150ml) water
4oz (100g) caster sugar
2oz (50g) cocoa powder

Put the water and sugar into a pan and heat gently until the sugar has dissolved. Bring to the boil and simmer for 1 minute. Whisk in the cocoa and bring back to the boil, whisking hard until the sauce is smooth.

Mocha Cream Sauce

This rich, creamy chocolate sauce spiked with coffee and brandy may be served hot or cold.

Ingredients
FOR ¾PT (450ML) SAUCE

½pt (300ml) double cream
1 tbs strong black coffee
8oz (225g) plain chocolate
1 tbs brandy

Put the cream and coffee into a heavy-based pan and bring just to the boil. Break the chocolate into small pieces and add to the pan. Heat gently until the chocolate has melted. Take off the heat and add the brandy, stirring until smooth.

Mocha Sauce

Coffee-spiked chocolate sauce which will pair with mocha puddings or with chocolate ones.

Ingredients
FOR 4

1oz (25g) butter
1oz (25g) plain flour
¾pt (450ml) milk
1 tbs coffee essence
2oz (50g) plain chocolate
1 tbs caster sugar

Put the butter into a pan and heat gently until melted. Stir in the flour and cook for 1 minute over low heat. Work in the milk and stir over low heat until smooth and creamy. Stir in the coffee essence and cook for 1 minute. Chop the chocolate finely and add to the sauce with the sugar. Stir until melted and serve at once. For added richness, stir 2–3 tbs cream into the sauce just before serving.

Chocolate Whipped Custard

A light chocolate custard, which is very good with steamed puddings.

Ingredients
FOR 4

½pt (300ml) milk
1 tbs caster sugar
1 egg
1oz (25g) plain chocolate

Put the milk and sugar into a small pan and bring to boiling point. Separate the egg and put the yolk into a bowl. Pour on a little of the hot milk and beat well. Strain back into the pan with the remaining milk and stir gently over low heat until thickened. Chop the chocolate finely and stir into the custard. Remove from the heat and cool slightly. Whisk the egg white to soft peaks and fold into the custard. Serve at once.

Chocolate Mousseline Sauce

Rich creamy sauce to serve with pancakes or light sponge puddings.

Ingredients
FOR 4

2 eggs and 1 egg yolk
2½fl oz (65ml) double cream
1½oz (40g) caster sugar
2 tbs sweet sherry
2oz (50g) grated plain chocolate

Put the eggs and egg yolk into a bowl with the cream, and place over a pan of hot water. Heat gently, beating until smooth and thick. Add the sugar and sherry and beat until the sugar has melted. Stir in the chocolate and remove from the heat.

Chocolate Mousse Sauce

———— ⋆ ————

A rich, foaming sauce for ices, mousses and puddings.

Ingredients
For 4

4oz (100g) plain chocolate
1oz (25g) butter
6 tbs water
2 eggs

Put the chocolate into a bowl with the butter and water and heat over a pan of hot water until just melted. Separate the eggs. Remove chocolate from heat and beat in the egg yolks. Whisk the egg whites to soft peaks and fold into the mixture. Serve at once.

Dark Chocolate Rum Sauce

———— ⋆ ————

Luscious chocolate sauce to serve with hot puddings or with ice cream. If preferred, strong coffee may be used instead of water and the rum omitted.

Ingredients
For 4–6

2oz (50g) caster sugar
4 tbs water
4oz (100g) plain chocolate
2 tbs rum
1/2oz (15g) unsalted butter

Put the sugar and water into a small, heavy-based pan over low heat and stir until the sugar has dissolved. Bring to the boil. Take off the heat and add small pieces of chocolate, stirring well. Stir in the rum and butter and serve at once.

Chocolate Butterscotch Sauce

———— ⋆ ————

A lightly flavoured chocolate sauce which is good with steamed or baked puddings or vanilla ice cream.

Ingredients
For 1/2PT (300ML) SAUCE

2oz (50g) unsalted butter
2oz (50g) demerara sugar
1oz (25g) drinking chocolate powder
6fl oz (175ml) creamy milk

Mix the butter, sugar and drinking chocolate powder in a heavy-based pan, and stir over low heat until the butter has melted and the sugar has dissolved. Raise the heat and cook for 2 minutes. Take off the heat and stir in the milk until evenly blended. Bring to the boil and cook for 2 minutes. Serve warm or cold.

Chocolate Fudge Sauce
*

A good sauce to serve hot or warm over puddings, mousses or ices.

Ingredients
½PT (300ML) SAUCE

6oz (175g) can evaporated milk
3oz (75g) plain chocolate
2oz (50g) light soft brown sugar
1oz (25g) butter
¼ teasp vanilla essence

Put the evaporated milk into a heavy-based pan. Break the chocolate into small pieces and add to the pan with the sugar and butter. Heat gently and stir continuously over low heat until the chocolate has melted and the sugar has dissolved, but do not boil. Remove from the heat and stir in the vanilla essence.

Mint Cream
*

A perfect filling for chocolate pancakes or topping for a rich chocolate mousse or gâteau.

Ingredients
FOR ½PT (300ML) CREAM

½pt (300ml) double cream
1 tbs caster sugar
3 tbs crème de menthe

Whip the cream to soft peaks. Add the sugar and continue whipping until the cream stands in stiff peaks. Stir in the crème de menthe until evenly coloured.

Coffee Custard Sauce
**

Coffee is the perfect complement to chocolate, and this rich custard is good with any dark chocolate pudding, whether hot or cold.

Ingredients
FOR 1PT (600ML) SAUCE

½pt (300ml) milk
½pt (300ml) single cream
1oz (25g) coffee powder
4 egg yolks
3oz (75g) caster sugar

Put the milk, cream and coffee powder into a heavy-based pan and bring to the boil. Whisk the egg yolks and sugar in a bowl until thick and creamy. Slowly pour the milk on to the eggs, whisking all the time. Return to the pan and stir gently over low heat until the mixture thickens and coats the back of a spoon. Strain and serve hot or cold.

Mars Bar Sauce
*

The secret treat of generations of bed-sitter dwellers, this instant chocolate sauce tastes wonderful over ice creams and puddings. Simply chop two large Mars Bars and heat very gently in a small, heavy-based saucepan. When melted, stir well and use at once. For incredible richness, stir in a spoonful or two of thick cream just before serving.

Raspberry Liqueur Sauce

*

Clear red fruit sauce is quickly made and provides a wonderful foil to chocolate dishes. Framboise, kirsch, cassis, rum or brandy may be used for the alcoholic content.

Ingredients

FOR ½PT (300ML) SAUCE

1lb (450g) fresh or frozen raspberries
8oz (225g) icing sugar
juice of ½ lemon
2 tbs liqueur

Sieve the fruit to make a purée. Stir in the sugar and lemon juice until the sugar has dissolved. Chill and stir in the liqueur just before serving.

Orange Sauce

*

Oranges go beautifully with chocolate, and this sauce helps to offset the richness of hot chocolate puddings.

Ingredients

FOR ½PT (300ML) SAUCE

2 oranges
½pt (300ml) water
1 tbs unsalted butter
1 tbs plain flour
½oz (15g) caster sugar
2 tbs orange liqueur

Grate the rind of the oranges and put into a heavy-based pan with the water. Bring to

the boil and simmer for 10 minutes. In another pan, melt the butter and work in the flour. Add the orange liqueur and simmer for 5 minutes, stirring well. Squeeze the juice from the oranges and strain into the pan. Add the sugar, stir well and simmer over low heat for 5 minutes. Remove from the heat and stir in the liqueur. Serve at once.

Crème Anglaise

**

The French version of custard is thin, sweet and creamy, and is delicious cold with chocolate dishes.

Ingredients

FOR 1PT (600ML) SAUCE

½pt (300ml) milk
vanilla pod
6 egg yolks
4oz (100g) caster sugar
½pt (300ml) single cream
2 teasp orange flower water

Put the milk into a heavy-based pan with the split vanilla pod. Bring to the boil. Take off the heat, cover and leave to stand for 10 minutes. Whisk the yolks and sugar together in a bowl until pale and creamy. Strain in the milk, whisking well. Put into a heavy-based pan and stir over low heat until the sauce coats the spoon. Remove from the heat and leave to cool, stirring frequently. When nearly cold, stir in the cream and orange flower water.

11

DRINKS

CHOCOLATE IS AN ALMOST universal comforter. There is nothing quite like a hot or cold chocolate drink to comfort, feed and yet stimulate. In warmer countries such as Mexico, they like their chocolate spiked with spices or contrasting coffee; in colder climates, the chocolate has to be lighter, sweeter and frothier, often served with cream or laced with spirits.

A smooth chocolate syrup is a good basis for cold chocolate drinks, quickly prepared with chilled milk or ice cream. For hot drinks, cocoa powder or drinking chocolate powder is now most easily used, although they were once prepared with melted, unsweetened chocolate in a long and laborious business.

Chocolate Nog

★

An old-fashioned way of making a nourishing milk drink for a cold morning.

Ingredients
FOR 2

¾pt (450ml) milk
1 tbs caster sugar
1 vanilla pod
1 egg
3oz (75g) plain chocolate

Put the milk, caster sugar and vanilla pod into a heavy-based pan and heat gently. When the milk is just at boiling point, remove from heat and take out the vanilla pod (this can be washed, dried and used again). Separate the egg, and whisk the egg yolk and milk together. Break the chocolate into small pieces and add to the mixture, stirring until creamy. Whisk the egg white to stiff peaks. Pour in the hot milk, whisking all the time. Pour into 2 warm mugs and serve at once. If liked, a blob of whipped cream may be placed on top of each serving.

Real Cocoa

⁕

Real men like real cocoa, made in the traditional way, preferably with Dutch cocoa powder, which has the finest flavour.

Ingredients
FOR 4

4 tbs cocoa powder
3 tbs sugar
pinch of salt
¼pt (150ml) boiling water
1½pt (900ml) milk

Mix the cocoa powder, sugar and salt in a heavy-based pan. Add the water and mix to a paste. Simmer for 3 minutes. Add the milk and heat slowly to just below boiling point. Whisk well and pour into hot mugs. If you are a sailor or wildfowler, add some rum.

Basic Chocolate Syrup

⁕

This syrup may be used as a sauce for puddings and ice creams, but it is useful to store in the refrigerator as the base for chocolate drinks.

Ingredients
FOR ½PT (300ML) SYRUP

½pt (300ml) water
10oz (300g) light soft brown sugar
4oz (100g) cocoa powder
pinch of salt
2 teasp vanilla essence

Put the water into a heavy-based pan and stir in the sugar, cocoa powder and salt.

Bring to the boil and then simmer for 5 minutes, stirring often. Remove from the heat and leave to cool, stirring occasionally. Stir in the vanilla essence. When cold, cover and store in the refrigerator.

Chocolate Toddy

⁕

A soothing bedtime drink with a very special flavour.

Ingredients
FOR 2

1pt (600ml) milk
2oz (50g) plain chocolate
2–3 tbs rum
1 tbs double cream
pinch of ground nutmeg

Put the milk into a heavy-based pan. Break the chocolate into small pieces and add to the pan. Bring to the boil, stirring occasionally. Take off the heat and stir in the rum. Divide between two warm mugs. Pour the cream over the back of a teaspoon on to the hot chocolate, so that the cream floats on the surface. Sprinkle lightly with nutmeg and serve at once.

Swiss Chocolate

Richly warming and comforting, this is the drink for a cold winter's night, or even for mid-morning after a brisk walk.

Ingredients
FOR 4

2pt (1.2l) milk
4 heaped tbs drinking chocolate powder
¼pt (150ml) double cream
pinch of ground cinnamon or cocoa powder

Heat the milk to boiling point. Take off heat and whisk in the drinking chocolate powder. Whip the cream to soft peaks. Pour the hot chocolate into mugs. Spoon cream on top of each mug and sprinkle lightly with cinnamon or cocoa powder.

Breakfast Chocolate

Thick hot chocolate makes a marvellous drink for a winter breakfast, to accompany croissants, brioches or a lightly fruited bun.

Ingredients
FOR 2

3oz (75g) plain chocolate
5 tbs boiling water
½pt (300ml) creamy milk

Break the chocolate into small pieces and put into a heavy-based pan with the water. Heat gently, stirring well, until the chocolate has melted and the mixture is thick. Heat the milk in another saucepan. Divide the hot chocolate between two mugs and pour in the hot milk. Serve at once.

Mexican Chocolate

Almost a complete meal, this spiced chocolate drink is very reviving in cold weather.

Ingredients
FOR 4

1pt (600ml) milk
½pt (300ml) double cream
½ teasp ground cinnamon
½ teasp ground nutmeg
pinch of ground allspice
pinch of salt
2oz (50g) plain chocolate
5 tbs water
2 egg yolks

Put the milk and cream into a bowl over a pan of hot water and bring just to the boil. Add the spices and salt, and simmer for 1 hour.

Just before serving, heat the chocolate and water in a small pan over low heat until the chocolate has melted. Take off the heat and beat in the egg yolks. Whisk in the spiced milk until the mixture thickens. Serve at once.

Chocolate Ice Cream Soda

A quickly assembled summer drink, which is easily made if all the ingredients have been well chilled in the refrigerator. The ice cream may be chocolate, vanilla or mint-flavoured.

Ingredients
FOR 1

3 tbs Chocolate Syrup (p116)
1 tbs double cream
1 scoop ice cream
soda water

Put the Chocolate Syrup and cream into a tall glass and stir until well mixed. Add the ice cream and top up with soda water. Stir thoroughly and serve at once with a straw and long spoon.

Mocha Cooler

A treat for a hot day which is filling enough to serve instead of a meal.

Ingredients
FOR 4

1pt (600ml) strong black coffee
2oz (50g) plain chocolate
8 scoops coffee ice cream

Make the coffee freshly and leave it to cool. Break the chocolate into small pieces and put into a basin over hot water. Heat until melted and then leave to cool.

Just before serving, put the coffee and chocolate into a blender and mix well. Add the ice cream and blend until thick and creamy. Pour into tall glasses and serve with straws.

Chocolate Milk Shake

Refreshing milk shakes are best made with milk which has been chilled in the refrigerator and whirled up in a blender with flavouring.

Ingredients
FOR 1

½pt (300ml) milk
3 tbs Chocolate Syrup (p116)
2 tbs finely crushed ice
pinch of ground cinnamon or nutmeg

Put the milk, Chocolate Syrup and ice into a blender and whirl until well mixed. Pour into a chilled glass and sprinkle with cinnamon or nutmeg.

Iced Chocolate

A refreshing but nourishing drink for a hot day. The syrup may be prepared in advance and stored in the refrigerator for a day or two.

Ingredients
FOR 4–6

8oz (225g) caster sugar
½pt (300ml) water
2oz (50g) cocoa powder
1 teasp coffee powder
2pt (1.2l) chilled milk

Put the sugar and water into a heavy-based pan and heat gently until the sugar has dissolved. Bring to the boil, but do not stir, and boil for about 5 minutes to make a thin syrup. Remove from the heat and whisk in the cocoa powder and coffee powder until there are no lumps. Refurn to low heat and simmer for 3 minutes. Pour into a jug and chill in the refrigerator. Whisk in the chilled milk just before serving.

Chocolate Liègeois

*T*he richest chocolate drink, which may be served at the end of a meal instead of a pudding and coffee.

Ingredients
FOR 4

¼pt (150ml) Chocolate Syrup (p116)
1pt (600ml) creamy milk
4 scoops chocolate or vanilla ice cream
¼pt (150ml) double cream
2 teasp caster sugar
cocoa powder

Mix the Chocolate Syrup and milk until evenly coloured and pour into four tall chilled glasses. Add a scoop of ice cream to each glass. Whip the cream and sugar to stiff peaks and divide among the glasses. Sprinkle lightly with cocoa powder and serve at once with straws and long spoons.

12

FANCY BITS

SINCE MOST CHOCOLATE DISHES are very dark in colour, they can also appear flat and dull. Their appearance is greatly enhanced by the addition of smooth, shiny chocolate decorations which are easily prepared.

Squares, Triangles and Other Shapes

Melt plain chocolate and spread thinly with a palette knife on a completely flat sheet of baking parchment. Leave to set at room temperature until firm but not brittle. Use a sharp knife to cut squares or triangles, or use cake or cocktail cutters for circles and other shapes. Lift carefully from the baking parchment. Any offcuts may be melted and used again.

Leaves

Choose fresh leaves which are not poisonous and which have an attractive shape and prominent veining (rose leaves are ideal). Wash and dry the leaves thoroughly. Brush one surface of each leaf thickly and evenly with melted chocolate, preferably using the heavily veined side. Arrange on a sheet of baking parchment and leave until the chocolate is hard. Peel off the leaves carefully.

Lace

Draw triangles or circles on baking parchment. Put melted chocolate into a small piping bag with a small writing pipe and pipe round the outline of each shape. Fill in with lacy lines. Leave to set at room temperature. Lift very carefully from the paper.

Palm Trees

Use a small piping bag with a writing pipe, and fill with melted chocolate. Pipe a six-pointed starfish shape on to baking parchment. Pipe on a trunk from the centre, giving a ringed effect by using short horizontal lines. Leave to set at room temperature.

Caraque (Long Curls)

Melt plain chocolate and spread with a palette knife less than ¼in (5mm) thick on clean dry marble or a laminated surface. Leave to set at room temperature. Using a long knife, hold the blade at an angle of 45° to the surface and push away from the body, shaving off long curls. Lift off carefully with a skewer or pointed knife. Small flakes which break off may also be used as decoration or may be melted and used again.

Short Curls

Use a thick block of plain chocolate or cake covering, as French cooking chocolate is too hard and brittle for this technique. Use at room temperature, and scrape off curls of chocolate with a potato peeler (the type with a light, thin rotary blade is easiest to use). Do not handle the curls which melt easily, but lift them with the point of a knife directly on to the surface to be decorated.

Grated Chocolate

Use a thick block of plain chocolate or cake covering and chill for 30 minutes in the refrigerator. Use the coarse side of the grater for preparing the chocolate.

Chocolate Horns

Use cream-horn tins which have been washed and dried. Rub the insides with kitchen paper to make them shiny. Pour in melted chocolate and tilt the horn moulds so that the inside is evenly coated. Leave to set and then repeat the process to make a thicker casing which will be easier to unmould. Leave to set in a cool place and when the chocolate has set hard, ease out with the point of a knife. For small horns which are suitable for *petits fours*, paint the chocolate only a short way up the outside of the horn moulds. Leave to set and repeat the process. When the chocolate is hard, slip it out of the moulds.

Cake and Sweet Bases

Put together paper or foil cake or sweet cases in pairs to provide a firm base. Paint chocolate thinly inside the inner case to cover completely. Leave until hard and then repeat the process. When the chocolate has set, peel off the outer cases and use the chocolate shapes for filling with liqueurs, truffle mixture, soft fruit, fondant, etc.

LIST OF RECIPES

Sweetmeats and Petits Fours

Sauces

Drinks

INDEX

C000108927

Ten Thousand Lights – Saffron Dusk
Yisei Ishkhan

This novel's story and characters are fictitious. Certain places and
historical figures and events are mentioned, but the characters involved in
the story are products of the author's imagination. Any similarities between
them and actual people, living or dead, is coincidental.

Copyright © April 2023 by Yisei Ishkhan
Cover design by Norshie
All rights reserved. This book or any portion thereof may not be
reproduced or used in any manner without the written permission of the
publisher, except for the use of brief quotations in a book review.
First edition: April 2023

Ten Thousand Lights

Saffron Dusk

Shadows of Blood

The Second Prince was thrown backward onto the ground. The back of his head smacked hard against the table. A wave of nausea washed over him. He tried to push himself up into a seated position, but a heavy weight on his stomach was pinning him to the ground.

"Qian Ming!" A voice cried out.

Qian Mingyue caught sight of a figure stepping out from the darkness. Amidst the shadows, the dim glow of lanternlight illuminated the room. Mingyue could just make out the young man's features—the lighting distorted his visage. His handsome face appeared haunting with his downcast expression; his jade-coloured eyes now flickered with a bloody, crimson tint.

"Do not move," the young man said. His gentle, rose-petal lips spoke the words firmly.

Mingyue's vision began to clear. The young man stood several steps away, a steel blade clenched tightly in his hand. But the blade wasn't pointing at Mingyue. The figure who had pushed Mingyue to the ground was enveloped by the darkness of the room; he had Mingyue pinned to the floor with his legs on either side of the prince's body. The edge of the jade-eyed man's sword flashed through the darkness against that individual's throat. Mingyue could sense the figure clad in shadows holding a knife that hovered just above his face. His heart was racing, but he managed to speak up with three simple words.

"Was it you?" His voice trembled as he asked the question.

The person above Mingyue was breathing heavily, simultaneously focusing on the prince beneath him and the man behind him, wondering who could strike faster. He didn't respond to Mingyue's question. To Mingyue's surprise, he felt a warm, wet drop drizzle down onto his forehead. The person on top of him was crying.

"It was you who killed them, wasn't it!" Mingyue reasserted. This time, it was an accusation, not a question. He channeled all the anger and disgust that had been pent up over the last three months into those words.

"I…I didn't have a choice," the shadow whispered. He sounded as though *he* were the one in pain, as if he'd been the one knocked against the floor with a knife pressed up against his throat.

"Step away from Qian Ming," the jade-eyed man warned again.

"You wouldn't understand," the shadowed figure spat. "None of you would understand!"

At this point, he was laughing hysterically. The jade-eyed man gripped his sword nervously, prepared to strike at any moment.

The laughing ceased. Several long moments of silence passed. Other than the lanternlight casting eerie shadows dancing across the walls, it seemed as if time had frozen.

"I'm sorry…" the figure said. His voice was soft, so soft that even amidst the silence, Mingyue struggled to understand what he was saying. "Please…forgive me…"

Before Mingyue could respond, the figure lurched forward. Mingyue could sense the knife coming toward his face. The jade-eyed man didn't hesitate. His sword swung down in an instant. Mingyue's eyes flicked toward him.

"Erik! Don't!"

It was too late. The sound of steel ripping through flesh slashed through the deafening silence of the room, splattering blood across the floor. The lanternlight went out, casting the world into darkness.

Book I

Saffron Dusk

Part I

One Thousand Years

I. The Stranger in the Garden

1/8/18th Year of the Golden Dragon Emperor

Year of the Wooden Goat

Three months earlier:

"Prince Mingyue? Prince Mingyue!" The young eunuch named Ao Neili shouted. He raced up and down the alleyways of the palace, desperately in search of his prince. Where could he have gone?

The boy stopped to catch a breath, leaning his hand against the twisted trunk of a tree as he hastily adjusted the black and silver futou[1] atop his head worn by all who served in the Palace of Lunar Serenity. He cursed silently. Why did the prince always cause him so much trouble? He *always* ran off like this whenever he had the chance, even though he knew he wasn't supposed to.

Neili groaned. "Wu Liqing is going to kill me!"

"Who goes there?"

Neili jumped back from the tree at the sound of the voice, his stomach doing somersaults. Sure enough, from the shadows of the terrace was a towering young man, his hand firmly clasped around the shaft of his spear, as if he was prepared to strike at any moment. Despite his best efforts to tie back his long, dark hair, it curled as it fell past his ears, peeking out from under the broad-rimmed hat atop his head. Those types of hats weren't worn for fashion—they were sturdy and rather uncomfortable. Whenever someone was spotted in one, everyone knew at once that they were a member of the Imperial Guard.

With his silky white robes contrasting with his dark complexion, Wu Liqing stood out from most of the other servants and guards in the palace. By birth, his parents had named him Olekina. However, this name was foreign to Wuyue, and therefore difficult for most to pronounce. Thus, he had been given the courtesy name[2] of Wu Liqing

---

[1] Fútóu (襆頭): A turban or hat-like headpiece commonly worn by men during some Chinese dynasties.

[2] Courtesy name: A name bestowed upon adulthood in addition to one's given name. In this case, many often use one's courtesy name when addressing them rather than their birth name as a sign of respect. In Wuyue, most foreigners have birth names in their native tongue, while Chinese courtesy names are bestowed upon them.

by the Crown Princess herself. This was the name by which he was known to most, though he still preferred his birth name.

Neili cursed silently as Olekina's gaze rested upon him. He didn't understand why he could never spot the man before the man spotted him.

"Ao Neili," Olekina addressed the young eunuch by his full name. He didn't need to say anything more. One look into his black eyes was more terrifying than any scolding Neili could receive from his superior. A shudder went up his spine. How could Olekina say so much with his words despite speaking so little?

"Wu Liqing!" He straightened up and bowed his head respectfully to the guard. "Ah…please forgive me!"

Olekina's face remained expressionless as he looked down at the boy. After a few moments, he pointed to his left—eastwards.

"The prince went that way."

Neili's gaze flicked in that direction. "The Palace of Heavenly Peace? Thank you, Wu Liqing! I promise I'll get him back here immediately!"

Olekina said nothing, his eyes following the young eunuch as he hurried off to find the prince.

***

I'm sorry, Neili. I hope I don't get you into trouble.

Qian Mingyue smiled himself. He found every opportunity he could to slip away from the watchful eyes of his servants and guards. It was boring to spend each passing day within the Palace of Lunar Serenity, going back and forth between classes in history, calligraphy, and music. Each day was the same as the previous one. He hardly ever had the chance to leave the Imperial Palace, and even visiting the sub-palaces *within* the palace was a rare occurrence.

Mingyue had covered himself in a cloak. With the elaborate golden and red robes he usually wore, anyone would easily recognize him as the prince and spoil his fun. Pulling the hood over his lengthy, tied-back hair, he snuck through the palace walkways, careful to avoid as many people as possible.

Unfortunately, the hood was pulled so far over his face that he could hardly see where he was going. After rounding a corner, he slammed into someone head-on and tumbled backward onto the ground. His hood was thrown back. In a panic, Mingyue hurried to throw it back over his face. But the person he had run into caught his eye. He was a young man, about his age, who stood a bit taller than he was. His skin was pale like snow; his golden hair was cut short, softly swaying in the breeze. It barely went past his ears, and wasn't done up in any sort of fashion, a rare sight to see in Wuyue. But what caught Mingyue's attention the most were his deep, jade-coloured eyes shimmering in the sunlight. He had never seen eyes like that before.

Mingyue blinked in surprise, "You—"

The boy extended his hand toward Mingyue, but Mingyue simply stared up at him in confusion.

"Sorry! I wasn't looking where I was going!" The golden-haired boy said. He spoke with a peculiar accent. Mingyue bit his tongue. He was having a difficult time holding himself back from laughter. This boy was clearly a foreigner, probably a Semu[3] from the west. Of course, there were many Semu living in Wuyue—Mingyue's own father was among them. But something about this young man struck him as peculiar. He was different than the others.

Before Mingyue could speak, the foreigner's rose-petal lips widened into a warm smile, the nervous glimmer in his eyes seeming to ask the prince for forgiveness. Mingyue didn't know why, but his heart suddenly fluttered.

Who does this boy think he is? Mingyue thought to himself. *No one has ever looked at me in such a way before. If someone had bumped into me, they'd be*

---

[3] Sèmù (色目): Literally meaning "coloured-eyes;" a Chinese term usually referring to foreigners who come from West or Central Asia. The term originates from the Yuan Dynasty (1271-1368 AD), when the Mongol rulers of China established multiple castes along ethnic lines.

cowering in the corner, kowtowing on the ground as they begged for mercy. But here is this boy, standing above and looking down on me. Is it possible that he doesn't realize that I'm the prince?

Mingyue noticed that the boy's arm was still outstretched toward him, waiting expectantly for him to take hold of it. Mingyue ignored him, pushing himself up from the ground and dusting off his robes.

"What are you doing here? Foreigners aren't allowed in the Palace of Lunar Serenity."

The jade-eyed man cocked his head in confusion. Mingyue waited for a few moments, wondering why he wasn't responding.

"Apologies, sir," a voice spoke out.

Mingyue glanced past the boy and spotted another young man, also a foreigner. He had more olive-coloured skin, darker hair, and was more average in height that the first gentleman. Both wore navy blue tunics adorned with gold buttons, though the outfit of the jade-eyed man was far more elaborate than that of the newcomer.

The dark-haired boy bowed to Mingyue respectfully. "I apologize on my lord's behalf. He cannot yet speak Wuyueyu⁴ with fluency and does not understand much of your culture. I apologize for his careless behaviour and any offense he may have caused."

Mingyue blinked. It was uncommon to come across a Semu who could speak even basic phrases in the Wuyue tongue, but Mingyue was taken aback by the elegance with which this young man spoke. Not only could he pass for a native speaker, but even a Yue noble. Who exactly were these men?

Mingyue didn't know what he should say. He furrowed his brow. "It is not a problem, but what are you doing here? Foreigners are not allowed in the Palace of Lunar Serenity."

The dark-haired boy quickly scanned the area around them. "You are correct, sir. But I do not believe that we have wandered off from the grounds of the guests' residence."

---

⁴ Wúyuèyǔ (吳越語): Meaning "the language of Wuyue. It is a dialect of the Wu language, spoken in the kingdom of Wuyue in the Jiangnan region of eastern China.

Mingyue glanced behind him, spotting a magnificent gate with large wooden doors and tiled-roofed watchtowers sitting upon the wall. He came to the sudden realization that the man was right. This *wasn't* the Palace of Lunar Serenity! While he was wandering through the back alleyways with his face covered by the hood, he must have accidentally stumbled into the Palace of Heavenly Peace, which neighboured the Palace of Lunar Serenity to the east.

Realizing his mistake, he quickly apologized. "Forgive me. I was mistaken."

His gaze flicked back toward the golden-haired boy, eyeing him curiously. The boy smiled back nervously before turning to his acquaintance and saying something to him in a tongue Mingyue couldn't understand. Were these two men *really* of Semu origin? The language they spoke certainly wasn't Sogdian,[5] or any of the other Semu tongues Mingyue was familiar with.

The darker-haired boy nodded. He turned back to Mingyue. "He says that just like the misty mountains and sleepy gardens, even the servants of Wuyue's palaces are alluring."

Mingyue was taken aback by the comment. His face flushed red, out of both embarrassment and annoyance. Alluring? Was this boy flirting with him?! And "servant?" Just who did this man think he was?

The golden-haired boy, gazing upon Mingyue's flustered expression, realized that there must have been a misunderstanding over what he had said. His acquaintance quickly spoke up.

"Apologies! Perhaps 'alluring' wasn't the proper translation—"

"Beautiful," the golden-hair boy said simply. He flashed Mingyue a smile. "The palace servants are beautiful, just like the gardens and mountains of Wuyue."

Every word he said was carefully enunciated. Once again, Mingyue felt that strange, fluttering sensation in his chest. He found

---

[5] Sogdian: An Eastern Iranian language spoken in the region of Sogdia in Central Asia. It was a common lingua franca among merchants who traveled along the Silk Road between the Middle East and China.

those words strangely poetic coming from the lips of a Semu, though he would've brushed the comment aside had it come from the tongue of a native Wuyueyu speaker.

"Such boldness, speaking to a prince in such a manner," he whispered under his breath. He couldn't help stifling a laugh.

"Pardon?" The dark-haired boy asked.

Before anything more could be said, they were interrupted by the shouts of a frantic voice.

"Prince Mingyue? Prince Mingyue!"

Mingyue cursed to himself as Neili's voice grew nearer and nearer. Neither of the foreigners seemed to notice that the prince in question was the young man standing before them. Before Neili had entered the area, they had already turned to depart.

"We best be off then," the dark-haired boy said to Mingyue.

The golden-haired boy turned and smiled gently back at him one last time before disappearing into the alleyway. Mingyue's heart fluttered as sunlight glimmered in his jade-green eyes. He reprimanded himself for not asking for the foreigner's name.

II. Princes of Yue

1/8/18th Year of the Golden Dragon Emperor

Year of the Wooden Goat

"Prince Mingyue? Prince Mingyue!" Neili called out frantically. As soon as he had spotted the prince standing aimlessly in the garden, he hurried over. He rested his hands on his knees, panting to catch his breath. "Your Highness, why did you run off on me!"

"*Hmm?*"

Mingyue turned to the young eunuch, blinking in surprise as if he'd just noticed him for the first time. He had been staring in the direction which those foreigners had gone for a while now, mesmerized as though lost in a trance. With Neili's arrival, he snapped back to reality.

"Why are you yelling so loudly?"

Neili looked up at the prince with annoyance but didn't dare to speak back at him. "Your Highness, your lessons with Mister Zhang begin soon! If you are late, I will be at fault!"

"*Mnn...*" Mingyue nodded but didn't seem to be listening. "Ao Neili, have any foreigners arrived at the palace recently?"

Neili was getting antsy. "Your Highness, I overheard that an envoy arrived last night."

"From where?"

"Sailing south from the Keliyete Khanate."

"*Hmm,*" Mingyue nodded. "He *is* a Semu then."

Neili became flustered. "Your Highness...did you encounter someone?!"

Mingyue turned to the eunuch. "A young man. His eyes were as green as the chambers of the Jade Palace—"

"Your Highness!" Neili silenced him with a gasp. "You can't be mingling with foreigners! Especially not before he has been formally received at the Hall of Harmony by the Emperor! Wu Liqing and Wei Hanxi will kill me if they find out! Your Highness, you really create a lot of trouble for me!"

Mingyue smiled slightly.

Neili bowed his head. "Your Highness, enough talking! We must hurry back, or you will miss your classes!"

"Yes. I apologize, Neili."

Neili sighed dramatically. "And stop calling me by my given name! What will others think? It's embarrassing! You should be calling me 'Ao Neili!'"

***

"In the second year of the old calendar,[6] the Year of the Fire Rooster,[7] the Keliyete Khanate annexed all the lands of the Hanguk Kingdom,[8] giving them widespread access to the Taiping Ocean[9] for the first time in their history."

Mister Zhang stood at the front of the room, pointing to a display of a large map as he spoke to the princes.

"Mister Zhang," Qian Zukang spoke up. "I have a question."

Zukang was the elder brother of Mingyue by two years. Like his younger brother, his long hair was tied back in typical fashion for Yue nobles. The handsome young man bore a similar visage to his younger brother, although one could easily tell them apart by looking at their expressions. Zukang was known for his mischievous nature, and one could detect the devious grin lurking behind his smile. Mingyue, on the other hand, was quite serious, though timid in his demeanor. Although he had his mischievous moments, such as running off from Neili earlier that morning, he generally was much better disciplined than his elder brother.

"Yes, Prince Zukang?" Mister Zhang said.

"When the Hanguk Kingdom was annexed, why was the ruling family not executed?"

---

[6] Old Calendar: Eras of Chinese history are marked by the reign of an emperor. When a new emperor ascends to the throne, a new calendar cycle begins.
[7] Year of the Fire Rooster: The traditional Chinese calendar revolves around a sixty-year cycle, each year corresponding to one of twelve animals and one of five elements. The Year of the Fire Rooster would be 58 years before the Year of the Wooden Goat.
[8] Hanguk: Meaning "Korea."
[9] Tàipíngyáng (太平洋): The Chinese name for the Pacific Ocean.

Mister Zhang smiled. "A good question, Prince Zukang. After the Keliyetes annexed the Hanguk Kingdom, the Yi Dynasty of Hanguk became assimilated into the Keliyete nobility. This is a common practice among the northern peoples. They do not tend to invoke such violent means in disposing of the nobility of conquered lands. They do not regard the nations they rule over as subordinate, but as equals with themselves. As a result, they treat all under the Eternal Blue Sky with respect and dignity."

"*Tch*, if only the whole world was just as respectful," sighed the young man to Zukang's right—Prince Narsieh Sasan.

Narsieh leaned back in his seat, only half listening to the conversation. Of the three students mentored by Mister Zhang, the two brothers Mingyue and Zukang, were both princes of the Yue Dynasty. Narsieh, however, was not. His courtesy name was Li Niexia, and he was the son of the head of the House of Sasan. After the fall of their dynasty in Persia more than a millennium ago, the Sassanians had found refuge under the Tang Dynasty, later rising to a prominent status in the court of Wuyue. They had been close allies of the House of Qian for centuries, with much intermarriage between the two families over the generations.

"Prince Niexia, would you like to speak?" Mister Zhang asked.

Narsieh sighed. "If only the whole world showed the same amount of respect as the Keliyete Khanate does to their conquered peoples."

Mingyue chuckled. He had grown accustomed to phasing out the conversations around him when it came to topics like this. It wasn't that he didn't take an interest in learning history, but Narsieh and Mister Zhang had this conversation nearly every class. Mingyue was far more interested in doodling at times like this, drawing his brush across the page in broad strokes.

"Prince Niexia," Mister Zhang said calmly, "it has been more than one thousand years since your dynasty was overthrown. Those who are responsible are long gone."

"Even so," the man sat forward in his seat, "the Khorasani Shah rules over the lands of my forefathers. You would not understand. You have never left the homeland of your people, much less been forced off of it."

"Li Niexia, I see that your attitude hasn't changed," a voice came from the door behind them.

All three princes spun around to see a tall, handsome young man, clad in fine silk robes, with his hair tied back in the same style as Mingyue and Zukang.

"Shenzhong?!" The brothers shouted in unison. All three princes jumped from their seats and rushed over.

The young man, Xi Shenzhong, was the grandson of the emperor's elder sister, making him Mingyue and Zukang's second cousin. His father, Xi Chengxin, was the governor of Suzhou.

"Shenzhong, what are you doing here?" Zukang said in surprise.

Shenzhong smiled. "Have you forgotten? The Qiantang Festival is approaching! I wouldn't miss such an occasion, especially considering that this year marks the thousandth anniversary of the empire's founding. It will be the biggest celebration in our history!"

It was true. Foreign ambassadors from all over the world would be arriving over the next few days to partake in the celebrations of the thousandth year of Wuyue's existence as an imperial dynasty. Everyone was excited as the Imperial Palace, the capital, and the entire empire prepared for the festivities. Even Narsieh managed to smile.

"Prince Shenzhong, I am happy to see you again," Mister Zhang said.

Shenzhong returned the greeting. "As am I! I am happy to be back."

"Shenzhong, how long will you be staying?" Mingyue asked.

"Probably a few months," Shenzhong replied. "I will most likely stay until after Zukang's wedding."

Zukang laughed. "Shenzhong, you're older than me by two years, yet I'll be married before you. Your parents still haven't found you a bride?"

Shenzhong chuckled. "I am not from the main branch of the family, Zukang. It is not as easy for me to find a bride as it is for you."

Zukang smirked. "Ah, yes. What a shame that you won't be getting to marry the Yi Princess."

Shenzhong rolled his eyes playfully. "Shut up."

Zukang jeered at him. The Yi Princess, a descendant of the ruling dynasty of the Hanguk Kingdom, was rumored to be the most beautiful maiden in all the north. Just as Mister Zhang had mentioned, the House of Yi held high status in the court of the Keliyete Khanate, not unlike the House of Sasan in Wuyue. A marriage alliance between Wuyue and the Keliyetes would be of significant political gain for both nations.

"How about you, Mingyue?" Shenzhong addressed him.

Everyone turned to Mingyue expectantly.

"That's right," Zukang piped up. "A-Ming[10] is now of an age when he would typically be engaged. But Father and Mother still haven't found a suitable maiden for him yet."

"But perhaps Mingyue has someone in mind?" Shenzhong nudged him.

"*Hm?*" Mingyue flashed his cousin a quizzical glance.

Shenzhong gestured to the papers on Mingyue's desk. Instead of taking down notes of Mister Zhang's lecture on the Keliyete Khanate, Mingyue had been doodling. He typically didn't pay much attention to what he drew, simply letting his hands slide subconsciously across the page as it brought to life whatever Mingyue had in mind. In most cases, this ended up being incoherent shapes and squiggles, though occasionally he would draw simple objects such as flowers or butterflies. But this time, there was something different.

---

[10] A-Ming (阿明): It is common to use "A" in front of a name as a form of endearment.

Mingyue's heart skipped a beat. He hadn't noticed until then, but on his page was a rough outline of a person's face. It wasn't a particularly good drawing, but one could still make out some of the details of his visage—his sharp jawline, the strong bridge of his nose, his thick, dainty lashes, and hair that barely went past his ears…

"Drawing again instead of taking notes?" Mister Zhang sighed.

"N-no…" Mingyue rushed to cover the drawing with a book.

"Who's she supposed to be?" Narsieh inquired. "She looks like a foreigner."

Mingyue's face flushed red. He hadn't intended to draw the golden-haired boy he'd met earlier that day, much less give him such a feminine appearance. But now that he thought about it, he realized that the young man he'd met in the gardens *did* possess such features, though perhaps Mingyue had exaggerated them to an extent in his drawing. His heart fluttered. He desperately wished for someone to change the topic of conversation.

"Speaking of foreigners, I heard that there was a foreign envoy that just arrived in the palace last night!" Zukang exclaimed. "Did you hear about that, Shenzhong? I wonder who they might be."

"Ah, yes." Shenzhong nodded. "The Second Prince of the Norden Empire."

Mingyue blinked in surprise. "Prince…?"

"Indeed. And just as the Yi Princess is the most beautiful woman in all the north, I have heard rumors that Norden's Second Prince is the most handsome man in all the west."

Mingyue's heart raced faster. Was that golden-haired gentleman he met earlier the prince? He was dressed far more elegantly than the dark-haired man who'd accompanied him. Now that he thought about it, the dark-haired man had referred to him as 'my lord'…

"When will he be received into the Hall of Harmony?" Mingyue asked.

"The Norden prince?" Shenzhong asked. "This evening."

III. The House of Qian

1/8/18th Year of the Golden Dragon Emperor

Year of the Wooden Goat

The Imperial Palace of Wuyue sat atop Dingjia Mountain, rolling down toward the West Lake to the east. Being built on sloped terrain, Mingyue could overlook much of the Imperial Palace when he was at the highest point of his quarters. He gazed out over the dozens of glazed rooftops of the many sub-palaces and buildings that made up the Imperial Palace, surrounded on all four sides by a towering, fortified outer wall. To both the left and right, steep mountainsides in the north and south crawled high into the sky, cradling the palace between them. Behind him, to the west, the inner palace sat further up, reaching toward the peak of Dingjia Mountain. Although from the top of the mountain, one could gaze upon the setting sun on the western horizon, Mingyue had never been to that part of the palace before. He had never seen the setting of the sun. He could only ever watch the east, as orange and pink clouds danced across the sky, and evening sunlight shimmered over the surface of the lake.

As the sky began to change colour, a frantic voice interrupted Mingyue's tranquility.

"Prince Mingyue! Prince Mingyue!"

Mingyue sighed. It was Neili again. The young eunuch burst through the doors of the terrace.

"Prince Mingyue! What are you doing standing out here? Do you know how much time it takes to get to the Hall of Harmony?! The Norden prince will be received at sundown! You mustn't be late!"

Reality flooded back to Mingyue. The imperial family would be waiting at the Hall of Harmony to officially welcome the foreign envoy. His heart began to beat faster. Meeting others for the first time was something he always found to be nerve-wracking, but he'd never felt as self-conscious as he did just then.

He spun to face Neili. "Do I look okay?"

Neili blinked in confusion. Mingyue had never asked that sort of thing before. Besides, Neili thought the prince *always* looked okay—

much better than 'okay,' in fact, though he would never admit this out loud.

The eunuch's face flushed bright pink, like the colour of the clouds in the setting sun. "Ah...um...why would you need to ask that question, your Highness? Heaven is always smiling upon the Yue Princes!"

"*Mnn*..." Mingyue managed a slight nod, though he wasn't entirely satisfied with the answer.

***

The Hall of Harmony was located at the center of the Imperial Palace, just to the west of the Outer Court and to the east of the Lake of Tranquility. It was one of the largest buildings within the palace, second only to the Hall of Heavenly Purity, and was where the Emperor received foreign guests and ambassadors.

As was customary, Mingyue entered the hall from its main doors, alongside his elder brother and sister, Qian Zukang and Qian Sheli. They kowtowed three times to the elderly man seated upon the throne—their grandfather.

Qian Jinlong, the Golden Dragon Emperor, had gentle eyes and was well-known for his integrity. He was loved by his subjects throughout the empire, and his nearly two-decade-long reign was filled with peace and prosperity. Although he was quite elderly, his hair had only just started to grey, and he appeared many years younger than he truly was.

His wife, Zhen Yinfeng, was called the Silver Phoenix Empress. She sat on the lower steps of the throne to her husband's right. The Empress was the younger sister of the King of Nanyue, and like her husband, also appeared rather youthful for her age.

Their eldest child, Qian Huamei, sat to the Emperor's left. She was his heir apparent, and mother to Mingyue, Zukang, and Sheli. The three siblings took their positions at the foot of the throne, next to their father, An Yanlu.

Unlike the other members of the Yue Dynasty, Yanlu was not of Tang[11] descent. His light-coloured hair and eyes set him apart from most who were gathered in the hall that evening. He was of foreign Semu origins, born of a mercantile branch of the former Sogdian royal family. They had been settled in Wuyue for many generations now, even before the western lands had been absorbed by the Keliyete Khanate. Of course, there had been some who opposed a marriage between the Crown Princess of Wuyue and a foreigner, but the Emperor pointed out their hypocrisy, stating that while none took issue over his marriage to Empress Yinfeng, who was born outside of Wuyue, they complained about Prince Yanlu, whose family had resided in Wuyue for generations. The Emperor may have been the father of the nation, but he cared first and foremost about his family. He did not object when his eldest daughter fell in love with the Sogdian prince. Emperor Jinlong was highly respected, and so his decision to honour this marriage was quickly accepted by the people.

Soon, the other members of the imperial family began to make their way into the Hall of Harmony, bowing before the Emperor. First was the family of Emperor Jinlong's elder sister, Qian Jinling. She arrived with her daughter, Xi Yanggui, the Princess of Ailao; her son, Xi Chengxin, the governor of Suzhou; and of course, her grandson, Xi Shenzhong. Next to arrive was Qian Jinxin, the youngest brother of the Emperor. He was regarded as a black sheep, with no family of his own, having long since renounced his princely titles, retreating to the mountains as a monk. The younger generations often mocked him for this behind his back. Only missing from the procession was the family of the Emperor's second daughter, Qian Zemao, as well as his eldest brother, Qian Jinyu.

"Is Prince Jinyu not attending?" Shenzhong whispered.

Sheli shook her head. "He is not well."

---

[11] Táng (唐): A reference to the Tang Dynasty, in this case denoting descendants of the subjects of the Tang Dynasty. They are also known as the Han ethnicity and are the dominant ethnic group within Wuyue, Nanyue, and the Xin Empire.

A silent understanding passed between them. She didn't need to say anything more—everyone already knew. Jinyu had disappeared on a visit to the Land of the Heavenly Mountains in his youth. After many years, it was presumed he was dead. When the previous Yue Emperor passed away, his second son, Jinlong, inherited the throne. However, a few years ago, Jinyu had been found safe and returned on a ship from Tsimshian.[12] But after being gone for nearly half a century, Jinyu was not the same man he once was. He was elderly and senile and hardly seemed to recognize his old home or family. No one could say what had happened during his many years in the eastern lands.

"And Princess Zemao?" Shenzhong inquired. "Jingli and Fengling?"

Jiao Jingli and Jiao Fengling were Zemao's children, making them Mingyue's cousins.

"Their travels were delayed," Sheli said.

"I see."

"Delayed," Zukang scoffed. "We all know why. She wants to spend as little time here as possible."

"Hush, Zukang," Sheli scolded her brother.

"What? We all know it's true."

Mingyue shared an awkward glance with Shenzhong and Sheli. Zukang was right, but none of them dared to admit it.

At last, one of the eunuchs stepped into the room, bowing before the Emperor.

"Your Majesty," he announced, "I present to you the envoy of the Norden Empire. They have traveled many months across the continent to take part in the celebrations of Wuyue's one-thousandth year."

Mingyue caught sight of the golden-haired gentleman as he entered the room. He was clad in deep blue robes, with the finest of furs lining his sleeves and collar. His jade-like eyes twinkled in the evening light as he knelt respectfully before the Emperor. His

---

[12]Tsimshian: The Tsimshian Chiefdoms are a confederation of unified territories with tributary status to the Wuyue Empire. They are located in the Land of the Heavenly Mountains, on the eastern shore of the Taipingyang.

26

attendants and servants flanked him on either side. Mingyue eyed them curiously. They were pale-skinned, and most had light hair and light eyes, even lighter than that of An Yanlu. He had heard rumors of lands far to the west where everyone had golden-hair and jade-like eyes but had never taken those stories seriously until now.

"Emperor Jinlong," the boy spoke in a smooth, clear voice. "A pleasure to meet you. I am the second son of the late King Sven IV, Prince Erik of Norden."

IV. Wonders of the World

The jade-eyed prince caught sight of Mingyue. For a moment, his eyes rested on him, though not long enough for anyone other than Mingyue to notice. As the prince faced the Emperor once again, a slight smile appeared on his face.

"Your Majesty, I bear gifts from the Norden realms."

He gestured to the attendants behind him. Among them, Mingyue spotted the dark-haired boy who had been accompanying the prince earlier. He was the one who stepped forward.

"I am Prince Erik's chief attendant, Caleb Selkirk. Please excuse my lord. He is not fluent in the Wuyue tongue, so I will be communicating with the Emperor on his behalf."

Emperor Jinlong nodded in approval. The attendants brought forth finely decorated wooden chests, each giving off the scent of the various types of wood they had been fashioned from. Everyone smiled in delight as the chests were brought before the throne. Mingyue closed his eyes. The potent aura of conifers made it easy to imagine himself in one of the northern forests.

Each box contained valued treasures from the Norden Empire— the finest pelts of reindeer and fox, polished stones from the lands across the Western Ocean, the softest down from northern species of birds. Finally, the last of the attendants knelt before the throne. The two remaining chests were opened, revealing many jars filled with oil within the first, and several beautiful ivory carvings in the second.

"This oil has been harvested from the finest whales in the Western Ocean, while these carvings are fashioned from the ivory of the mythical Yinshu.[13]"

Everyone marveled at his words.

"Norden hunts whales?" Asked Xi Yanggui.

---

[13] Yīnshǔ (隐鼠): Meaning "hidden rodent," it is the old Chinese term used to refer to the Woolly Mammoth, which were believed to be creatures that dwelt underground in the far north.

Caleb nodded. "Whaling is a common practice undertaken by our people. Whale oil is highly sought after in the west. It is long-lasting and used to create soaps and oil lamps."

"Impressive," smiled the Emperor. "It is clear that among the world's navies, the Norden fleets are the masters of the western seas."

Caleb lowered his head humbly. He unveiled a jar in his hands, prying open the lid to reveal a crystalline substance contained within. "This is the next gift I present before the Emperor. It is the jewel of the Northern Ocean—an elixir made of the ground horn of the narwhal, the unicorn of the sea."

Emperor Jinlong seemed pleased. "I express my gratitude to your brother, the king. His gifts seem to have been carefully chosen."

Erik smiled. "That is not all. I have heard that the Yue Dynasty has a great love of animals, and so, I also present the Emperor with these."

Outside the hall, at the bottom of the steps in the palace's central square, several people walked forward with a large, brown mammal in tow. Several people gasped.

"A bear?" Shenzhong's father Chengxin exclaimed.

"Is it safe?" Asked Huamei.

Caleb nodded assuredly. "Dancing bears are very popular in the European court. They are brought up around humans since they are cubs, thus are tame and gentle. There is nothing to fear."

As one of the attendants began playing a melody on the violin, the bear stood on its hind legs and swayed from side to side with the music.

"Wow!" Shenzhong exclaimed. "So good!"

The court broke out into applause. Mingyue's eyes widened in wonder. Though foreign envoys to the Imperial Palace were quite common, they typically came from Ayutthaya, Karnata, Abyssinia, or the many other lands of the Southern Ocean. He had grown up seeing the elephants, monkeys, and the many strange species of birds brought over by these envoys, though they never ceased to amaze him. But

29

never had he seen such a ferocious, dangerous-looking creature act so calm and docile, almost human-like.

One more attendant hurried in, carrying a large bird perched on his arm.

"This is the last gift that we present to the Yue Emperor," Caleb said. "This falcon is of the finest breed of all falcons in Sogdia. We acquired it during our travels through the Keliyete Khanate and thought that Prince Yanlu would appreciate the gift as a reminder of the homeland of his forefathers."

Mingyue's father, Yanlu, smiled in gratitude. "This indeed is a wonderful gift."

Emperor Jinlong nodded slowly. "Prince Erik, each of the gifts presented before us was more magnificent than the last. I am grateful for the respect that you have shown, and hope that both Norden and Wuyue can further cultivate this budding relationship between us through trade and friendship."

Erik smiled as he and his attendants bowed before the Emperor.

Mingyue felt a spark within him. He had always desired to discover the world, but he had never given it a serious thought before. Now, however, gazing into Prince Erik's jade eyes, Mingyue saw the wonders that the world beheld. Lands of vast forests. Seas of ice where unicorns dwelt. Endless expanses of the open steppe. Mingyue could see the world in Erik's eyes.

Suddenly realizing that the prince had caught him staring, Mingyue quickly glanced away.

Erik suppressed a smile. "Your Majesty, forgive me for any rudeness I may have shown."

Emperor Jinlong blinked in surprise. "Nonsense. Your gifts have been well-received, and you seem like a man with honour and utmost integrity."

Erik's eyes met Mingyue again. He continued addressing the Emperor.

"Early today, I encountered one of the imperial princes. Due to my carelessness, I accidentally caused him harm and knocked him to the ground. Because of my ignorance, I was not aware that he was an imperial prince, and I showed him great disrespect."

To Erik's left, Caleb's face went pale in terror. He opened his mouth to speak but didn't dare let any words come out. The language Erik was using made it seem like he had acted in a poor manner and had caused injury to the prince.

"Y-your Majesty…" Caleb finally said in a panicked tone, lowering his gaze even further, "forgive my lord. This was a grave embarrassment and should not have occurred. I am willing to receive any punishment for any harm or disrespect caused to the Yue prince."

Everyone was surprised by these comments, most of all Mingyue. He quickly stepped forward and addressed his grandfather.

"Your Majesty, what the prince says is not false, but he is not at fault. I was the one who took on the disguise of a servant and left the boundaries of the Palace of Lunar Serenity without my permission. I was not looking where I was going, which is why I bumped into Prince Erik. But he did not show any rudeness or disrespect toward me. Rather, he was gentle and kind, even though I appeared to be a servant who had disrupted a prince."

Now, everyone was even more surprised. Erik himself grew silent, turning to Mingyue and thinking slowly as he struggled to understand the words he was speaking.

The Emperor smiled at Erik. "Prince Mingyue has no complaints of any harm or disrespect shown by Norden's prince. Why would you make it seem like you were at fault?"

Erik laughed sheepishly. "I…apologize for any misunderstandings…"

"Nonsense, nonsense," said the Emperor. "As Prince Mingyue has said, you showed great honour and respect to him, even when you believed him to be only a servant acting out of line. Prince Erik, I hope that you and my grandson can continue to have meaningful interactions. May the cultivation of your friendship reflect the

31

strengthening of these newfound ties between Norden and Wuyue. From now on, I will grant you the freedom to visit the Palace of Lunar Serenity any time you wish. You are a welcomed guest of the Yue Dynasty."

V. Dawn in the Ambrosial Garden

5/8/18th Year of the Golden Dragon Emperor

Year of the Wooden Goat

Over the next several days, numerous envoys from many nations began arriving in the ports of Qiantang. Bearing many treasures and gifts from around the world, they all came to show their respect to the Yue Emperor. In a few weeks, Wuyue would be marking the Qiantang Festival, the thousandth year of the founding of the imperial dynasty. It was to be the largest celebration in their history.

Just a few days ago, the eldest daughter of the Oghuz Rumeli sultan had arrived, bearing the finest of glass, fabric, fruit, and oil from the Mediterranean and Arabia. Other nobles from the many lesser kingdoms to the west and south had also been received into the Emperor's court, some from places Mingyue hadn't even heard of before.

"Neili," the prince spoke up. From his terrace, he could see the early rays of dawn breaking forth from behind the mountains far to the east.

"Yes, your Highness?" Neili replied. He draped Mingyue's robes over the prince's body, dressing him for the day ahead.

"Will there be more envoys arriving today?"

"I believe most of the guests have already been received," the eunuch replied. "Rajah Devaiah, the Nipponese envoy, and the Yi Princess will be arriving within a few days."

"And the Xin delegation?"

Neili shuddered. "Oh, don't tell me that they're coming too! I can't stand the Crimson Emperor."

Jiao Hongli was who Neili was referring to. He was also known as the Crimson Emperor and ruled over the Xin Dynasty to Wuyue's north. Even though the Xin wielded control over most of the Tang Realms,[14] they lacked the wealth and prosperity of the southern

---

[14] Tang Realms: Lands formerly ruled by the Tang Dynasty (618-907 AD) where the Tang ethnic group is predominant. This includes the territories stretching from the Gobi Desert in the north to the South China Sea, and the Himalayas in the west to the East China Sea. Lands south of the Yangtze River are primarily controlled by Wuyue and Nanyue, while lands north of the Yangtze River are primarily controlled by the Xin Empire.

kingdoms. While the south had maintained relative stability for the past millennium, the north had seen several dynasties rise and fall over the centuries and been subject to numerous invasions and conquests by the nomadic peoples of the steppe. In contrast, Wuyue and Nanyue had histories stretching all the way back to the collapse of the Great Tang, and thus had centuries to consolidate their borders, build up armies and navies, and expand their maritime trade across the world. This led them to develop into fabulously wealthy nations. This was particularly true for Wuyue, which now had numerous overseas colonies and tributary states throughout the Taiping and Southern Oceans.

"He is not coming," Mingyue responded. "Only my cousins will be attending. And Princess Zemao, of course."

Neili didn't find that reassuring. Mingyue's cousins, Prince Jingli and Princess Fengling, were a pair of twins who were a year his junior. They were the children of Princess Zemao, Princess Huamei's younger sister. Being married off to the previous Xin Emperor as one of his consorts for political purposes, Zemao harboured some resentment toward the Yue Dynasty. Unsurprisingly, her children seemed to share in her resentment. Whenever the twins visited, Mingyue could always sense a great deal of unspoken tension between them.

There was a knock at the door. Mingyue turned to see a dark-skinned woman, only a few years older than himself, standing at the door. Her silky, black hair was braided over her shoulders, blending in with the deep violet dress she was wearing. Despite her delicate frame, she gave off a stern aura with one look in her eyes. This woman was Hansini, known by her courtesy name Wei Hanxi, and she was the principal attendant of Mingyue's daily affairs.

"Miss Wei," Neili bowed.

Hansini didn't give him a second glance. She spoke directly to the prince. "Your Highness, Lady Ramanantsoa has just returned from her voyage. She has invited you to the Imperial Gardens to present the finest treasures of her travels."

Mingyue nodded. "I will be there shortly."

Mingyue always enjoyed being the first to gaze at the exploits brought back by voyagers upon their return to Qiantang. Of all the voyagers, however, he was always most excited to see Lady Arivetso Ramanantsoa. She was a young maiden, the daughter of the lord of one of Wuyue's many tributary states—Merina, a large island off the coast of the Dark Continent. Once a year, she would arrive in Qiantang with wonders from across the Southern Ocean.

Mingyue soon arrived in the gardens, accompanied by his guard, Olekina, as well as Hansini. He quickly caught sight of Arivetso. She was an elegant, dark-skinned noblewoman as tall as he was, dressed in bright green and yellow robes. The fabrics she wore gave her body a very angular appearance. Her posture was upright and firm, her eyes wide and glowing with wonder.

"Your Highness," she bowed to the prince.

Mingyue didn't have time for such formalities—he was much too excited to see what she had brought back with her. Nearby, he caught sight of several enormous birds with lengthy, firm necks and legs. Each stood nearly twice his height, with a beak large enough to crush an entire melon in half. Mingyue stared in awe at the sight of them. He had seen many ostriches before, but those didn't compare in size to the creatures standing before him.

Lady Ramanantsoa chuckled at the look on the prince's face. "Prince Mingyue, I present to you the vorompatra, a bird native to my homeland of Merina."

Mingyue glanced at her in bewilderment. "If these are native to Merina, why have you never told me about them before?"

"Apologies, your Highness," Arivesto bowed to the prince. "The vorompatra is a rare species. It was not even known whether they still existed. Their numbers have suffered greatly due to hunting for their meat. My father thought it was best to send this group back to Qiantang, for their own protection, and as a gift to the Emperor."

Hansini muttered under her breath, "What do you expect us to do with these?"

Mingyue, overhearing her comment, responded without addressing her directly. "These creatures will be looked after and taken care of. They will be given sanctuary in the Imperial Gardens and will be provided with an adequate habitat and resources to ensure their well-being."

Hansini bowed with a sigh. "Of course, your Highness."

Arivesto laughed. "You two still address one another as if you are siblings bickering."

"We are not siblings," Hansini and Mingyue both said in unison.

They glared at one another. Amidst Arivesto's laughter, Mingyue detected other voices in the distance. He turned to Olekina.

"Are there other visitors in the gardens?"

Olekina replied with a nod. "I heard that some of the guests would be visiting today."

Past several of the bushes and trees, Mingyue glimpsed a flash of golden hair. A young man turned his face upwards. His jade-green eyes shimmered in the sunlight. Mingyue's heart skipped a beat. It was the Norden prince.

VI. The Prince and the Sultana

Stepping through the clearing, Mingyue saw that indeed the person before him was Erik. However, he wasn't alone. Next to the prince was the attendant from the other day, Caleb, along with a girl with fiery-red hair. Mingyue had heard that some of the Westerners had red hair but had never seen it for himself before and was skeptical as to whether that was true.

Hansini and Olekina quickly followed their prince. The trio from the Norden envoy faced another group of three individuals. Mingyue recognized the woman in the middle clad in violet robes—she had arrived with an envoy a few days prior and had been received into the Hall of Harmony. This was Aysun Sultana, the eldest daughter of the Oghuz Rumeli Sultan. She was no more than a few years older than Mingyue, her posture regal, and her face bearing a stern expression. The others accompanying her, a woman and an androgynous figure whom he thought might be a eunuch, were clad in much simpler attire, with cylindrical hats atop their heads. They must've been her attendants.

Mingyue overheard Erik and Aysun exchanging words, but the language they spoke was a foreign tongue he couldn't understand. Luckily for him, Arivesto came up beside him. She had traveled widely throughout the Oghuz Rumeli realms and quickly began translating the conversation for Mingyue's ears.

Erik was the first to speak, "Aysun Sultana, what an honour to see you again." He bowed his head.

Aysun's response wasn't as polite. "I was hoping not to encounter any of you Norse here in Wuyue. Let us keep our interactions to a minimum."

"Aysun Sultana," this time it was Caleb speaking. "The Second Livonian War is over. The peace treaties have already been signed. Prince Erik had hoped that there would be no tension between our nations anymore."

Aysun's expression remained unchanged. "My elder brother was killed in the war. I will not be at peace until justice is served."

"If I may ask," said Erik, "how can we bring his death to justice? The soldier who delivered the fatal wound to the Rumeli prince was killed at the Battle of the Neris River."

Aysun raised an eyebrow. "Is the life of a mere soldier equal to that of my brother's? Our Crown Prince was killed. Don't you think it is only fair for the Norse to pay with the life of their own Crown Prince?"

King Erlend II, Erik's elder brother, had only just ascended to the throne. He was still young, not yet having any children of his own, and thus for the time being, it was Erik himself who bore the title of Crown Prince.

Both of Erik's attendants went wide-eyed in shock at Aysun's suggestion, but Erik himself didn't react.

"Absurd!" Yelled the red-haired girl. "What sort of request is that? It would only lead to another war!"

One of the Rumeli attendants, the androgynous individual with dark, curled locks, grew defensive. "How dare you address Aysun Sultana in such a manner!"

Erik waved the red-haired attendant's comment aside. "Agnes, please apologize to Aysun Sultana."

The red-haired woman, Agnes, glared at Aysun as she reluctantly obeyed the prince's request. The Sultana stared back at her expressionlessly. Mingyue finally decided it was time to step forward and interrupt the conversation.

"I think I agree with Miss Agnes in her assessment. Such a demand is unreasonable."

Everyone's attention turned toward the Yue prince, noticing his presence for the first time.

"Third Prince Qian," Aysun said in surprise.

Both she and Erik bowed upon his arrival. They were at first confused as to how he had been listening to their conversation but understood when they caught sight of Arivetso.

Aysun quickly switched from the Oghuz to the Wuyue tongue so that he could understand.

"I apologize, your Highness. However, you should not concern yourself with European affairs. This is between the Oghuz Rumelis and the Norse."

Mingyue thought for a moment before speaking up. "The Emperor has declared mutual friendship between Wuyue and Norden. If a conflict emerges that disrupts trade and interaction between our two nations, then Europe's affairs will be our affairs as well."

Aysun seemed shocked by his comment. Hansini also stepped in to interrupt.

"Your Highness, the relationship between Wuyue and the Oghuz Rumelis is one of balance and harmony. They are the west. We are the east. Yin and Yang. There must not exist any animosity between these two."

Aysun raised an eyebrow. "Third Prince Qian, does even a servant understand Heaven's Will more than a Yue prince?"

"Do not disgrace His Highness," Arivetso spoke calmly. "Of course, Wuyue's Third Prince would not dream of challenging the Oghuz Rumelis. However, the Sultana must also understand that her request for the life of Norden's Crown Prince is unreasonable. I am sure she is merely speaking out of mourning for her late brother. After all, was not the previous Khorasani Shah killed by the Oghuz Rumelis during the Third Gulf War? I am sure that the current Shah would not request the head of the Oghuz Rumeli Sultan as justice for his father's death."

"*Tch*," sighed Aysun Sultana, waving away Lady Ramanantsoa's comment. "Of course, I would never make such an outrageous demand, but I will not forget my brother's death. I wanted to see how Norden's Crown Prince would respond to such a request. I must say, I am disappointed he did not speak out to defend himself."

"Of course not," Erik said at last. "I was aware that you were testing me, Sultana. I have heard that you are a woman of great integrity, not one to speak with a malicious tongue."

Aysun huffed. "And *I* have heard that Norden's Crown Prince speaks honeyed words." Her eyes flicked toward Mingyue. "Be careful not to let the serpent's tongue seduce you."

She whipped herself around and disappeared further into the garden, her two attendants following closely behind.

A long while passed as Mingyue watched the princess depart. He raised an eyebrow at Erik, repeating the words that the Norden prince had said to him on the first day they'd met.

"'Just like the misty mountains and sleepy gardens, even the servants of Wuyue's palaces are alluring.' Is it true that you speak 'honeyed words'?"

He expected Erik to become flustered, but instead, the jade-eyed prince smiled.

"Aysun Sultana claims I speak sweetened phrases. However, I merely state what is the truth. The only fault with my words that day was to wrongly refer to you as a servant. I apologize, your Highness. But I must say, I am surprised that you remember the exact wording I used during our first meeting. It seems that Third Prince Qian has spent a lot of time thinking about our encounter."

It was his turn to raise an eyebrow. Erik's comments caught Mingyue off guard. The Yue prince found that *he* instead was the one who was now flustered.

"You—" his face flushed red. He didn't want Erik to think that he'd been paying much attention to him. He decided to change the conversation. "You have improved in your comprehension of Wuyueyu since I last saw you."

Erik laughed. "It looks like Third Prince Qian also uses honeyed words."

Mingyue's face grew even brighter. "Not 'honeyed words.' It was merely an observation."

Erik nodded in agreement. "Indeed. Caleb has been trying his best to teach me as much as he could in the past few days. However, I think it would be better to practice with a native speaker. Don't you agree?"

A moment of silence passed between them. Both Mingyue and Erik's servants, along with Lady Ramanantsoa, had slipped away into the shadows. This awarded the princes some sense of privacy in their discussion, despite knowing very well that the others could still hear every word passing between the two.

"You sound almost fluent," Mingyue noted. "How is that possible when only a few days ago you were struggling to get by?"

"As I said, I've been practicing," he chuckled. "Picking up a new tongue is much easier the more languages you already know."

"And how many would that be?"

Erik paused for a moment to think. "Norse, my mother tongue of course. There are several dialects, of which I can speak three or four. Oghuz, as you just witness. Agnes and Caleb taught me Gaelic, Anglish, and Vinlandic. I also know Volga Slavonic, Avar, Gallic, Venesian, Frisian, Saxon, Livonian, Suomi, a bit of Sami, some Oghuzi, Latin, Greek, and Persian—"

"Alright, alright, no need to brag."

"Hey! You're the one who asked."

"Yes."

"And how many do you speak?"

"Wuyueyu, Nanyueyu, Xinyu, Sogdian, and some Persian and Syriac."

"Ah, so we share Persian in common," he chuckled. "I picked it up on our way to Wuyue when we were passing through Khorasan, but I haven't actually been to Persia myself. Have you?"

"I've never left Wuyue."

"Never left Wuyue?! Really?"

"I've never even left Qiantang," he added. "In fact, I hardly ever leave the palace."

"How?" Erik's face was one of disbelief.

Mingyue shrugged. "It is not our custom."

"Well, all the more impressive that you've been able to pick up so many languages!"

"Not really. Xinyu is fairly similar to Wuyueyu, so it is easy to pick up. My grandmother is from Nanyue, and my father is Sogdian. There are many Persians in the court, and Syriac is commonly spoken among the priests and monks in temples."

"I see…" Erik nodded. "I suppose if *I* lived in a palace such as this, I too would have little reason to leave."

"Are the palaces in Norden much smaller?"

"Oh, far, *far* smaller. Not just in Norden, but just about everywhere that I've traveled. I wouldn't be surprised if this palace alone was larger and housed more people than Norden's entire capital, haha!"

"You must tell me more. I don't think I've ever met anyone as widely traveled as you. Well, other than Lady Ramanantsoa, but she primarily travels throughout the Southern Ocean."

"I'd be happy to," Erik smiled. "Why don't we take a stroll through the gardens?"

Mingyue's heart skipped a beat. What was this strange feeling? Excitement? Nervousness? Both? He didn't know why, but he felt content with the idea of spending time with the Norden prince.

VII. Ephemeral Garden

For much of the day, Mingyue and Erik spent their time touring the Imperial Gardens. Mingyue brought the Norden prince to see the vorompatra birds that Lady Ramanantsoa had just brought to the palace. The creatures strutted gracefully through the foliage, stirring up much curiosity and bewilderment from those who passed by. Erik's jade-green eyes lit up at the sight of them.

"Wow!" He beamed. "I've never seen such large, strange-looking creatures before!"

Arivesto spoke up from the side. "They are the largest birds in the world. Just as Wuyue has the Silver Phoenix, Merina has the vorompatra."

Erik's mouth hung agape. "These are birds? How can they fly?!"

Mingyue turned to the Norden prince in confusion. He tried to suppress his laughter, but it slipped through his lips. "Prince Erik, not all birds can fly."

"Really?" He blinked in confusion. "Then what makes them birds?"

Mingyue thought for a moment. "Not all who possess wings know how to fly. Does that make them any less than what they are?"

Erik responded after several moments of silence. "I suppose not."

"Bats can fly. So can butterflies. But they aren't birds. On the contrary, chickens have wings, but they can't fly. Yet they are still birds."

"But chickens *can* fly," Erik asserted.

"No, they can't."

"You've never seen a chicken fly? They aren't very good at it, but I can assure you that I have seen chickens fly down from trees before and hilltops before."

"That isn't flying, that's falling."

"Still! They can use their wings to steer their direction and slow their descent. I can't imagine a creature like those vorom...vorom-whatevers using their wings for anything. Look how tiny they are!"

Arivesto raised an eyebrow at him, "I am surprised that Norden's Crown Prince has never encountered such creatures. Surely during your travels, you have come across many strange and magnificent wonders."

Erik nodded in agreement. "Indeed, I have. But I have never seen a bird so large before. We do not have creatures like that in the north."

"I have heard stories of the north," Mingyue said. "Is it true that it is a land of eternal darkness and winter?"

Now it was Erik's turn to laugh. "That is only the case in the very far north of the empire. In the winter, it is shrouded in two months of darkness. However, in the summer, there are two months of eternal light—we call that the midnight sun."

"Amazing. What does the sunset look like? I have never seen one before."

Erik tilted his head in confusion. "You've...never seen the sunset?"

Mingyue shook his head. "The mountains block the view from here. One cannot see the western horizon unless one goes to the highest point in the palace, which I am not permitted to enter."

Erik turned to gaze toward the west. Indeed, the misty mountains looming overhead blocked out much of the sky. He smiled.

"Every evening, it is the same sun setting on the horizon, yet somehow, each sunset is different. I have seen the glowing sunsets over the dark shadows of the Rainbow Mountains, the shimmering sunsets reflected in the Western Ocean, and the glittering sunsets of lands covered in ice."

Mingyue marveled at his words. Erik stretched his arm out toward him. "Come. Why don't we go together to see the sunset together?"

Those words struck Mingyue. He blinked in confusion. "Together...now...?"

"His Highness has other matters to attend to this evening," Hansini interjected.

She had been standing in the shadows since the two had started talking, and now stepped forward into the light, lowering her head respectfully as she addressed the Norden prince.

"I apologize, but it is my duty to attend to the Third Prince's affairs and ensure that he fulfills his obligations."

From the corner of her eyes, her gaze met Mingyue. He shot her a disapproving look but knew that she was right.

"Wei Hanxi is correct," he admitted reluctantly. "Perhaps I can accept your invitation another night."

It was Hansini's turn to shoot the prince a disapproving glare. Mingyue fought hard to suppress a smirk.

Erik smiled at both of them. "That would be wonderful."

***

Erik watched as Mingyue was called back to the Hall of Harmony. Neili had entered the gardens to inform him that guests had arrived. He was required to be present among the Yue court while they were being received, just as he had been when the Norden envoy arrived a week earlier.

Erik was soon left alone in the gardens as Mingyue and his attendants hurried back to the palace for preparations. He admired the peonies and appreciated the warm climate at the base of Dingjia Mountain. At this time of year, much of the Norden realms would already be shrouded in gray, overcast skies, as the days darkened, and winter approached. In Wuyue, however, the atmosphere still gave off the aura of summer.

"My lord," Caleb said from the garden pathways.

"Yes, Caleb?" Erik turned to him.

The dark-haired man stood next to a cherry blossom tree, alongside Erik's guard, the red-haired woman named Agnes.

The attendant spoke up, "The Third Prince of Yue has returned to the palace to welcome the Xin envoy, is that correct?"

Erik nodded. "That is what the servant just said, is it not?"

Caleb nodded slowly. "By this point, most of the envoys have already arrived to celebrate the Qiantang Festival in a few days. However, the Roman envoy has not yet landed in Wuyue."

Erik knew that what he was saying was true, but he didn't want to appear troubled by those words. "Neither have the Keliyetes, Nipponese, or Karnatan envoys," he pointed out. "Is that of concern?"

Caleb hesitated. "N-no…your Highness. However, there has been no word at all from the Tsar since we departed from the Tsardom. It has already been several months since then…"

Erik brushed his words aside. "I'm sure we will hear from them soon."

Caleb and Agnes eyed one another nervously. They both knew how strange the silence from the Roman Tsardom was. Erik received letters from them on a regular basis, and it had never been more than a few weeks before he would hear from them again. But by now, nearly half a year had passed. Though none of them dared to say anything out loud, they all knew that something was not quite right.

VIII. Crimson Whirl

Mingyue arrived in the Hall of Harmony that evening dressed in some of his finest attire. Considering the prince's wardrobe consisted almost exclusively of top-quality silk, the black and gold robes he donned were of the utmost elegance. After all, they were welcoming one of their most important guests—the Empress Dowager Zemao of the Xin Dynasty.

Qian Zemao, the second daughter of Emperor Jinlong, was married off to the previous Xin Emperor in her youth. After the death of the previous Xin Empress, Zemao was elevated from the status of Noble Consort to Empress and bore the Xin Emperor two children—Prince Jingli and Princess Fengling. Being a pair of twins, they were known as the Yin and Yang of the Xin Dynasty. They were the pride and joy of their late father. After his death, however, it was Jiao Hongli, the Crimson Emperor, who ascended to the throne. Being the eldest son of the Emperor, and the son of the first empress, this was only natural. While Jiao Hongli would not be attending the Qiantang Festival, he had sent the Empress Dowager and his younger half-siblings in his place.

Upon the envoy's arrival, the Yue court was all donning black and gold, the official colours of the Xin Dynasty. Mingyue had grown bored after having received so many envoys the past few days. None had excited him the way the Norden delegation had. However, he was still curious to see how his cousins Jingli and Fengling had matured. He hadn't seen them for several years and hoped that perhaps the historic tension between them would dissipate. Zemao had been elevated to the status of Empress since they'd last seen her. Perhaps now she would feel less bitterness toward her relatives in the Yue court.

After the typical formalities of greetings, gift-bearing, and paying respect to the Yue Emperor, Zemao stepped forward. With a single glance at her regal posture and features, one could instantly tell she was an Empress. However, Mingyue couldn't help but notice the smug appearance on her face. When she had been married off to the Xin

Emperor at a young age as a consort, she had harboured much resentment toward her family in Wuyue. Now that she had risen to the status of Empress, however, she seemed to be full of herself, almost looking into Emperor Jinlong's eyes as if she were his equal in status. Mingyue found this amusing.

"I have heard that Second Prince Zukang has been engaged to the Yi Princess," she said. It was easy to hear the distaste in her voice. "The Crimson Emperor sends gifts to congratulate this joyous arrangement."

As she gestured for her attendants to bring forth gifts, Mingyue noticed Jingli's eyes grow wide in horror. The boy seemed like he wanted to speak up, but he held his tongue.

Zemao's attendants approached alongside a young man. He wore a white, turban cloth around his head and ornately decorated strips of fabric hung loosely over his body, exposing his arms and much of his chest. The boy's light hair and handsome features reminded Mingyue of Erik. The two could pass for brothers at a glance. The one difference, however, was his eyes. Unlike the Norden prince, this man didn't have soft, gentle, jade-green eyes, but rather a devilish, serpentine gaze that was tainted with a crimson glow. If it weren't for the cuffs and chains bound around the man's wrists and ankles, one might easily mistake him for a noble.

"What is this you have brought here?" Asked Empress Yinfeng. Her voice sounded almost accusatory as she gazed at the chains around the young man's limbs disapprovingly.

Zemao smiled at her aunt. "The Crimson Emperor's gift to the Second Prince, of course. In congratulations for his betrothal to the Yi Princess."

The Yue court turned to one another in confusion, murmuring among themselves. What did it mean that the Crimson Emperor had sent a man in chains as a wedding gift to Wuyue's Second Prince?

Mingyue's eyes flicked toward his elder brother. Zukang seemed most confused of all.

"Pardon if I may ask," he spoke up, "but what exactly is the purpose of this gift?"

Zemao raised an eyebrow. Jingli and Fengling recoiled at their mother's actions as if they wanted to disappear altogether.

"What is the purpose?" She repeated. "Your Highness, surely you must understand. This man is the most skilled huxuan[15] dancer in all the west. The Crimson Emperor hoped to honour the prince by presenting such an individual as a gift."

A long, empty silence rang out across the hall. It seemed as if everyone wanted to speak, but no one dared to say anything.

Finally, Emperor Jinlong's elder sister, Qian Jinling, broke the silence. "Forgive my interruption, but is it not typically a woman who performs the dances of the Sogdians?"

Zemao smiled. "In the Tang Realms, yes, that is the tradition. However, in the former Sogdian Kingdom, young men were also used as…entertainers. Is that not so, Your Highness?" Her eyes rested upon Mingyue's father, An Yanlu.

Yanlu blinked momentarily before responding. "Yes, that is correct."

Though no one spoke it out loud, they all knew that the Crimson Emperor's choice of a young Sogdian man as the gift to Zukang was no mistake. Yanlu, the father of Zukang, Sheli, and Mingyue was a descendant of the former Sogdian royal family. Despite this, he had been granted the title of First Prince of Yue. Though he would not be heir to the throne, a foreigner as the father of three of Wuyue's potential future successors naturally attracted much disapproval from others in the court. The most prominent disapproval, however, came from Zemao. The Xin Dynasty had also been opposed to this marriage. Presenting such a gift to the Second Prince of Yue was a deliberate act of mockery. It was shocking. Never before had a Xin Emperor shown such outright disrespect to Wuyue. But now, the Xin Dynasty's new

---

[15] Hú xuán (胡旋): A dance originating in Central Asia brought to China during the Tang Dynasty. Literally meaning "Dance of the Whirling Barbarian," it is also called the Sogdian Whirl.

49

Crimson Emperor clearly saw himself at least on equal footing with the Golden Dragon Emperor, if not above him.

Despite all the tension boiling beneath the surface in the Hall of Harmony, the Emperor managed to smile at his daughter.

"We will accept this gift. Such a talented performer will surely be welcomed into the palace. Please present my gratitude to the Crimson Emperor."

Jinlong knew better than to act based on emotion. While this gift had been accepted out of integrity, the clear message that the Crimson Emperor was sending with it would not be forgotten.

***

After the court was dismissed, Mingyue hurried to catch up with his cousins. Around an hour or so from then, they would gather on the terrace by the Lake of Tranquility at the center of the palace to dine with the Emperor. Before then, they had time to prepare themselves for the feast.

Mingyue spotted Jingli and Fengling in one of the alleyways on their way back to their guest residence. Sheli and Zukang had already arrived before him.

"Jingli!" Zukang called out.

Walking ahead of them, Jingli halted. He paused for a moment before slowly turning to face his older cousin.

"Prince Zukang, my title is Prince Jingli."

Zukang scoffed. "What exactly was your elder brother thinking when he decided to gift me a dancer?! A *male* dancer at that? I am not a cut-sleeve![16]"

"*Tch*," Jingli sighed, rolling his eyes.

It was clear during his reaction in the Hall of Harmony that he disapproved of the gift as well. However, he had very little say in the diplomacy of the Xin Empire. If the Crimson Emperor decided to present such a gift to the Yue court, he could not argue against it.

---

[16] Cut sleeve: A Chinese colloquial term for a homosexual man.

"An Yanlu is a Semu prince," stated Jingli. "A male dancer is nothing bizarre in Sogdian culture. If the Emperor can accept a barbarian as his son-in-law, surely he can accept their culture as well."

At the word "barbarian," Zukang fumed. Jingli realized too late that he had just referred to the First Prince as a barbarian. Calling those who hailed from lands outside the Tang Realms "barbarians" was a common manner of speech but had grown out of fashion.

Unsurprisingly, this was taken as an insult.

"YOU!" Zukang easily took offense. He lunged at his younger cousin.

"A-Kang!" Sheli called out.

She didn't want her brother to get into a fistfight with Jingli. Such occurrences had been common in their youth. Perhaps "fistfight" wasn't the best way to put it. Typically, Zukang would tackle an unresistant Jingli to the ground. Needless to say, it was always Zukang who was reprimanded by his elders, while Jingli was pitied.

Luckily, this time someone intercepted Zukang, grabbing hold of his wrist. It was Shenzhong. Somehow, he was always present when his two younger cousins got into a fight and had grown used to breaking them up. Jingli didn't even flinch at Zukang's fist, which had come within inches from his face.

Shenzhong sighed. Shaking his head, a nostalgic smile appeared on his face. "Still getting into fights, even after all these years? Will you ever grow up?"

He said it in a teasing manner. Zukang glared back at him. Luckily for Shenzhong, he was respected by both Zukang and Jingli, being the eldest of all the cousins. Though he had a rather carefree personality, and wasn't particularly formidable, none of them would dare get into a fight with him.

"Forgive my brother," Fengling spoke up, stepping between Jingli and Zukang. "Jingli sometimes lets his tongue slip."

Shenzhong nodded in agreement. "I am sure the Crimson Emperor meant only good intentions with his gift. If Zukang does not appreciate the Sogdian dancer, I would be happy to take him into my custody instead."

Zukang pulled his sleeve away and huffed with a smirk. "Is perhaps the reason your father hasn't yet found you a maiden for marriage because you don't have a taste for women?"

Shenzhong threw his head back in laughter. "Certainly not! I can assure you that I do not have an interest in men. Nevertheless, I could use some entertainment. Unlike Qiantang, Suzhou is an awfully boring place to reside."

***

That evening, the huxuan dancer performed as entertainment at their feast on the terrace. Against the backdrop of the Lake of Tranquility in the heart of the palace, the sparkling jewels and gold of the young man's outfit sparkled like stars in the sky as he spun and whirled his body around in circles. Mingyue was captivated by his movements.

"How fascinating!" Sheli exclaimed to Mingyue's left. "I wish they had gifted this dancer to me! Perhaps we should find our own!"

"*Mhm...*" Mingyue responded to his sister without a second thought.

He turned his gaze upwards at Sheli. She and Fengling both stared back at him blankly. It was then that Mingyue realized his sister hadn't been speaking to him, but rather to their cousin. His face flushed red in embarrassment. Both Sheli and Fengling broke out into ceaseless giggling, attracting much attention from the other tables. This only led to further embarrassment on Mingyue's behalf. He turned his face away from them, hoping they would soon forget about him.

In the corner of his eye, Mingyue caught sight of the dancing man. He glimpsed his smooth, pale skin and toned muscles on his exposed chest and abdomen. A strange sense of guilt washed over him for staring there, and he quickly fixed his eyes instead on the man's face. His light hair swirled through the air gracefully as he spun, like leaves in the wind. Without being able to get a clear look at his face, Mingyue could almost imagine that the man dancing before him was Erik. For

52

some reason, his heart skipped a beat at that thought. His face grew redder.

Mingyue was surprised when the dancer's eyes landed on him as well. He had just finished one of his spinning cycles, allowing Mingyue to finally stare into those deep, crimson eyes. They had a sharp, mysterious glow to them. The boy shot Mingyue a devilishly handsome grin. Mingyue quickly averted his gaze. His stomach was doing somersaults.

How could one look from a man make him feel so flustered?

IX. King Qian Shoots the Tide

10/8/18th Year of the Golden Dragon Emperor

Year of the Wooden Goat

A week later, the celebration of Wuyue's one-thousandth year as an empire, the Qiantang Festival, was held.

The envoys from the Keliyete Khanate and Empire of Nippon had been delayed due to storms in the northern seas, but the Roman delegation was also mysteriously absent, without any news of their whereabouts. Though Caleb and Agnes continually brought up their worries to Erik, he waved them aside each time. What could he do about it? The Volga Romans were traveling along the same route through the Keliyete Khanate that the Norden envoy had passed through, from the Volga River to the Bohai Sea. If anyone would have news of them, it would be the Keliyetes. They would have to wait a few days for the Keliyetes to arrive before they could take any further action.

The most important guests, however, were present for the celebrations. Rajah Devaiah, along with his daughter and his son-in-law, had landed in the city the previous evening. As the heir to the throne of Karnata, one of Wuyue's closest and most important allies and trading partners, their presence in Wuyue was significant. Much of the past day had been spent celebrating their arrival with lively music and elaborate dance performances.

Mingyue remembered getting along well with Ahi, the Karnatan princess, during one visit she had made to Wuyue several years prior. Like him, she was much quieter and more reserved than those around her, and so the two of them would often slip into discussion at the back of the room while everyone else was busy conversing with one another.

Mingyue was surprised to see that though Princess Ahi was more than a year younger than he was, she was already married. Her husband, Prince Sundar, was a tall, handsome young man, clad in snowy white robes with a turban around his head. Both Sundar and Ahi were respectful and reserved individuals. Though they seemed somewhat aloof when one first met them, both had rather gentle and friendly demeanors. Mingyue couldn't help but think just how perfect the two seemed for one another. He knew that he would soon be arranged to marry too and wondered if the match would be just as admirable as this young couple.

That afternoon, each of the delegations stood alongside one another on the Qiantang Bridge that spanned the length of the river just outside the city. It was one of the few occasions each year in which Mingyue had the chance to leave the palace. He relished basking in the cool breeze blowing across the river. The Imperial Palace, surrounded by mountains on most sides, had a warmer and more humid climate than the rest of the region. Mingyue appreciated the cooler temperatures and fresh air.

"Today marks the one-thousandth anniversary of the Wuyue Empire," an announcer's voice rang out. Near the middle of the bridge Mingyue spotted a woman dressed in elegant black and gold robes, donning a rectangular hat atop her head. The hat was adorned with floral embroidery around the edges of each of its four sides, surrounding the symbolic cross emerging from a lotus at its center. She appeared to be of Tang descent though several of her features—the slight hook of her thin nose and hooded lids of her eyes—suggested that she likely had at least some foreign ancestry. Mingyue recognized her as Si Lu, the High Priestess of Qiantang who served within the palace's temple.

"One thousand years ago, the Great Shatuo[17] sent their navies upon the Wuyue Kingdom up the Qiantang River from the east, and down the Qiantang River from the west in an attempt to subjugate the Wuyue Kingdom. As they razed every city and village along the river and closed in on the capital, Wuyue's eighth king, King Weiyue, rallied together the citizens and soldiers of Qiantang for one final stand against the invaders."

---

[17] Shatuo: A Turkic tribe that heavily influenced northern Chinese politics from the ninth to tenth centuries. They are noted for founding several dynasties after the collapse of the Tang Empire.

"It was on that day, the tenth day of the eighth month, in the year of the Wooden Tiger, the Shatuo ships arrived in Qiantang from the east and west. The citizens of Wuyue stood along the banks of the river, burning the entire length of the shore to prevent the ships from landing. Archers stood along this very bridge, aiming the flaming arrows toward both west and east as the enemy approached. When the tidal bore[18] came in, King Weiyue ordered the army to destroy the dikes constructed by the first King of Wuyue more than a century before. The waves of the tide caught the Shatuo ships off guard, sinking many. At the same time, the archers unleashed their volley of flaming arrows. The Shatuo fleets were ultimately annihilated, with not a single life of a Wuyue soldier or citizen lost. This great battle, the Battle of the Qiantang River, marks the birth of the Wuyue Empire. Following the defeat of the Shatuo invaders on the night of the full moon, King Weiyue of Wuyue had the title 'Emperor of the Moon'[19] bestowed upon him by his people."

"The Shatuo lost the Mandate of Heaven. They have long since disappeared off the face of this earth. But Wuyue still stands, today and forevermore! May Heaven's Will bless the Yue Emperor, sovereign of a thousand years, may you reign for ten thousand more!"

At this point, everyone standing along the bridge drew their flaming arrows. Villagers along the shores lit ceremonial fires to commemorate the Battle of the Qiantang River. As the annual tidal bore came in from the east, everyone prepared to release their arrows.

Once the waves were visible in the distance, Emperor Jinlong gave his command. "Fire!"

The burning glow of ten thousand lights shot forth from those gathered along the bridge and the shore, sinking into the waves as it

---

[18] Tidal bore: A tidal phenomenon in which the leading edge of the incoming tide forms waves of water that travel up a narrow river against the direction of the river current. The Qiantang River has the largest tidal bore in the world.

[19] Emperor of the Moon: In Chinese, the word for 'moon' is 月 (yuè). The official name of Wuyue's Dynasty is the Yue Dynasty, of which the House of Qian is the ruling family.

passed them by. The waters glowed a deep orange before the flames were extinguished.

***

As Mingyue headed back to the palace in his palanquin, he continuously glanced out toward the west, hoping to catch a glimpse of the sunset before the sky was hidden behind the mountains. He sighed in disappointment as they slipped into the shadow of the cliffsides.

Neili peaked his head into the palanquin at the prince. "Your Highness, is everything alright?"

"*Mnn*," the prince nodded.

The palanquin suddenly stopped moving. Mingyue peered out to see what was going on and spotted Olekina with his spear blocking Mingyue's servants. In front of him stood a woman with flaming-red hair. Mingyue recognized her as Erik's guard, Agnes.

"Lower your spear," Mingyue ordered Olekina. The guard obeyed the prince's command reluctantly.

Agnes flashed Mingyue a grin, bowing before him. "Third Prince Qian, I present a message from Norden's Crown Prince."

Off to his left, Erik came riding up alongside him on horseback. His jade eyes flicked toward the Yue prince expectantly.

"Go on," Mingyue nodded to Agnes.

She smiled. "Prince Erik wonders if Prince Mingyue would like to view the setting of the sun with him over the Qiantang River."

Mingyue found himself blushing at the invitation. Before he could think of a response, however, a voice to his right spoke up in his place.

"The invitation is appreciated. However, it is the prince's duty to be present at the palace for the evening festivities."

It was Hansini who spoke. Her eyes were sternly fixed on Agnes in front of her. Hansini's unwavering expression told the red-haired woman that she would not accept any objection. Agnes lowered her gaze.

Mingyue's heart sunk in disappointment, but he knew that Hansini was right. He would likely get scolded later if he wandered off with the Norden prince.

"Miss Wei is correct," he said reluctantly. "Unfortunately, I will not be able to accompany the prince this evening. But perhaps another night, after the festivities are over."

He glanced at Erik, a small smile involuntarily tugging at his lips. The jade-eyed prince nodded in understanding, returning a smile.

X. The Qiantang Incident

That evening, all the delegates gathered in the Hall of Splendour to celebrate the Qiantang Festival. The palace gates were open for all the citizens of the city to gather in the main square of the Outer Palace. Ten thousand people stood among the crowd as performers from each of the envoys showcased the traditions of their homelands through music and dances down the center of the square toward the pavilion.

The Karnatan princess, Ahi, sat near Mingyue alongside her husband. Rajah Devaiah was seated next to Qian Jinlong himself, as the Emperor's honoured guest, friend, and ally. Only the Karnatan and Xin envoys had been graced with being seated on the platform alongside the imperial family. All the other delegations stood out in the square among the crowds. Mingyue scanned the thousands of people, hoping to catch a glimpse of the Norden prince.

"Is there perhaps someone you are looking for?" Ahi wondered, noticing his distant gaze.

Mingyue quickly glanced from the crowd. "No...I was just observing."

He strained as Zukang threw an arm over his shoulders. He laughed. "Perhaps A-Ming has caught sight of the Yi Princess, and is staring upon the beauty of my betrothed."

Mingyue rolled his eyes and shrugged his brother off.

"Now, now, Zukang," interrupted Shenzhong. "The Keliyete delegation has yet to arrive in Wuyue. Your fiancée is not among the crowd."

"True," Zukang sighed in disappointment. He shot a sideways glance toward Jingli. "I haven't yet been able to enjoy the company of the Yi Princess, but at least I have a dancing boy to entertain me. Isn't that right?"

Jingli glared back at him.

"Perhaps Mingyue is not looking for the Yi Princess, but rather your dancing boy," laughed Fengling.

"Fengling!" Jingli spoke with a scolding tone at his twin sister.

Mingyue shook his head and averted his attention from the others. Their chatter simmered down into an awkward silence for several moments as the songs and dances across the square continued.

Ahi cleared her throat, hoping to reignite the conversation. "Sheli, Mingyue, we have all heard of your brother's engagement to the Yi Princess. Tell me, have you two also been arranged to marry?"

Sheli responded with a shy smile. "The youngest son of the Ansei Emperor of Nippon is my betrothed—Prince Hyousuke. He should be arriving in Qiantang shortly."

Mingyue, on the other hand, replied to Ahi's question with a simple shake of his head. "No."

"I have heard rumors that Mother and Father have already sent out letters of courtship to all ends of the empire and beyond," Zukang remarked, raising an eyebrow at his younger brother. "Don't worry. It's only a matter of time before A-Ming is engaged as well."

"*Hm*," Mingyue sighed, looking out at the crowd once again. At that moment, his gaze met the gentle glow of two jade-green eyes. Out in the square, the Norden's Crown Prince gave a small wave to Mingyue. He flashed a smile. For a moment, Mingyue felt as if they were the only two people in the world. His face flushed red as he involuntarily smiled back.

Everyone on the terrace seemed to catch sight of Mingyue blushing.

"Perhaps A-Ming already has his eyes on someone," Sheli suggested.

"No," Mingyue said quickly. He straightened his back and tore his eyes away from the square once again, covering his reddened face by taking a sip of tea.

"Where?" Zukang clamoured to get a glimpse at the person his brother had been staring at. "Is there a beautiful maiden here tonight?"

Shenzhong laughed. "I'm sure there are many beautiful maidens out there."

Jingli scoffed. "Are you sure? It seemed as if Mingyue was looking at the Oghuz Rumeli sultana."

Everyone's gaze rested on Aysun Sultana, who stood just a short distance from where Erik was. Her face bore the same, stern expression that it had during their previous encounters.

Zukang shivered. "Mingyue, is *that* really what you consider to be beautiful?"

None of them could resist laughing.

"Zukang, what are you suggesting," Ahi managed to ask. "I would say that the Oghuz Rumeli sultana is quite beautiful—in a sharp, rather refined manner."

"Perhaps *too* sharp," Zukang interjected with a shudder. "I find her intimidating."

"An acquired taste," Shenzhong suggested.

They all broke out into another round of laughter.

Sheli's gentle gaze rested on Mingyue. While none of the others could make sense of him, Sheli knew her younger brother better than most. She realized immediately that Mingyue hadn't been looking at the Oghuz Rumeli sultana, but at the Norden prince.

At the center of the pavilion, First Princess Huamei rose from her throne and stepped forward to address the crowd.

"It is my honour to stand here tonight before you," she smiled. "From all the ends of the earth, you have gathered here today to celebrate with us the one-thousandth year of our imperial dynasty. May Heaven smile down upon you."

After a few moments of applause, she continued. "This evening, I would like to take some time to announce the engagement of my youngest son, Third Prince Mingyue."

Mingyue froze at her words. He looked up at his mother with a frantic expression in his eyes. Engagement? For *him*? Where was this coming from? Had he heard her correctly?

"Mingyue," she smiled. "Step forth."

After a moment of hesitation, Mingyue slowly rose from his seat. He could feel all eyes glued to him as he took a shaky step toward the middle of the platform. He could barely process what was happening. His body seemed to be on autopilot, carrying his legs across the pavilion toward his mother against his will. His heartbeat boomed through his ears. Mingyue had never enjoyed being the center of attention. Now, standing before so many people, he thought he might pass out.

Click, click, click. The sound of his footsteps echoing against the tiled floor was deafening. Step by step, he rose higher and higher onto the platform until he had come before his mother.

"Son," Huamei addressed Mingyue simply.

"Mother," he replied, bowing respectfully.

Huamei turned back to the crowd.

Mingyue was confused. The engagement of an imperial prince or princess would usually be revealed in a private chamber by the parents. Only then would it be announced to Wuyue's subjects. However, even then, neither Zukang's nor Sheli's engagements had been proclaimed at such a major festival.

"Prince Mingyue shall be engaged to marry—"

BOOM!

The ground rattled. Mingyue nearly lost his balance. Just as Huamei pronounced the name of Mingyue's betrothed, an explosion rang out to their left. One of the towers on the wall that surrounded the square erupted into a burst of light. Sparks of colour shot out in all directions. There were gasps from the crowd, some even screamed out in surprise.

Huamei furrowed her brow. "The fireworks aren't supposed to go off this soon…"

At the tower, there was movement amidst the darkness. Several figures rushed out from the building as smoke rose from the roof. But one individual wasn't fleeing—instead, they leaned out one of the windows. Mingyue couldn't make out the individual's features, whether they were a man or woman, soldier or civilian, young or old. Whoever it was, they were clad in loose, black robes, and had their entire face obscured with a dark mask. What Mingyue did notice was the long, sleek object clasped in their hands. Its shape stretched as the black clad figure pulled back. By the time Mingyue realized what it was, it was too late.

The bow was released. Within a fraction of a second, the whiz of an arrow zipped past his ear. He didn't even have time to react. The world flashed white. An explosion rang out from just behind him. He was thrown forward from the blast, tripping down the steps of the pavilion and tumbling into the square below.

At this point, the crowd erupted into chaos. Guests scattered and fled in all directions. Some of the guards hurried toward the prince, but none of them could push their way through the mayhem.

Mingyue felt a hand rest gently on his arm.

"A-Ming…" Huamei whispered. Her voice was soothing, eerily calm amidst the chas.

Huamei held her son against her. Mingyue was still dazed from the explosion and his fall down the palace steps. He couldn't make sense of what was going on. Up on the wall, where that figure clad in shadows had fired the arrow from, the tower was now engulfed in a sea of dark flames. Whoever had fired the arrow was long gone.

Turning his gaze toward the terrace, Mingyue found the scene unrecognizable. The throne had been blasted apart by the exploding arrow. The surrounding area was charred black and stained red with blood. Several bodies lay on the ground. The prince blinked in confusion.

"Mingyue," Huamei repeated. She hugged him tighter against her.

Over his mother's shoulder, Mingyue saw several people storming the terrace. They seemed to be Karnatan soldiers judging by their attire—dressed in loose robes, with turbans wrapped around their heads. As all the other guests scattered every which way, that group of men grabbed hold of a young woman. Mingyue's vision cleared. It was Princess Ahi.

"Let go of her!" A man shouted—her husband, Prince Sundar. He unsheathed a sword and engaged the attackers. The others that

63

Mingyue had been sitting with, his siblings and cousins, were nowhere to be found. He hoped they had managed to escape.

Although Sundar bravely fought off the attackers, he was overwhelmed by their numbers. After only a few moments, he was struck down by a blow.

"Ahi!" The young man called out as his body hit the ground. His terrified eyes were fixed on the Karnatan princess as she was dragged to the center of the terrace. The soldier who held her had a dagger to her throat.

Mingyue couldn't make sense of what was going on. Who were these men that had suddenly attacked? They had been hiding among the crowd and were waiting for the perfect opportunity to strike. That opportunity came when the shadowed figure had fired an exploding arrow into the throne.

This was a well-orchestrated attack. But Mingyue still didn't understand why this was happening. What motives did anyone have for causing so much death and destruction?

Despite the chaos, Mingyue felt tranquility in his mother's embrace—it was as if he were a child once again. He knew that he should be afraid right now, but he wasn't. Instead, he felt safe—safe, and warm. That warmth was spreading across his abdomen and limbs. In fact, it wasn't just warmth he felt, but also wetness.

Mingyue pulled away from his mother, his eyes widening in horrified realization. Blood was seeping through Huamei's robes, staining not only herself but him as well.

"M-mother...?" He whispered fearfully.

Huamei smiled weakly at her son. It was only then that Mingyue noticed the arrow protruding from her back. How long had that been there?

"Mother!" He shouted. He caught her in his tainted hands as she collapsed forward from the blood loss.

"Ming...yue..." her voice was barely audible. "I'm sorry...I had to leave you...so soon..."

64

"No…" Mingyue's words choked up in his throat as his mother's head drooped downwards. This couldn't be happening.

Up on the terrace, Sundar was still trying to push himself to his feet to save his wife. Unlike her husband, the young princess had a serene expression in her eyes. Her face appeared radiant as she was held in the center of the terrace before all below to see. It was as if her soul had already left her body, as if she had already departed from this world.

As her attacker raised his dagger against her, Ahi's eyes met Mingyue. The blade slashed against her throat. Mingyue's vision went black as a stream of blood splattered down the steps of the palace.

Part II

Black Fire

I. The Bloodstained Palace

12/8/18th Year of the Golden Dragon Emperor

Year of the Wooden Goat

"You cannot enter," Olekina said simply.

The guard stood outside two burgundy doors, spear clenched in hand as he blocked Jingli and Fengling's path. The twins were dressed in black robes that fluttered gently in the breeze, having arrived at the infirmary where Mingyue was taken following the attack. Two days had passed since then.

"I have been sent to inquire upon Third Prince Qian's condition," explained Jingli. "How is he?"

"Recovering," Olekina stated bluntly, staring down at the Xin nobles. He refused to step aside.

Jingli was unsatisfied with this vague answer. He simply nodded. "The funeral is to be held this evening. I was wondering if Third Prince Qian would be attending."

"Second Prince Qian," Olekina corrected.

"Pardon…?" Jingli blinked in confusion.

"Second Prince Qian," the guard repeated. "After Prince Yanlu's passing, Prince Mingyue has risen to the rank of Second Prince."

"That…is correct…" Jingli nodded slowly. It still hadn't fully set in for any of them. "Will Second Prince Qian be attending the funeral?"

"He will," Olekina spoke with stern certainty.

Jingli and Fengling nodded, thanking Olekina for relaying this news to them. As the two departed, Mingyue's attendant Hansini stepped out through the infirmary doors behind Olekina. She closed them silently behind her.

"You should never make absolute statements," she narrowed her gaze, her voice filled with disapproval.

"He will go," insisted Olekina. "He *must* go. As the son of Prince Yanlu and Princess Huamei, he must show respect to his parents."

Hansini lowered her voice. "Have you seen him? He is in no condition to go anywhere."

"Why not?" Olekina wondered in confusion. "He wasn't badly injured."

Hansini sighed. "He just lost both his parents before his eyes. He is traumatized. I do not think he will soon recover from that."

Olekina remained silent. He too was an orphan, having lost his parents suddenly at a young age. Unlike Mingyue, however, he hadn't had the opportunity to mourn them after their passing. He never would have survived otherwise.

Olekina nodded slowly as he took in Hansini's words. The prince would need time to recover.

Inside the infirmary, Mingyue lay motionless on the bed. He stared blankly at the ceiling, having been in this position for several hours now. The boy cocked his head to the side as a figure entered the room.

"Your Highness," a young man said softly. His long, dark hair was braided over his shoulder; his olive skin and chocolate-coloured eyes glowed in the dim candlelight. The man knelt next to the prince's bed with a cup of tea in his hands. "Drink. You will feel better."

Mingyue waved him aside. "I don't want any."

Nearby, a man broke out into a heavy fit of coughing. With haste, the olive-skinned man hurried over to the neighbouring bed.

"Prince Sundar, are you awake?"

Besides those who had been killed, many others were injured in the attack on the festival. Among them was Emperor Jinlong. Unfortunately, the palace was ill-prepared to deal with such catastrophes. Thus, Prince Sundar, who was among the worst of the injured, was recovering in the infirmary at the Palace of Lunar Serenity alongside Mingyue. Sundar groaned in pain but remained unconscious. He had suffered much blood loss from being stabbed during the attack. It was unknown if he would survive.

There was a knock at the door. After a moment, it creaked open. Stepping foot into the room was Qian Sheli, Mingyue's elder sister. She was dressed in all white—the colour of death. A veil of mourning hung over her face.

"Princess Sheli," the olive-skinned man said in surprise, bowing to the princess.

"Doctor Chu," Sheli addressed him. "Thank you for taking care of my brother. Is there anything I can do for you?"

Kanen, whose courtesy name was Chu Kening, was the chief physician of the Palace of Lunar Serenity. The young man stared at Princess Sheli before his gaze shifted toward Mingyue.

"I must change the Karnatan prince's bandages. Your Highness, perhaps you can take your brother out for some fresh air?"

Sheli smiled softly. "Of course."

Mingyue leaned on his sister for support. He had been injured from the shock wave of the explosion and from falling down the stairs, but more than anything, he was simply drained of energy. He still could not process exactly what had happened. Despite witnessing it before his very eyes, he found it difficult to accept it as true.

"Did they find him…" he whispered.

"Find who?" Sheli asked gently.

"That person…" he couldn't bring himself to look at his sister. "The one in the shadows. The one who fired the arrow—"

The one who had killed their parents. Sheli gently placed a finger to Mingyue's lips before he could say it. Not that he could even bring himself to say it anyways. His voice was trembling. He felt that if he spoke those words out loud, what had happened would become real. He couldn't accept that reality.

"Do not concern yourself with that," Sheli whispered. "The guards are doing everything they can to find those responsible."

"How…? Everyone that they've caught has already killed themselves by ingesting poison capsules. What if those who are responsible are never brought to justice? What if we never even know why…?"

What if we never know why our parents were killed?

The princess flinched at his words. The loss of their parents had affected her just as much as it had him, but Sheli knew she had to remain strong for her little brother.

"Judging by their attire, the assailants were from Karnata," she said calmly. "If they came with the envoy, someone is sure to recognize their corpses. If not, someone in the Yindu[20] Quarter must know who they are."

Sheli gentle placed her hands onto the sides of Mingyue's face, turning her brother's distracted gaze toward her. "It is not your duty to bring them to justice. Leave that to others. Right now, your duty, as the son of the Crown Princess, is to mourn. That is all you need to do. All you *can* do."

Mingyue said nothing.

The two stepped out onto the terrace at the back of the infirmary, overlooking a small, isolated garden with a pool in the middle.

"Why are we here?" Mingyue wondered.

"It is good for you to get some fresh air."

Mingyue noticed several figures near the other end of the garden. He caught sight of Erik, accompanied by his attendant, Caleb. With them was Lady Arivesto Ramanantsoa, along with a young woman carrying a small jar.

The siblings watched in silence. Shadows from the terrace roofs overhead kept them obscured from sight.

"May I ask why we are here?" Erik pondered the same question Mingyue had just uttered.

Arivesto smiled. "I just wanted to check up on your condition. I hope you are recovering from your injuries."

"It was just a scratch," responded the prince. "Nothing severe. I am more worried about the others, especially Prince Mingyue. I have not been told of his condition. How is he doing?"

---

[20] Yindù (印度): The Chinese word for India. The Yindu Quarter is one of the many quarters in the city of Qiantang home to merchants and migrants who have arrived in Wuyue from around the world.

"He is resting," Arivesto said simply. "Thanks to your interference, the prince was unharmed."

At first, Mingyue didn't understand Arivesto's words. Everything that had happened that night was a blur; he had forgotten most of it. However, now that it was brought up again, his memories started to come back to him.

After the blade sliced across Princess Ahi's throat, Mingyue found himself frozen in shock. A completely innocent young woman, someone who he considered a friend, had just had her life ended so ruthlessly before his very eyes. And for no apparent reason.

In front of him, his mother's body lay face-first on the cold, tiled ground of the square—the Crown Princess of Wuyue, sprawled out on the floor in such a degrading manner, a single arrow protruding from under her left shoulder blade. Thick, warm blood pooled around Mingyue's legs, staining the edges of his robe as he knelt next to her. His eyes were wide in horror, but he was completely silent, unable to even draw a breath.

"Get to the prince!" Someone shouted. Mingyue couldn't tell who, whether friend or foe. At this point, it didn't matter. Nothing mattered. Mingyue didn't care anymore.

Someone grabbed his shoulders and pulled him around. He gazed up at the man, who was clad like a Karnatan warrior. The soldier lifted his sword to strike.

A streak of red flashed before Mingyue's eyes. Within a moment, the man who had been prepared to kill him slumped to his knees and dropped his weapon. Erik's guard, Agnes, had plunged a knife into the man's side.

"Run!" She yelled at him as she fended off two more attackers.

Mingyue was still dazed. He didn't react. Someone took hold of his hand. The person's grasp was firm, yet gentle at the same time. It was Erik.

The Norden prince pulled Mingyue to his feet. One of the men Agnes was holding off suddenly broke free, lunging toward Mingyue with his sword. Erik quickly threw himself between the two of them.

His sword was drawn from its sheath, clashing against the other man's weapon with a deafening screech. Erik's defensive move was rushed and ill-prepared. He didn't have a proper grip on his sword, and the blade was knocked out of his hand upon impact, clanging to the ground. The prince's wrist was strained by the strike, twisting under the force of the other man's momentum. He recoiled in pain. But his move had managed to carry out its purpose—the attack was deflected away from them. As the soldier brought his weapon around toward the prince once again, he was suddenly impaled through the stomach from behind, collapsing to the ground. Behind him stood Olekina, clasping the bloody spear that had just pierced through the dying man's body.

Mingyue felt queasy recalling these events. He had been unconsciously blocking them out over the past few days. But now, seeing Erik before him, he couldn't suppress them any longer.

The prince stumbled forward. Sheli caught her brother's hand to steady him.

"Are you alright?"

He nodded, slowly drawing in a breath. "It's nothing…"

Below, Arivesto gestured to the individual accompanying her, a young, dark-haired, olive-skinned woman who appeared to be of Melayu[21] descent.

"Keiy, come forward."

The woman, Keiy, stepped forth, holding out the jar to Erik.

"This will help you recover from your injuries," Arivesto explained. "Please take it."

The Norden prince declined the gift with a polite smile.

"Please, take it," Arivesto repeated. "If not for yourself, then at least for your guard who was injured. It would be irresponsible of me to not tend to the injuries of Wuyue's guests. Especially one whom Third Prince Qian seems to have taken such a liking to."

---

[21] Melayu: A Wuyueyu term referring to the people of insular Southeast Asia, particularly the Malay and Philippine Archipelagos. Many of these islands are overseas colonies of Wuyue or home to kingdoms that give Wuyue tribute.

Erik chuckled at her words as he took the jar of ointment from Keiy. "Has the prince taken a liking to me, then? I couldn't tell, considering how many times he's turned me down."

"The prince has many other duties to attend to," Arivesto sighed. "He is also not the best at expressing his emotions. But the fact that he even speaks to you is a sign that he at least feels comfortable in your presence."

"Haha," Erik smiled in embarrassment. "I'm glad to hear that. I hope he's been doing alright."

Arivesto nodded. "It will take time. But I'm sure the prince will appreciate your concern. He will be at the funeral later this evening."

Sheli continued guiding her brother through the palace grounds in silence, before circling back around to the infirmary. Returning her brother to his bed, Sheli finally spoke up.

"A-Ming, are you going to the ceremony?"

"Of course I am," he said defensively. "I have to, don't I?"

"It is expected that you do, but you should only go if you're able to. I know it's painful. Ao Neili will bring your clothes here later. The procession will head out shortly afterwards."

Mingyue nodded. "I will be ready."

II. Every Sun Must Set

12/8/18th Year of the Golden Dragon Emperor

Year of the Wooden Goat

The funerary procession set out in late afternoon. It was strange to be holding a funeral only a few days after the Qiantang Festival. Whoever was responsible for the attacks had planned out and executed their plot with utmost precision. Every soldier who was captured instantly committed suicide by biting down on poison capsules that they had hidden behind their teeth. These were not ordinary soldiers, but highly trained assassins who were willing to carry out their orders to the death. Strangely, no one had yet been able to identify any of the corpses of those they had captured.

Several of the attackers were known to have fled the scene, including the mysterious shadow-clad figure who had fired the exploding arrow, as well as the arrow that had killed Qian Huamei. With each hour that passed, Mingyue grew more and more anxious. Not only did he want the perpetrators to be caught and brought to justice, but he also knew that this would not be the last of them. It was only a matter of time before they struck again.

Security was high. More soldiers were flanking either side of the procession than those who were taking part in the funeral itself. The caskets for Princess Huamei and Prince Yanlu were at the front of the procession in a large, tiled-roof structure, almost a small building, on a bamboo palanquin being carried by dozens of servants. Behind them was a similar, smaller structure. This one was carrying the body of Princess Jinling, Emperor Jinlong's elder sister, who was Shenzhong's grandmother. The elderly princess had been among the casualties of the exploding arrow.

Mingyue's palanquin was riding alongside Shenzhong's as the procession made its way out of the palace.

"I am sorry about Aunt Jinling," Mingyue muttered. "May her soul rest in peace."

Shenzhong kept his eyes fixed forward. "I am sure the last few days have been much more difficult for you than for me."

Mingyue said nothing. To his right, Olekina walked alongside the palanquin. He was always within arm's length of the prince whenever they left the palace, but today he was even closer than usual. The guard clasped his spear tightly in his hands, alert, and prepared to strike at any moment if anyone dared to step too close. Mingyue eyed the tip of his spear. It was the same blade that had pierced the Karnatan soldier the other night, but today not a trace of blood stained the weapon.

"Wu Liqing..." Mingyue managed to say. "Thank you for protecting me."

The guard's eyes flicked toward the prince momentarily before his focus returned to the surrounding area. "That is my duty, Your Highness. There is no need to thank me. I should have gotten to you sooner. Perhaps I could have prevented any harm from befalling your parents..."

"It is not your fault," Mingyue interrupted. "I don't want to hear you blame yourself for it."

Olekina fell silent but spoke up again after a moment. "Your Highness, if anyone deserves your gratitude, it is the Norden prince. He went out of his way to protect you, even putting his life in danger. If it wasn't for him, I wouldn't have had enough time to get to you..."

Mingyue nodded. "I will be sure to thank him later. Perhaps I will accompany him to view the sunset..."

Olekina's eyes met Mingyue, but neither of them said anything else.

They arrived at the docks at the main gate of the palace, which opened up onto the West Lake. Mist hung heavy over the water, with only the peaks of the mountains on the other end of the lake being visible. Dozens of boats lined up along the shore to carry the procession across the water. From there, they would travel to the canal leading to the Qiantang River, then upstream to where the Imperial Burial Grounds were located further west of the palace.

***

Thousands of civilians lined the shores of the river as the procession made its way upstream. They each lit a lantern, casting them out onto the river, where they floated along the gentle waves—ten thousand lights flickering across the surface of the water like stars in the night sky.

It took some time for the dozens of ships to arrive upriver, and even then, they still had to travel the mountain paths to reach the burial grounds.

Priests accompanying the procession played their gongs and bells in a noisy, celebratory manner. Loud music was customary for such processions, said to drive away demons and evil spirits as the souls made their way to the afterlife.

Nearly the entire royal family was present for the funeral, even Qian Jinyu, the senile, eldest brother of the Emperor. However, notably absent from the ceremony was the Emperor himself. Jinlong had lost both his legs in the explosion. While it seemed he would survive his injuries, he would remain incapacitated for a while as he recovered.

Rajah Devaiah of Karnata had unfortunately been killed in the attack alongside his daughter. Rumors were going around that he had thrown himself in front of Emperor Jinlong at the last second before the arrow exploded, saving the Emperor's life by sacrificing his own. To the very end, he had remained Wuyue's closest friend and ally.

At last, they reached the burial grounds, climbing one of the highest hills, where the deceased would be laid to rest. Statues and enormous tombstones commemorating the ancestors of the Yue Dynasty decorated the mountain peaks—dozens of generations, thousands of graves.

The burial grounds were surrounded by rolling green mountains. To the south was the Qiantang River. To the east, one could see the rear walls and towers of the Imperial Palace peaking over the top of Dingjia Mountain. To the west, the sun already hung low in the sky, painting the clouds orange and pink.

Everyone took their assigned positions before the caskets. As per custom, the children of the deceased stood at the highest step of the hill—Mingyue, Sheli, and Zukang, the children of Princess Huamei and Prince Yanlu. Alongside them was Shenzhong's father, governor Xi Chengxin of Suzhou, as well as Xi Yanggui, princess of Ailao. Both were the children of Princess Jinling.

Along the lower steps were Empress Yinfeng, Shenzhong, and Qian Jinxin, the Emperor's youngest brother. Following them were the other members of the dynasty, and then the nobles and delegates from Wuyue and beyond standing at the base of the hill.

High Priestess Si Lu presided over the ceremony, repeating each prayer and chant in Wuyueyu, followed by Sogdian in honour of An Yanlu, and Syriac, the liturgical tongue. Her reverberated throughout the valley. Incense hung heavy in the air as the sun set low on the horizon. Soon, it disappeared behind one of the mountains. The burial grounds were cast into darkness.

"Every sun must set," Chengxin whispered.

Mingyue and the others all glanced at their mother's cousin, but none spoke any words.

I have never even seen the sunset, Mingyue thought to himself. *And yet I have already seen the light of many souls burning out.*

Everyone circled the mound, marching with banners and flowers in hand as the priests continued chanting and clanging their bells and gongs. After what seemed like an eternity, they gave their final bows, each kowtowing to the heavens, the earth, and the sea in unison with one another. After the caskets were entombed, flowers were decorated over the mound, and offerings of food were placed before the gravestones. The priests then lit these all aflame. Against the backdrop of the evening atmosphere, flames pierced the night sky. Thick, black smoke choked the mountainside. The moon was beginning to rise above the peaks, but all Mingyue could see was the blanket of darkness hanging overhead.

Si Lu finally spoke the last words of the ceremony, "Let the flames burn away these offerings, and the smoke carry its essence to the heavens. Let the flesh of these bodies return to the dust, and the souls of the deceased return to the Eternal Heavenly Light."

The journey back to the palace was tense. They had buried their dead, but there were sure to be more to come. Wuyue hadn't seen such a violent, catastrophic attack in a long time. Whoever was responsible had clear intentions and would certainly strike again. The question was, who were they targeting? And why?

The Karnatan princess had been singled out and slaughtered in cold blood, but three members of the House of Qian had also been killed in the attack, including the Crown Princess. In addition, the Emperor had been heavily injured.

The attackers seemed to be from the Karnatan Empire, judging by their attire. If that was the case, they were most likely targeting the Karnatan royal family and had managed to kill both the heir to Karnata's throne and his daughter. However, something didn't add up. If Karnatan rebels were responsible for the attack, why had they brought Wuyue into the situation by carrying out their attack in Qiantang and killing members of the Yue Dynasty as well? The perpetrators were certainly aware that such an attack would make them the enemies of the world's most powerful empire. The death of Huamei and Yanlu, and the maiming of the Yue Emperor were surely not accidental or merely collateral damage. They were directly targeted as well. For what reason, Mingyue didn't know. The only person who may be able to offer some insight was the sole member of the Karnatan royal family who had survived the attack—Prince Sundar. As he was currently incapacitated, they would have to either wait for him to regain consciousness, or wait for the attackers to strike once again, before they could gain insight as to who these individuals were and what their motivation was.

As they arrived back at the river at the base of the mountains to return to the palace, a group of half a dozen soldiers rode up on horseback. The guards at the front of the procession cautiously raised their weapons. Empress Yinfeng waved them aside.

"Commander Wang, come forth."

The leader of the group rode up to the empress's palanquin, speaking in a somber tone, just loud enough for her to hear. "Your Highness, I do not mean to concern you, but there are reports of a disturbance in the city."

"What sort of disturbance?"

Commander Wang hesitated. "There have been tensions in the Yindu Quarter the last few days. After news that Rajah Devaiah and his daughter were killed, riots have broken out demanding that the perpetrators be caught and brought to justice. Even worse, factions within the community are growing suspicious and turning on one another. There are rumors that the attackers were Karnatan soldiers, perhaps loyalists to northern separatists rather than the ruling family. A temple has been burned to the ground, and the central bazaar is also in flames."

Yinfeng nodded slowly. "I understand. Thank you for informing me. Enforce a curfew over the Yindu Quarter and surrounding districts until we can restore order."

"Yes, your Highness."

III. Whispers in the Shadows

"Another funeral?" Zemao sighed. It was the day after the burial, and the Empress Dowager of Xin was sitting in her guest quarters as servants stood to the side fanning her.

"Yes," a eunuch confirmed. "The Shah of the House of Sasan has succumbed to his injuries and passed away. The funeral is to be held at the Tower of Silence in the Persian Quarter later today."

His words hung heavy in the air. The Shah, Prince Narsieh's father, had been present at the Qiantang Festival the other night and was among the many who were injured in the attack. His injuries had not been too severe, and thus it was expected that he would survive. However, that wasn't the case. He was one of the highest-ranked officials in Wuyue, thus his death had cast yet another dark shadow over the empire.

Zemao sighed. "This is a bad omen. Must we really attend *another* funeral? And of all places, the Tower of Silence? The Feng Shui of that place is very negative. Merely visiting it is sure to bestow more ill fortune on us, not to mention participating in those barbaric rituals—"

"Mother," Jingli interrupted Zemao sternly.

She gazed at him in confusion. "Is it not true? We simply cannot partake in such a ceremony that will only bring more bad luck to the Emperor. He is severely injured. We should be offering prayers and burning incense for his health and prosperity. The balance of Wuyue has been upset by what has taken place. The Yue Dynasty cannot afford to further defy Heaven's Will."

The servants and eunuchs all kept their gaze averted from the Empress Dowager, none of them daring to object.

Jingli shook his head, "Mother, the House of Sasan is very close to the House of Qian. They hold a high position in Wuyue's court. Failing to attend this funeral would be highly disrespectful."

Zemao gave a half smile at her son. They both knew that she didn't need to be told that. After all, she had grown up in Wuyue and was familiar with the court.

Jingli continued, "Besides, I know that you are not really concerned with the Feng Shui of the Tower of Silence. After all, even the Imperial Palace is not built on a north-south axis in accordance with Feng Shui regulations."

Everyone in the room could sense the disapproval beneath Zemao's light smile. No one dared to breathe. The Empress Dowager knew she shouldn't cause a scene in front of the servants, especially with her son. Gossip spread quickly, and any sign of tension from within the Xin Dynasty could be viewed as a weakness to be exploited, even by members of her own family.

"Very well," she huffed. As she turned to depart, the maids whisked her from the room before the situation could escalate any further.

Fengling reproached her brother, "Jingli, you should show some filial piety when addressing Mother. It is out of line for a son to speak to his mother in such a manner, and even more so for a prince when addressing the Empress Dowager."

The frustration in Jingli's face lessened as he turned to his sister. "Fengling, Mother should also know her place when she is in the presence of the Yue court, especially His Majesty the Emperor. The amount of arrogance she has shown since our arrival is inappropriate, as is the wedding gift that was presented to Zukang."

Fengling considered her brother's words, nodding slightly in agreement. "You are not wrong. However, that gift was ordered to be presented by Hongli himself. Our brother is the Crimson Emperor, how can mother deny his commands?"

"*Tch*," Jingli scowled. "Hongli may be the emperor, but Mother is the Empress Dowager. If you ask me, her authority should be at least equal to that of Brother's."

Fengling chuckled. "That is not how it works."

"No," sighed Jingli. "Unfortunately not."

Several moments of silence passed before Jingli spoke up again, this time in a much more hushed tone. His nervously scanned the

83

room to be sure that no one was listening in. When it was clear that there were no servants present, he spoke.

"Fengling…you don't think that Mother could be involved in what happened…do you…?"

Fengling's eyes widened, but the question her brother had asked wasn't surprising to her. Both siblings were aware of the contempt their mother had toward her relatives in Wuyue.

Fengling shifted uncomfortably, "W-what would she have to gain from that…?"

Jingli shrugged. "If Hongli asked her to do it, do you think she would?"

Fengling opened her mouth but didn't know what to say. The truth was they weren't sure of how she would act in such a situation. And that's what they found scary.

"We both know that Hongli wishes to expand the canal system and reduce the tariffs on goods traveling through Wuyue," Jingli noted. "Whatever Brother wants, he always finds a way to get. Through any means necessary. And we both know of his other intentions…"

Fengling hushed her brother. "Don't speak of such things out loud. If Hongli or Mother were responsible, there is still no evidence of it yet. And even if they were, what are we supposed to do about it?"

Jingli stared back helplessly at his sister. "That is what I don't know."

***

Elsewhere in the palace, Jinlong lay resting in his room, with Empress Yinfeng seated at his bedside. The elderly emperor's face was pale and sweaty as he lay asleep, his maimed body covered by a blanket. The curtains hanging over his bed swayed gently in the breeze wafting through the open windows.

Jinlong coughed.

Yinfeng waved at the servants standing by the doorway. "It's too cold for him. Close the windows."

The Empress felt a gentle hand rest on her. She looked down to see Jinlong open his eyes weakly.

"It's fine. I'm not cold."

Yinfeng nodded and waved the servants back. There was a knock at the doorway. The two turned to see Princess Yanggui enter the room. She bowed respectfully in the presence of her aunt and uncle.

"Your Highness," she spoke with reverence, "we are departing the palace shortly for the Tower of Silence."

Yinfeng nodded. "I will not be attending."

Yanggui blinked at her words in surprise. "Your Highness, everyone expects the Empress to attend the funeral."

Jinlong looked up at his wife, "Yinfeng, you should not neglect your duties to our subjects."

Yinfeng breathed with a heavy sigh. "As the Empress, my duty is first to my subjects. As a wife, my duty is first to my husband. Others can take on my duties as Empress, but none can bear my responsibilities as a wife."

Jinlong knew he couldn't argue with her on that.

Yinfeng turned back to Yanggui. "Yanggui, your uncle and I will not be around forever. Now that Huamei is gone…things are different. Huamei was to succeed Jinlong to the throne. Now that she and Yanlu are no longer with us, a new successor must be appointed."

"Sheli is the eldest child of Huamei," Yanggui said. "Now that Huamei and Yanlu have passed, Sheli would naturally be elevated to the status of First Princess, and Zukang to that of First Prince."

Jinlong nodded slowly. "Sheli is the eldest. However, she is a woman. Unfortunately, it will be difficult for her to gain the legitimacy to rule, especially at such a young age."

"Your Majesty, Huamei was also a woman," Yanggui noted, "and yet you appointed her to be your successor."

Jinlong nodded. "That is true. But seeing as I had no sons to succeed me, that only made sense. On top of that, Huamei already held a very high reputation in the court before I appointed her as my successor. And her husband, though a Semu prince, was still a resident

85

of Wuyue and a subject of the empire. Sheli's fiancé is a foreign prince from Nippon. When their engagement was arranged, it was not expected that Sheli would rise to the throne so suddenly, if at all. I am not sure how the Emperor of Nippon will react to his youngest son becoming the husband of the Wuyue Empress. Their marriage was arranged to ensure strengthened ties between our nations, and for the further development of our navies and trading policies to combat the Wokou Pirates. I fear that the Ansei Emperor will feel threatened by his son should he become emperor over the most powerful nation in the world."

Yanggui considered her uncle's words. "Perhaps the engagement can be called off?"

"That is not a matter that can easily be arranged," Yinfeng interrupted. "Besides, I am sure Nippon would take great offense to such a decision."

Jinlong sighed. "There are a great many decisions that still need to be made, and such a short amount of time left. With my condition as it is, we may only have a few years, perhaps less."

"Your Majesty, do not speak of such things," Yanggui snapped. "It will bring a bad omen."

Yinfeng lowered her gaze. "What your uncle says is true. It would be best to appoint Sheli or Zukang as a co-regent, to ensure a smooth transition of power when the time comes."

Jinlong nodded solemnly.

Yinfeng continued, "That is why I will not be attending the funeral. You must go in my place, acting as the representative of the Empress. We will not be around forever. The next generation must cultivate an adequate reputation and earn the respect of Wuyue's subjects if they are to govern over the empire in the future."

"Your Highness, it isn't my position to take on such a role. Wouldn't Zemao be a more suitable representative, seeing as she is your daughter?"

"Zemao," Yinfeng scoffed. "She hasn't even bothered to pay her own father a visit over the last few days. Besides, she is the Empress Dowager of Xin; you are the wife of the Crown Prince of Ailao. Ailao is on much better terms with Wuyue than Xin, and that is in no small part thanks to you, Yanggui. I trust you more than I do Zemao, you know that."

There was a knock at the door from a servant. "Your Highness, your palanquin is ready to take you to the Tower of Silence."

"I will be out in a moment," Yanggui replied. She bowed to Yinfeng and Jinlong before her departure. "Of course, Your Highness. I will do everything I can."

As the princess turned to leave, Yinfeng spoke up. "Yanggui, one more thing. During the Qiantang Festival, Huamei announced that she and Yanlu had chosen a maiden for Mingyue to wed. Were you made aware of this decision beforehand?"

"I was not. I had assumed that she would have told you or Mingyue before it was announced."

Yinfeng shook her head. "I am afraid that no one seems to know who was chosen as Mingyue's bride."

"I see…" Yanggui muttered. "I will be sure to look into the matter."

Yinfeng smiled. "Thank you."

IV. The Tower of Silence

The Persian Quarter of Qiantang was eerily silent. Mingyue and the others arrived in the district by midday, crossing the West Lake from the palace to the main center of the city. Most of the central districts had been put under lockdown under Empress Yinfeng's command the night before. As Mingyue was carried through the city on his palanquin, the only sound that he could hear were the footsteps of his guards clicking against the cobbled street. Most windows had been shuttered and doors sealed, but the prince still sensed an ominous aura, as if dozens of people were watching him from the shadows at that very moment.

The Tower of Silence was an enormous, cylindrical structure atop a hill just beyond the Persian Quarter that towered over most of the buildings below. As the only site where traditional Persian funerary rites could be held in the city, it was a place of great significance. In the millennia since the House of Sasan had arrived in Wuyue, the Three Persian Teachings[22] that had arrived during the Tang Era had gradually overlapped with one another until the boundaries between them were blurred. This primarily led to the decline of those who followed the Teachings of Zoroaster and Teachings of Mani as they were assimilated into the community of those who followed the Luminous Teaching, the most prominent of the three in Wuyue. Of course, this did not mean that the old customs of the other traditions disappeared. They continued to live on in Wuyue, albeit altered as they were absorbed into Tang culture, syncretized with the Luminous Teaching, and the Teachings of the Dao and the Buddha. The House of Sasan was emblematic in upholding these traditions, even if they themselves no longer adhered to the same religion as their Persian ancestors.

---

[22] Three Persian Teachings: A reference to Zoroastrianism (祆教; Xiān Jiào), Manicheaism (明教; Míng Jiào) and Christianity, the Luminous Teaching (景教; Jǐng Jiào), which all arrived in China from Persia during the Tang Dynasty.

Typically, for the death of a major figure within the community, especially the Sassanian Shah, the streets would be crowded with mourners. Under the curfew, however, they were completely deserted. The occasional flame burning at the windows and doorsteps to commemorate the Shah was the only sign of life in the district.

Next to the tower was the fire temple, where most of the other nobles had already arrived. Inside, Mingyue caught sight of Erik, to whom he gave a slight smile. The Norden prince was dressed in dark black robes, contrasting with Mingyue's pure white attire. In the middle of the room burned the sacred fire, considered holy for the followers of the Teachings of Zoroaster. Narsieh stood near the flames alongside several priests, with the body of the Shah laid out on a stone in front of them. Dressed in plain white as opposed to his typical violet royal garb, Mingyue almost didn't recognize the young prince. He blended in with the crowd of other Sassanian nobles. The two princes each gave a nod of consolation toward one another as they waited for the ceremony to begin.

After a while, a large, white bull was brought into the room, wandering over to the corpse.

Fengling whispered, "What is that for?"

"Part of the ceremony requires the corpse of the deceased to be washed in the urine of a white bull before it is laid out on the tower," one of the nobles replied.

Zemao scoffed, "Putrid."

"You are not required to participate in the ceremony," Jingli muttered.

Zemao huffed.

Sheli spoke up, "I have heard that bull urine is cleansing."

They all turned to her in surprise.

"Of course, the daughter of a Semu would understand the ways of barbarians," Zemao whispered under her breath.

"Mother," Jingli hissed.

Mingyue too had overheard her comments, but seeing as how no one else seemed to, he paid no attention.

The priests came around with long sheets of cloth, handing them out to each person. "This is for suppressing the corpse-demon that emerges from the body's decay after death."

"Corpse demon?!" Fengling exclaimed.

The priest nodded, "Everyone must be tied to at least one other individual using this cloth during the ceremony. This repels the demon; the force of two or more beings is stronger than one."

Shenzhong raised an eyebrow, "Sounds intense."

Each of them turned to one another, pairing up as they tied themselves together in preparation for the ceremony. Naturally, Jingli and Fengling paired together. Zukang and Sheli bound their hands, while Zemao went with her brother, Chengxin. This left Mingyue and Shenzhong as the only two remaining. Mingyue turned to his cousin expectantly but was surprised to see him already with someone.

He eyed the girl—a foreigner. She had wavy, brown hair, speckled with strands of gold, brushed over her shoulder. Her eyes were a matching colour, shimmering in the firelight.

"Oh," Shenzhong chuckled as he noticed that Mingyue had wanted to pair up with him. "A-Ming, this is Alaneya Fatima Maria. Her father controls most of the foreign trade in Suzhou. She is a relative of the Oghuz Rumeli sultana."

Mingyue's gaze flicked from Alaneya to Aysun Sultana at the other end of the room.

"Princess…?" He asked, turning his attention back to Alaneya once again as he wondered what her title might be.

Alaneya smiled sheepishly, "Not princess. My uncle is merely a duke—the Doge of Venesia. My father runs the maritime trade between Venesia and Wuyue. His sister is the mother of Aysun Sultana."

Mingyue nodded. "A pleasure to meet you, Lady Alaneya."

He glanced at Shenzhong, wondering what the daughter of a Venesian trader based in Suzhou was doing in Qiantang, and what relation she had with his cousin. Alaneya blushed the moment her hand made contact with Shenzhong. No one except Mingyue seemed to notice. He wondered if perhaps there was a deeper relationship between the two that he wasn't yet aware of.

Seeing as how everyone else had been paired off, Mingyue awkwardly stood alone amidst the crowd. He was unsure as to what he should do.

A sudden tap on the shoulder caught him by surprise, Erik stood behind him with his arm stretched out, clasping his strand of cloth. He flashed a small smile at Mingyue.

"It seems we both remain without a partner."

Mingyue nodded, "It would seem so."

Erik blinked, waiting for Mingyue to say something more. However, Mingyue also remained silent. He expected Erik to continue speaking. A few moments of awkward silence passed between them.

"Would you—"

At the same moment Erik started speaking, Mingyue offered out his palm to the Norden prince, in an unspoken request for Erik's hand. Both froze as soon as they realized that the other had taken the liberty to make the first move. Mingyue's face flushed red. Erik smiled nervously.

Sheli interrupted the two, taking Erik's left and Mingyue's right hand and binding them together with the cloth.

"Took you two long enough," she smiled as the two princes awkwardly stood together.

Erik clasped Mingyue's hand in his. "I believe the ceremony is starting."

Just as Sheli had said, the corpse of the Shah was ritually washed in the urine of the bull as before it was carried to the roof of the Tower of Silence. The roof was a large, circular area that opened over a pit in the center in which the body was laid out. In ancient times, it was customary for bodies to be laid out on the Tower of Silence to be consumed by scavenger birds. Cremating and burying corpses was seen by the followers of Zoroaster as desecrating the fire and earth, and thus this was the only acceptable means of laying a body to rest.

91

However, in the centuries that they had resided in Wuyue, this practice had gradually fallen out of favor. Instead, bodies were now wrapped in a white cloth before being set alight by a certain powder that turned the fire black. These flames were seen as being distinct from regular fire, and thus could not be contaminated by a corpse.

As the priests began lowering the Shah's body into the pit, the sight and smell of his dead body brought Mingyue back to memories of that night—that night when his mother had died in his arms and the Karnatan princess had been ruthlessly executed before all to see. He felt himself becoming faint.

Erik noticed his discomfort. He quietly whispered to Sheli, asking her for permission to take the prince away for a breath of fresh air. The princess nodded.

Erik led Mingyue toward the edge of the Tower of Silence, peering over into the Persian Quarter below. The streets were still desolate, without a single soul to be seen in any direction other than the guards who stood at the base of the tower.

"What are we doing here?" Mingyue asked. "I should be at the ceremony."

He gazed back at the center of the tower, where the black fire began to burn up the Shah's body.

"It seems you weren't well," Erik said. "I'm sure Prince Narsieh will understand. After all, it would be worse if you made a scene and threw up in front of everyone, wouldn't it?"

Mingyue felt a smile tugging at his lips. "That would be embarrassing."

Erik chucked. After a few moments, his expression softened. "I am sorry for your loss. I haven't had the chance to speak with you since the Qiantang Festival. How are you doing?"

Mingyue blinked. "I'm fine. My injuries from the fall were not severe."

"I wasn't talking about your injuries."

Mingyue looked up at the Norden prince, but his gaze flitted away once again. "I'm fine."

The two of them stood together, side by side in silence as they overlooked the ledge.

"I lost my parents and younger sister several years back," Erik said softly. He gazed distantly out over the desolate streets of the Persian Quarter.

Mingyue blinked in surprise. "I'm sorry to hear that..."

Erik smiled nostalgically. "My sister Anna was always causing trouble. She was a feisty kid who always wanted to play and explore. She said she wanted to travel the world, and visit many strange and distant lands, but she was still too young at the time. She never got the chance to fulfill that dream. She and Mother died from the Pestilence when I was ten."

Mingyue was at a loss for words, "...that must have been difficult."

Erik took a deep breath and nodded slowly. "It was. But everyone's time comes eventually. We just have to make the most of what we are given. I decided that I would live out my sister's dream. Upon my twelfth birthday, my brother granted me permission to travel on a diplomatic mission to our territories across the Western Ocean. Since then, I have traveled widely throughout Europe and the Mediterranean. My sister always wanted to visit Wuyue, the empire of the eternal sun. And now, here I am."

"It is honorable for you to live for your sister's memory," Mingyue said awkwardly. He didn't know what else he was supposed to say.

Erik's gentle, warm hand was still clasped in his thanks to the cloth binding the two of them together. With each passing second, Mingyue was growing more and more anxious. He wanted Erik to let go of his hand, but at the same time, he also wished for them to remain like this for a while longer. He didn't know why, but despite having just met the Norden prince, Mingyue felt he could trust him.

The air suddenly went still. Something was off. It was far too quiet, even if the Persian Quarter below was currently devoid of people. He quickly scanned the empty streets but didn't notice anything unusual.

Erik cocked his head. "Is something wrong…?"

Mingyue looked directly beneath them. The two guards who had been standing at the entrance to the Tower of Silence were slumped against the wall. An arrow protruded from each of their chests.

"The guards—!"

Just as Erik noticed what had happened, Mingyue felt a hand on his shoulder. He spun around. A cold, sharp blade was pressed against his throat.

"Your Highness—!" Erik cried.

"Nobody move," the man holding Mingyue captive commanded. His face was obscured by cloth, but the prince could tell that his attire was that of a Karnatan soldier—the same as the men who had attacked the festival and slaughtered his parents.

At the center of the tower, everyone's attention turned toward them, freezing in shock and horror at the sight of the Second Prince being held hostage.

"Any sign of movement and the prince dies," the man warned. This time, his voice was lower. He was gazing out of the corner of his eye at Erik as if that command was given specifically to him.

Everyone remained motionless, but Mingyue caught sight of movement in the crowd. As all attention was fixed in Mingyue's direction, no one noticed as two more masked figures crept up behind the Sassanian prince. Within a fraction of a second, a blade was raised against Narsieh's throat.

At this point, panic ensued. People gasped and screamed, and others pushed and shoved as they made a desperate attempt to escape. One of the priests bolted toward the stairwell that descended the tower. A moment later, he collapsed to the ground, a knife embedded in his back.

"He said not to move," one of the masked figures growled.

Shenzhong narrowed his eyes at the attackers. "What do you want?"

"We want safe passage," the man holding Mingyue captive replied. "If that can be assured, then no harm shall come to the Yue or Sassanian princes."

"If you are looking for a hostage, take me instead and let the princes go," Shenzhong insisted.

"Our orders are to bring back Prince Mingyue and Prince Narsieh to our superior. From there, negotiations will be made."

Zemao gasped. "Surely we cannot negotiate with terrorists!"

Shenzhong's father Chengxin stepped forth. "Do we have any other choice?"

Zemao glared back at him but said nothing.

The man holding Mingyue severed the cloth binding him together with Erik and slowly began to lead him toward the staircase. Mingyue caught Erik's gaze one last time as he was led away. The Norden prince's jade-green eyes were full of worry. He seemed as if he wanted to lunge forward and attack the man holding Mingyue hostage, but Mingyue gave him a slight shake of his head, warning him against retaliation.

When they slipped into the shadows of the staircase, the princes' captors covered their heads in bags and swung them over their shoulders. They hurried out of the Tower of Silence as suddenly as they had arrived.

V. The Scapegoat

14/8/18th Year of the Golden Dragon Emperor

Year of the Wooden Goat

As soon as Mingyue's kidnappers slipped into the stairwell, Yanggui ordered the soldiers to go after them. They came back within moments.

"They've vanished," one soldier said.

"How could they vanish?!" Yanggui fumed. "You were right behind them!"

The soldier hesitated. "Smoke bombs have been released in the stairwell. It's impossible to see which direction they went in."

Yanggui cursed.

"Your Highness!" Someone shouted from the edge of the tower. "The temple is on fire!"

Next to the Tower of Silence, the Fire Temple was ablaze. Smoke rose from its roof, blackening the sky.

"Evacuate the tower!" Chengxin shouted.

"That stairwell is the only exit," one of the priests quivered.

It was Chengxin's turn to curse.

Erik drew their attention over to him, waving the cloth that had been used to bind him and Mingyue together. "Everyone take your cloth and tie them over your face to block out the smoke!"

They did as they were told, and after several long minutes managed to escape from the tower unharmed. The flames had already begun to spread from the temple to the tower, but the priests hurried over to put them out.

"Forget about the temple!" Zemao shouted. "Prince Mingyue has been kidnapped!"

Yanggui turned to the soldiers, "Search every building. Inform the Empress of the situation and place the entire city on lockdown. Mobilize the army. Arrest anyone you see on the streets."

"Yes, your Highness."

"Everyone else, return to the palace immediately."

As the nobles frantically searched for their palanquins and horses to take them back to the palace, Erik slipped away from the group amidst the chaos, disappearing into an alleyway. Just as he thought he'd managed to escape without anyone noticing, two shadows approached from behind. He spun around, unsheathing his sword.

Agnes swooped under the blade, dodging the prince's strike, and taking the weapon into her hand with a twist of Erik's wrist.

"Careful where you swing, my lord," she smirked.

Erik's expression relaxed. "Agnes. Caleb. I apologize, I didn't know it was you."

"My lord, the Yue princess ordered all nobles to return to the palace," Caleb said.

Erik clenched his jaw. "Yes, I am aware."

Agnes raised an eyebrow. "Then where were ya headin' off to all on your own?"

"I…"

Agnes shook her head. "Caleb, take the prince back to the palace. I will go after the Yue prince."

Erik gave her a surprised glance. "Agnes—?"

Before he could protest, Caleb nodded and whisked the Norden prince away. As Agnes headed in the opposite direction, she caught sight of several looming shadows breaking through the fog to the west. On the surface of the lake, a fleet of ships sailed into view from the canal. Three different flags were visible from the masts—the first was that of a golden chrysanthemum amidst a magenta background; the second was that of the sun and moon amidst the eternal blue sky; the third depicted a double-headed golden eagle.

"Huh," Agnes smiled. "It seems our guests have finally arrived."

***

As the bag was pulled off Mingyue's head, he squinted as his eyes adjusted to the light. He found himself in a dimly lit room, illuminated only by the glow of candlelight. Narrow archways spanned the length of each of the room's four walls, leading down darker corridors. The room was empty, besides the elaborate radiant patterns that decorated the floor and walls.

Narsieh was next to Mingyue, both princes on their knees with their hands tied behind their backs. The men who had brought them here had left as suddenly as they'd appeared.

"Where did they take us?" Mingyue wondered. "Is this the Yindu Quarter? I don't recognize this place."

"No," Narsieh shook his head. "Not the Yindu Quarter. The Yindu Quarter is to the south of the Persian Quarter, but after we left the Tower of Silence, we traveled north."

"North?"

Narsieh nodded. "I knew that something didn't add up. If the attackers that night were really Karnatan separatists, then they would have no business with the House of Qian or the House of Sasan. However, both of our families were affected by the attack. You lost your parents and the Emperor's sister. I lost my father. That was no accident."

Mingyue's heart was racing. He had been thinking the same thing, but so far, all the evidence had pointed to the perpetrators being from the Karnatan Empire.

"What are you suggesting?"

"I had my suspicions the night of the Qiantang Festival," Narsieh continued. "True, those men may have been dressed in Karnatan attire and wielded Karnatan weapons, but their fighting style was certainly not of Karnatan origin. My suspicions were confirmed when we were kidnapped. If those men had truly been Karnatan soldiers, then I shouldn't have been able to understand their language. But I can. They are speaking a dialect of Persian."

Narsieh was correct. Now that Mingyue thought about it, the soldiers *had* been speaking Persian.

"Are you saying—?"

"These were not Sassanians," Narsiehs shook his head, finishing Mingyue's thought. "Their dialect is not one I am familiar with—it is a corrupted form. On top of that, they took us quite a distance from the Tower of Silence. I am certain we are no longer in the Persian Quarter.

However, if we were traveling to the northeast, as I suspect, then our current position should place us directly in the heart of the Semu Quarter."

"The Semu Quarter...?" Mingyue repeated.

Narsieh studied their surroundings. "This architecture is definitely Persian. However, it is not Sassanian, but Khorasani."

Mingyue finally dared to speak. "Emir Abdullah ibn Amin's residence."

Narsieh nodded. Emir Abdullah ibn Amin was the nephew of the Khorasanshah,[23] and resided within Qiantang serving as his uncle's ambassador to Wuyue.

Mingyue still didn't understand. "But why...? Why would the Khorasanis target Wuyue? Why would they go after the Karnatans?"

"It seems fairly simple now that we have all the pieces, doesn't it?" Narsieh said. "Karnata is an old nemesis of the Khorasanis. For centuries they've vied for control over Sindh and the Hindu Kush regions. But lately, the northern territories of Karnata have grown rebellious. Khorasan wished to take advantage of that fact and assassinate Rajah Devaiah while he was in Wuyue, framing the attack on Karnatan rebels in order to further weaken the empire. News of the Rajah's death will likely reach the subcontinent within a few weeks at most. The ensuing unrest that will follow could tear the empire apart. Once Khorasani's main rival in the region is eliminated, they will be in the perfect position to fill the power vacuum left behind."

Mingyue was amazed at Narsieh's ability to piece all of this together. "But that still doesn't explain why the House of Qian and the House of Sasan were also targeted..."

Narsieh smiled bitterly. "Do you ever pay attention to Mister Zhang's lectures? Wuyue is the closest ally of Karnata. In fact, it was your ancestors who supported the Karnatan rulers in the south during their unification of the subcontinent centuries ago. The Khorasanis know that Wuyue won't merely sit by and watch as their closest ally is

---

[23] Khorasanshah: A title for the ruler of the Khorasani Empire.

overrun. Wuyue must be weakened to prevent interference. And the House of Sasan? We are the oldest enemies of the Khorasanshahs. They have sought to eliminate us since the days we were driven out of Persia. Now, they might finally have that chance."

Mingyue let the gravity of their situation sink in. "During the Qiantang Festival, they tried to kill me after killing my mother. Why...? Why haven't they killed us yet if that is their intention?"

Narsieh shrugged. "Who can say? Perhaps they want us for insurance, as they said. Or maybe they have other intentions. After all, a living prince is a better bargaining chip than a dead one."

Sudden shouts disrupted their conversation, coming from the outer courtyard of the complex.

"Seems we've been discovered," Narsieh smirked.

Mingyue breathed a sigh of relief.

"I wouldn't get my hopes up," Narsieh said dully. "If our captors lose the upper hand, they may resort to killing us."

Mingyue gulped. He wiggled his body but couldn't undo the rope restraining his arms behind his back.

The doors in front of them suddenly flew open. Several soldiers rushed into the room. Unlike the men who had captured them, they were clothed in Khorasani rather than Karnatan attire.

One of the soldiers furrowed his brows. "Prince...Mingyue...?"

Before he could say anything else, a volley of arrows from the left struck all of them down.

"Your Highnesses!" Agnes gleamed as she strutted into the room. With a swipe of her blade, she slashed through the ropes restraining them. "Glad to see yer in good condition. Prince Chengxin has subdued the enemy within the complex. I'll be takin' ya both back to the palace now."

***

The place where Mingyue and Narsieh were taken indeed turned out to be the residence of Emir Abdullah ibn Amin, located right in the heart of the Semu Quarter. Narsieh's assessment had proven to be correct.

Emir Abdullah wasn't present in the complex at the time of the kidnapping. Incidentally, however, he had just returned to Qiantang on a Keliyete vessel, one of the ships that had docked in the city earlier that day. The man was quickly apprehended and brought before the Empress immediately, into the Hall of Harmony to prostrate himself before the throne. His face was full of confusion.

"Your Highness, a pleasure to see you again…" his voice wavered. "Will the Emperor be coming?"

Yinfeng rose from her throne, jabbing an accusatory finger at the young nobleman. "You are one to speak!"

Abdullah's expression grew concerned. "Apologies. Have I offended your Highness in some way…?"

"My daughter, my son-in-law, my sister-in-law, and now you attempt to take my grandson away from me?! I will have your head!"

Abdullah sprung to his feet. "Your Majesty, there must be some misunderstanding—!"

"Guards seize him!"

Abdullah stood paralyzed. "Wait—!"

As the guards closed in on him, Chengxin entered the room. He bowed respectfully to the Empress, "Your Highness, excuse my interruption. Perhaps executing the emir would not be the wisest decision."

"Then how would you have me carry out justice?"

Chengxin thought for a moment. "Emir Abdullah is the nephew of the Khorasanshah, and an ambassador to Wuyue. I fear that his execution would be regarded as a declaration of war on Khorasan."

Yinfeng waved his comment aside. "As far as I am concerned, the Khorasanis have already declared war on us when they attacked the House of Qian. This act of treachery shall not go unpunished."

Chengxin lowered his gaze from the Empress. "Of course, Your Highness. However, we are not yet aware as to whether the Khorasanshah is complicit in what has taken place here. In fact, Emir Abdullah himself may not have been involved either, although we can at least be certain that the attackers were of Khorasani origin. I just wish to ensure that no decisions are made rashly."

Yinfeng clenched her fists, though she didn't disagree with her nephew. She waved her hand to the guards. "Take him away. Chengxin, you will oversee this investigation. Emir Abdullah will be placed under house arrest within the palace until evidence of his involvement, or lack thereof, is uncovered."

Chengxin kowtowed before Yinfeng as the guards removed a resistant Abdullah from her presence.

"Understood, Your Majesty."

VI. The Princess, The Governor, and the Dowager

14/8/18th Year of the Golden Dragon Emperor

Year of the Wooden Goat)

Yanggui quickened her pace to catch up with Chengxin as he departed the Hall of Harmony.

"Chengxin!" She called out.

Chengxin bowed to his sister. "Your Highness."

"Thank you for rescuing Mingyue."

"No need to thank me," Chengxin assured. "Mingyue is the First Prince. It is my duty as a subject of Wuyue to protect him."

Yanggui stifled a laugh. "Chengxin, I think you are getting your nephews confused once again. After Yanlu's passing, Zukang is now the First Prince; Mingyue is the second."

Chengxin thought for a moment. "Ah yes. My mistake. Speaking of the First Prince, is he prepared to ascend the throne? With the Emperor's condition as it is, I fear we may only have a few months."

"Do not speak of such things. They will only bring about ill fortune."

"Apologies, but I do not believe that my words are misplaced."

Yanggui shook her head. "Regardless, Sheli is the successor to the throne, not Zukang."

Chengxin nodded slowly. "True. However, the First Princess is engaged to the Ansei prince. If she becomes empress, he will be emperor. Is it the wisest decision for him to rise to such a position at such a young age?"

Yanggui sighed. "The Emperor brought up a similar concern. Do you really believe that Zukang should inherit the throne?"

"It was merely a suggestion."

Yanggui sighed. "In the end, I suppose the Emperor has the final say."

"Yanggui, may I inquire about Mingyue's engagement?"

Yanggui hesitated. The scene from the night of the Qiantang Festival came flooding back to her. Huamei's announcement regarding Mingyue's engagement had been cut off abruptly by the attack.

"I was not informed of Huamei's decision to have Mingyue engaged until the announcement. Unfortunately, I am also unaware of who they had chosen as his bride. The Emperor has entrusted me with finding a suitable maiden for Mingyue before I return to Ailao."

Chengxin produced a letter from his robes, "Then perhaps I should inform you of what Huamei's decision was."

Yanggui eyes widened. She took the letter from her brother, glancing over it. "This…this is the maiden Huamei chose?"

Chengxin nodded. "She asked a few months ago that I send her a list of potential maidens for Mingyue's engagement. However, I did not think that she would have chosen this maiden."

"And what is your opinion on her decision?"

Chengxin thought for a moment. "When Huamei first sent me that letter, I was surprised. However, when I thought more about her decision, it seemed to be a good choice. Marriage with this maiden would form close ties between Wuyue and the west, and would strengthen trade. Plus, considering the recent developments with Khorasan, it would be beneficial to forge these relations."

"Indeed," Yanggui nodded slowly. "If this was my sister's decision, then it should be honored."

Unbeknownst to Chengxin and Yanggui, a third figure had been lurking in the shadows, eavesdropping on every word of their conversation thus far. Zemao suddenly decided to make her appearance, approaching her cousins from the terrace.

"My parents left it up to *you* to find Mingyue a suitable bride, did they?" She narrowed her gaze.

"Your Majesty," both Chengxin and Yanggui said in unison, bowing before their cousin. As the Empress Dowager of Xin, she was of higher status than both of them. But this was also true in Wuyue, as she was the daughter of the Emperor himself.

"They merely asked for our insight," Chengxin replied. His eyes were averted from her, not out of intimidation, but out of respect.

"Chengxin, I must say that I am impressed at how quickly you were able to track down Mingyue's kidnappers earlier today," Zemao mused, her tone indicative of intrigue, mixed with suspicion.

Chengxin smiled. "It wasn't me, Your Majesty. One of the Norden prince's soldiers spotted them heading toward the Semu Quarter. We merely followed until we reached the emir's residence."

Zemao folded her arms, "And what business did you have interfering with the Empress's decision regarding the emir's punishment?"

A look of bemusement crossed Chengxin's face. "Empress Zemao, it would be a disadvantage for Wuyue to execute the emir, wouldn't you agree? Substantial evidence must be uncovered first to convict him of his crimes."

Zemao frowned, "And in the meantime, the entire city is under curfew. I was hoping to return to Kaifeng[24] in a few days, but at this rate I will be stranded here until the situation can be resolved."

"Surely you wouldn't be leaving so soon?" Yanggui asked. "I thought you would at least be staying until Zukang's wedding."

"Of course, of course," Zemao assured. "And speaking of marriage, I also have a young maiden in mind to offer for the Second Prince's courtship."

Chengxin raised an eyebrow, "Oh?"

"Fengling."

Yanggui gasped, "Fengling?!"

"Fengling and Mingyue are an ideal match—"

"They are cousins!" Yanggui interjected. "I don't know about Xin, but in Wuyue that sort of practice is prohibited."

"Pardon me for asking," Chengxin interrupted, "but what purpose would Mingyue's marriage to Fengling serve? Strengthening ties between Wuyue and Xin? Wasn't your marriage to the Xin Emperor supposed to accomplish that?"

---

[24] Kāifēng (開封): A city in central China on the south bank of the Yellow River. It is the capital of the Xin Dynasty.

Zemao's face burned bright with rage. "You—!"

"Did Emperor Hongli agree to this decision?" Yanggui asked.

Zemao froze for a moment, "Of course he did! The Crimson Emperor desires increased trade with the south, reduced tariffs, and the construction of another canal in the east—"

"All of which can be accomplished without a marriage between Fengling and Mingyue," Chengxin pointed out. "I think that a marriage alliance with the maiden that Huamei had chosen would be much more beneficial for Wuyue."

Zemao clenched her jaw. "Then I am afraid that the Crimson Emperor will have to rescind his naval assistance in combating the Wokou Pirates."

"Is that the Crimson Emperor's decision?"

Zemao's lips curved into a smirk, "Jiao Hongli may be the Emperor, but I am the Empress Dowager. I think you underestimate my influence in the Kaifeng Palace. Hongli is lucky to have my support, as despite being my late husband's eldest son, he is rather unpopular among the court."

Chengxin smiled coldly. "Then it is rather unfortunate that Wuyue can no longer count on Xin's naval support. I am afraid that the Golden Dragon Emperor will likely increase the tariffs on goods passing north along the Grand Canal as a result."

Zemao snorted. "*Hmph*. The Golden Dragon Emperor is *my* father, not *yours*! If they wish to maintain amicable ties with Xin, they will listen to what *I* have to say over *you*."

Chengxin and Yanggui shared an amused glance with one another. Both of them knew that what Zemao was saying was false, and that she herself was aware of that fact. Her tone wavered with each word she spoke, yet she continued to raise her voice as though doing so would make what she was saying true.

"If my parents do not listen to what Xin wants, they will come to regret it."

"What *Xin* wants?" Chengxin grinned. "Or what *you* want?"

"*Tch*," Zemao glared at the two of them, whipping around gracefully with her robes fluttering behind as she turned to depart.

Chengxin and Yanggui watched on in silence as their cousin disappeared down the corridor. When she was finally out of earshot, Yanggui sighed.

"She hasn't changed since we were young."

Chengxin smiled, "Have any of us?"

"Chengxin, tell me, is this the right decision to make?"

Chengxin thought for a moment. "Sometimes there are no 'right' decisions. The animosity between the north and south is unfortunate. However, relations have been souring for decades now. Xin has been declining as of late, while on the other hand, the influence of the west is rising to greater prominence. We should cultivate growth rather than decay. Wouldn't you agree?"

Yanggui nodded slowly. "Please inform the girl's family so we can initiate the engagement."

Part III

Spring and Autumn

I. Deception and Remedy

15/8/18th Year of the Golden Dragon Emperor

Year of the Wooden Goat

The silence of the infirmary was deafening enough to hear a pin-drop. Kanen, the young physician, shuffled back and forth across the room preparing his medicines. Despite his quick movements, his feet slid soundlessly over the ground.

Mingyue opened his eyes, sitting up drowsily as he slid the blanket from his body.

"Your Highness," Kanen rushed over, "you're awake."

Mingyue looked around the room in a daze. He began to recall the previous night—being kidnapped alongside Prince Narsieh Sasan and held in the residence of Emir Abdullah before he was saved by Chengxin and Agnes. Upon returning to the palace, he was so exhausted from the ordeal that he simply passed out and was taken to the infirmary to ensure he was healthy and hadn't been harmed during the kidnapping.

Mingyue noticed another person in the room, seated on the other bed, fumbling his hands.

"Prince Sundar…?"

The Karnatan prince turned to him. His hollow gaze seemed to regain some life after glancing at the prince.

"Third Prince Qian…?"

Mingyue froze at those words—Third Prince Qian. Mingyue's father, Yanlu, had bore the title of First Prince, with his eldest son Zukang being the Second. But now, Yanlu was gone, and Zukang had ascended to the title of First Prince.

"It is 'Second Prince' now."

Sundar's eyes widened. "Your Highness, I apologize." He frantically bowed himself to the Yue prince. "I did not mean to offend. I wasn't aware—"

He suddenly clutched his side in pain. Kanen hurried over, helping the Karnatan prince lay back into a resting position.

"Your Majesty, you are still recovering from your injuries. You should not overexert yourself."

Sundar grimaced.

"There is no need to apologize," Mingyue said. "I should be the one apologizing to you. You lost your wife and your father-in-law while you were guests in our house. That is unforgivable."

Sundar's expression softened as he lay back in the bed. "It's not your fault. The only ones who are to blame are Emir Abdullah and those responsible."

Mingyue turned to the prince in sudden realization. "We must send word to Karnata immediately. News has already left Wuyue that Karnatan rebels were the ones who killed the Rajah and Princess Ahi."

Sundar shook his head. "Too many days have passed since the assassinations. By the time an envoy returns home to correct any false information, it will already be too late."

"But we can send an envoy to inform the palace before things get out of control…"

"Prince Mingyue, there is a power vacuum for the Karnatan throne, now that the Rajah…and Princess Ahi are…gone," Sundar strained to speak those words. "Rajah Devaiah's relatives will begin fighting among themselves upon news of his death."

"That's why you must return immediately," Mingyue insisted. "As the husband of the Crown Princess, you have a responsibility—"

"I have no power," Sundar interrupted. "I do not hail from the royal house of Karnata, and as the son of a regional lord in the northern territories, I'm afraid I have little support from the court."

"Then…?"

"The empire will collapse," the Karnatan prince said simply.

Mingyue fell into silence.

"Even if they knew that the Khorasanis were responsible for the assassination, they would still blame it on one another to frame their enemies and take the opportunity seize power," Sundar sighed. "The Karnatan Empire was already growing weak and could only be held together by a strong leader. A power struggle will ensue now that the heir is gone."

"You...you can't let that happen to your homeland..."

"There is nothing I can do about it." The prince's voice lowered into a whisper. "Besides, Princess Ahi is gone. What more is there for me in Karnata?"

Mingyue gazed at the young prince, unsure of what else he could say.

"There is another matter to consider," at the doorway, a figure stepped into the room—Hansini. She folded her arms and glanced at the two princes. "The entire city has been placed under curfew, and all ships and roads leading in and out have been blockaded. What's more, there are rumors of a rebellion in the east. The governor of Qinglong has seized control of the region and is preventing any ships from passing through the mouth of the Qiantang River. Even if you wished to send an envoy back to the Karnata, it would be seized in Qinglong."

Mingyue's heart sank. "A rebellion? How can that be?"

Hansini sighed. "I doubt it's a coincidence. The governor has likely taken advantage of the chaos taking place here and figured that Wuyue would have little means to put them down at a time like this."

"You said they were rumors?" Sundar asked.

Hansini nodded. "A fleet of ships arrived in Qiantang from the east yesterday. They consist of the Keliyete, Nipponese, and Roman delegations, who were supposed to arrive in time for the Qiantang Festival but were delayed because of a storm at sea. They claim to have come in contact with the Qinglong governor's forces. They were the last to pass through the region before the mouth of the river was seized."

"The delegates have arrived...?"

That news was like a stab to Mingyue's chest. The Yi Princess would be arriving on the Keliyete delegation and the Ansei Prince with the Nipponese ships. They were engaged to Mingyue's siblings, Zukang and Sheli, and were arranged to be married within a few months. Mingyue was pained that his parents would not be around to see the marriages, and that they hadn't even had the chance to meet the future spouses of their children.

113

Hansini nodded. "All three delegations are being received into the Hall of Harmony shortly. Prince Mingyue, I am here to inform you that the Empress requests your presence at the reception." She turned to Kanen. "Is he fit to attend?"

Kanen, who had remained silent for most of the conversation as he continued preparing his medicines, turned to Hansini.

"He should be."

The young physician quickly hurried over to Mingyue's bedside with a teacup in hand. He stirred several herbs into the liquid.

"Your Highness, your injuries are still not completely healed. The Empress has ordered that you be given the proper medication to ensure a full recovery."

He raised the fragile, porcelain cup to the prince's mouth. The smooth rim of the cup rested gently between Mingyue's lips, warm steam from the tea tickling his face.

Hansini raised her hand. "Wait."

Her eyes met Kanen's. The two shared a long, intense gaze.

"A servant is always supposed to test the prince's food and drink before he consumes it," she said.

Mingyue paused before taking a sip. Hansini was right. It was common protocol for a servant to taste everything a member of the imperial family consumed, to ensure that it wasn't poisoned.

Kanen slowly withdrew the cup from Mingyue's lips. He paused for a moment. Hansini seemed just about ready to speak when Kanen raised the cup to himself and took a sip. He lowered the cup, glancing back at Hansini. She nodded in satisfaction, permitting him to pass the cup back to the prince. Mingyue took it from Kanen's hand and drank the remaining liquid. The warm bitterness of the herbal remedy slid down his throat. Kanen received the cup again and returned it to the table.

"Miss Wei, please tell Ao Neili to bring my clothing here to prepare for our guests," he requested.

Hansini bowed. "Yes, your Highness."

II. Four Realms

The Golden Chrysanthemum—the emblem of the Ansei Emperor. The flag flew high and proud in the courtyard as the delegation from Nippon arrived. A row of a hundred drummers, fifty on the left and fifty on the right, lined the path to the Hall of Harmony. They drummed in unison as the Nipponese prince was carried across the courtyard on his palanquin. Ansei Hyousuke was the youngest son of Nippon's emperor, who ruled over the archipelago northeast of Wuyue, and also had territories far to the north and on the other side of the Taiping Ocean, in the Land of the Heavenly Mountains. After Wuyue, Nippon was the most powerful empire in the east. It was significant that Wuyue's First Princess was engaged to the Ansei Prince.

Ansei Hyousuke had elegant, handsome features, and wore a navy-blue kimono as he sat with a regal posture. He had a friendly, yet sly smile perpetually plastered on his face, as if he found amusement in everything he encountered. Despite his somewhat foreboding appearance, the prince gave off a light-hearted, gentle aura.

Mingyue stood next to his sister as the Nipponese prince was carried into the Hall of Harmony. She smiled bashfully as she gazed upon her betrothed for the first time. Ansei Hyousuke smiled in return.

"Ooh, he *is* handsome," Fengling fawned.

Sheli covered her face, hushing Fengling with a whisper, "A-Ling don't embarrass me!"

Fengling giggled.

As the Ansei Prince's palanquin arrived at the steps of the palace, his attendants rushing over to help him to the ground. He moved in a monotonous manner as if every step he took was planned out with precision. He kowtowed before the empty throne of the Emperor. Under most circumstances, the Emperor's absence during the arrival of a foreign envoy was unacceptable. However, this was a special case— Qian Jinlong was much too unwell to leave his quarters as he continued to recover from his injuries. Instead, Ansei Hyousuke addressed the Empress.

"Your Highness, it is my honour to bow before you. I am deeply saddened to hear of His Majesty's condition, and of the passing of Prince Yanlu, Princess Huamei, and Princess Jinling."

He made no error in the etiquette of his speech or presentation. To the surprise of all of those present, he spoke Wuyueyu with perfect fluency, despite being of foreign origin and having never stepped foot in Wuyue.

The procession of the Keliyete Khanate came next, waving the flag of the sun and moon amidst the eternal blue sky. The pounding of drums was now accompanied by the rattling of shakers and the deep hum of traditional throat singing. The atmosphere within the square completely shifted from a deep and steady to a lively and upbeat tone. The Yi Princess, Yi Seo-Yeon, was carried in on her palanquin next. The young woman wore robes of the finest silk, adorned with innumerable jewels and precious stones. Her long, black hair sat pinned up in elaborate fashion, high atop her head. The court held its breath as she entered. The stories they had heard of her beauty were not exaggerations. She had deep, sparkling eyes, lips like rose petals, and pale skin like that of a pearl. Her lashes fluttered as they landed on Zukang. She smiled softly at her fiancé. Shenzhong nudged Zukang. He became flustered as he nervously smiled back at the princess.

"Ooh wow! How beautiful!" Fengling swooned, clasping her hands together giddily.

The last envoy to arrive was that of the Volga Romans, under the flag of the two-headed golden eagle, accompanied by trumpets and an ensemble of drums. The Roman princess had skin and hair as fair as snow; her eyes were the colour of rubies. To Mingyue, her appearance was more like that of a porcelain doll than a human. He was uncomfortable looking into her eyes. It wasn't just their unnatural tint, but also her sharp, piercing gaze that made him feel as if she were staring into his soul. The princess bowed before the Empress three times.

"Your Highness," one of her attendants announced, "I present her Highness, Princess Irina Aleksandrova, sister to Her Majesty, Tsarina Sofia Aleksandrova III."

The Roman princess smiled softly, speaking with a heavy accent. "Your Highness, I apologize for my delayed arrival."

The Empress replied with a nod. "It is of no concern. In fact, it was perhaps better that you were absent. You may have also lost your lives had you been present during the Qiantang Festival. I believe that the storm that delayed you must have been Heaven's Will."

The three young nobles, Ansei Hyousuke, Yi Seo-Yeon, and Irina Aleksandrova shared a hesitant glance.

Ansei Hyousuke took his chance to speak. "Your Highness, perhaps I should not mention such a matter here, but it was not merely a storm that delayed us."

The Empress's expression immediately became agitated. "What is it?"

Ansei Hyousuke hesitated. "A day after my fleet set sail from Nagasaki, we encountered several ships belonging to the Wokou Pirates. They had seized control of the Roman and Keliyete envoys, which were accompanying one another. We attempted to negotiate, but the pirates held the two envoys hostage. We were forced to follow them to Qinglong. This was seven days ago. By the time we arrived, we discovered that the governor of Qinglong had already initiated his rebellion and was planning on using us as tools for bargaining."

"Seven days ago...?" Yinfeng repeated.

"Unbelievable!" Yanggui exclaimed. "That was before the Qiantang Festival! The governor was not simply taking advantage of the current situation in the capital, but his plot was simultaneously being carried out."

Chengxin nodded, "Indeed. It would seem that there is more to these circumstances than we suspected."

"Are you saying that the Qinglong governor and Emir Abdullah are conspiring with one another?" Zemao wondered.

118

"Silence!" Yinfeng demanded, rising from the throne. Then in a low voice, she turned to her nephew, speaking just loud enough for him to hear. "Chengxin, Suzhou is the closest administrative division to Qinglong. Send out word immediately to mobilize all military garrisons in the city."

"Yes, your Highness."

"Our first task is to prevent the rebellion from spreading," Yinfeng said. "Then we will need to assess the military capacity of the governor. Does he have complete control over the entire military stationed in Qinglong, or are there dissenters? From there we will uncover the weaknesses in his defenses, and strike. I want him deposed of as soon as possible. Qinglong has control over the main ports leading in and out of Wuyue. The longer we wait the stronger they will become, while we will only grow weaker."

Chengxin nodded. "Of course, your Highness. I will send out word immediately."

The Empress finally seemed to relax.

"I apologize, your Highness," Hyousuke lowered his head. "I did not mean to deliver such unfortunate news after what you've already been forced to endure this week."

"Nonsense! Nonsense!" Yinfeng insisted. "We are glad that you've arrived safely. Today is the Moon Festival. Despite these circumstances, I think we should celebrate accordingly."

"Of course," Hyousuke nodded. "Your Highness, before the court is dismissed, there is one more guest I would like to introduce."

"Oh?"

The Ansei Prince gestured to the entrance of the hall. There stood a young tan-skinned man with regal features who approached the center of the room. He wore long red and gold robes that hung loosely over his body and exposed much of his skin, a golden pendant around his neck, and an elaborate headdress adorned with feathers of the same colour. The most striking features of the man were his piercing green

119

eyes and strangely elongated head. Mingyue had never seen someone with such peculiar features before.

"I present to you the grandson of the Emperor of Tahuantinsuyu, Prince Amaru Huancahuari."

The Empress was intrigued, "Tahuantinsuyu? The land of gold?"

Hyousuke gestured to the attendants, who hurried in with chests filled with gold and jewels. "During my travels in the Land of the Heavenly Mountains, I met with the Tahuantinsuyu Emperor. His grandson wished to accompany me back to Nippon to see the world, and bestow these gifts before the Emperor."

Prince Amaru bowed to the Empress. "Your Highness, I am honoured to be in the court of Wuyue."

***

Typically, the Moon Festival was one of the most celebrated festivities in the city. This year, however, Qiantang was under curfew, with soldiers patrolling nearly every street. Guards stood at all the watchtowers and walls in the palace to ensure that no one was out of place. All gates were sealed, preventing anyone from entering or leaving the Imperial Palace, or even traveling between the sub-palaces. Nevertheless, Mingyue managed to sneak away from the main courtyard. As the imperial family gathered under the pavilion to feast, he slipped into the shadows, bumping into his sister.

"Sheli…?" He gasped in surprise.

"A-Ming?"

"I'm…returning to the Palace of Lunar Serenity for the night," he muttered.

The princess smiled softly. "I will not stop you. You should rest. I wish I could return to my palace as well, but I must fulfill my duties."

Mingyue noticed his sister's distant gaze. "Is something wrong? Is…your fiancé not as you expected him to be?"

She immediately composed herself once again. "No, no, that's not it." She blushed. "He is handsome and seems very charming and intelligent. I could not hope for a better arrangement. It's just…I wish that Mother and Father were here…"

"So do I," Mingyue fell silent.

Sheli shook her head. "Never mind, never mind. If you're leaving, you better go before someone else notices. I'll cover for you."

Mingyue smiled, "Thank you."

Upon leaving the pavilion, he headed for a section of the wall that he knew was relatively unguarded. He scaled a nearby tree, swinging himself over the top of the wall rather than going through the gates, where he knew he would be prevented from passing through. Sure enough, as he gazed further down the path, he noticed several figures approaching.

Slowly, he slid himself down the other side of the tiled roof, careful not to make any sounds or alert the guards. As he reached his hand out toward a branch on the other side, preparing to shift his weight onto the tree and make his way to the ground, a voice suddenly spoke out.

"Well, well, who do we have sneaking around here?"

Mingyue was startled. His hand lost its grip on the branch. The next thing he knew, he was falling from the roof, and not in a graceful manner. Rather than landing face-first on the hard ground, he felt himself collide with something softer—a person. They both hit the ground with a thud.

The person beneath Mingyue groaned. Their arms were wrapped tightly around Mingyue's waist in a failed attempt to catch him as he fell. Unfortunately, the weight and the momentum from the prince's fall had simply been too much. They both ended up on the ground, Mingyue on top with his face buried in the other person's left shoulder.

The person beneath him loosened their grip from his waist and gently stroked his hair. "Your Highness, you should really be more careful."

Mingyue quickly pulled away from the man's shoulder. He recognized that voice. As he looked up, two glowing green eyes stared back.

"Prince Erik…?"

III. One in a Million

15/8/18th Year of the Golden Dragon Emperor

Year of the Wooden Goat

"Prince Erik…?" Mingyue said in surprise.

He found himself laying on top of the Norden prince. He tried to roll himself to the side but felt something pinning him in place—the edges of his robes were trapped beneath Erik's body. Mingyue was stuck until Erik decided to move. The jade-eyed prince groaned beneath the weight of Mingyue's body, but he managed to smile—or rather, half smile, half grimace.

"Let's stay like this for a while," he suggested.

"W-what…?" Mingyue's face flushed red. "Why…?"

"My back hurts," he muttered. "I don't think I can move at the moment."

"Are you okay?" Mingyue asked, his voice a mix of concern and embarrassment.

The golden-haired prince chuckled. "I will be fine."

Mingyue tried to push himself up from Erik once again, but the ends of his robe were still pinned between Erik and the ground. Mingyue was snagged and lost his balance, falling forward back into the position they were first in.

Erik groaned in pain, pulling Mingyue close. "Don't move. It hurts."

Mingyue gave up resisting, nestling his face into the Norden prince's shoulder. His heartbeat was racing, but Erik's was calm and steady, beating in a soothing, rhythmic manner. His body was warm. He smelled of lavender—there was a strange familiarity about that scent. A sense of tranquility wash over Mingyue, as if he could fall asleep in the prince's arms. He pushed that indecent thought aside. What would someone think if they saw the two of them lying here in the middle of the ground? Mingyue prayed that no one was watching.

"What were you doing sneaking over the wall at this time of night?" Erik asked, bringing the Yue prince back to reality. "Shouldn't you be at the festival?"

"Why does that concern you?"

Erik smiled with a shrug. "I guess it doesn't. It's none of my business what the Second Prince does in his own palace, after all."

"I could ask the same of you," Mingyue said. "*You* should also be at the festival."

"Someone asked to speak with me," Erik admitted. "I was granted permission to meet here with them. But the fact that you were sneaking over the walls makes me think that you are here without permission. Were you sneaking away to pay someone a secret visit?"

Mingyue's face grew even redder. "And who is this '*someone*' you are suggesting?"

Erik shrugged. "It is none of my business who the prince has relations with. I hear that many princes in the east have…what's the word…harems—harems filled with lovely maidens all to themselves."

Mingyue scoffed. "No such thing. Wuyue abolished concubinage generations ago. Many neighbouring kingdoms continue the practice, but I would never engage in such indecency."

"In…decency…?" Erik cocked his head as he repeated the word in Wuyueyu. "What does that mean?"

"Something that is not appropriate," Mingyue explained. "Something that is not socially acceptable."

Erik laughed. "And what would one say if they saw you now, in such a situation? You are still lying on top of me. Wouldn't you say that is indecent?"

Mingyue's heart raced. "Y-you…! You're the one laying on *my* robes! I can't move anywhere unless you move first!"

"Ah. I apologize, I didn't realize you were stuck in this position. You could've told me! I would've removed your robe from beneath me." Erik raised an eyebrow. "The fact that you remained silent gives me the impression that you were not against us remaining like this."

"No such thing!" Mingyue protested, turning his gaze away from the prince. "You said you were in pain, so I didn't want you to move. I was merely being considerate."

"*Mhm*," Erik smiled. "Your consideration is appreciated. And you were right, I am in pain. Why don't we remain like this for a while longer?"

Mingyue wanted to resist, but something inside him prevented him from doing so. As Erik's gentle arms wrapped around his waist, Mingyue relaxed into his body. He felt completely at peace, a sense of serenity that he'd never felt before.

Please don't let anyone see us like this, he thought to himself.

Of course, they were interrupted at that very moment.

"Erik!" A voice yelled out. It was a woman, her voice filled with rage and disbelief.

Panicked, Mingyue tore himself away from the Norden prince. This time, he was successful. His robes broke free from Erik, and he found himself tumbling backward onto the ground. Unfortunately, the motion had been so forceful that it had torn his robes in the process. Much of the fabrics and silk still lay beneath Erik's body, while a large tear now exposed most of Mingyue's right leg.

The woman who had called out Erik's name stormed over.

"We were apart for a few months, and you already are fooling around with foreign girls?!"

She yelled at Erik in a foreign tongue, one which Mingyue couldn't understand. The woman leaned over Mingyue, prepared to strike. Mingyue caught a glimpse of the woman's snowy-white hair. Amidst the darkness of the night, it was difficult to make out her other features.

Just as Mingyue was prepared to be slapped across the face, an arm grabbed hold of the girl's wrist, freezing her in place.

"Your Highness, please do not strike. Don't you know who this is?" Though he wasn't speaking in Wuyueyu, Mingyue still recognized the voice as Erik's attendant, Caleb.

The white-haired woman took a step closer to Mingyue. Realization washed over her face as she was illuminated by the lanternlight.

"Second Prince Qian?!" She gasped, quickly switching her speech to Wuyueyu. "My sincerest apologies! I was not aware that it was you!" She fell on her knees and prostrated before the prince, her forehead touching the ground.

Mingyue blinked in confusion. "Princess…Irina…?"

The Roman princess raised her head but didn't dare make eye contact with Mingyue. She spoke in a slow, careful manner, her voice heavy with a Volga Roman accent as she carefully enunciated her words.

"Your Highness, I overreacted. I was simply overcome with emotion when I thought my fiancé might be laying with another woman…or…man…"

"Fiancé…?" Mingyue repeated.

"Princess Irina and Prince Erik are engaged to be married," Caleb explained.

The Roman princess's gaze flickered toward Erik, giving him a stern look before she turned back to Mingyue once again.

"I apologize for any indecency my fiancé may have shown toward you. Ah…but if the Second Prince is pleased with him…I suppose I can look the other way. After all, he is a free man until we are wed…"

Mingyue and Erik's eyes met, embarrassment washing over both of their faces. Mingyue raised his hands defensively.

"No such thing! I fell from the roof and landed on top of the Norden prince. That is all that happened. I should be the one apologizing."

Irina blinked in confusion as she looked Mingyue up and down. "Your robe is open…"

Mingyue looked down at himself, the tear in his robe exposing most of his right leg. The prince quickly covered himself and jumped up from the ground.

Erik smiled sheepishly as he sat upright. "Sorry…that's my fault."

Mingyue's face was burning so brightly by this point that he feared it would outshine the lanternlight. He bowed quickly to the others.

"I apologize for any misunderstandings, but I really must be leaving now."

Before anyone else could say anything, he had already slipped away into the darkness.

"Caleb, please accompany the Yue prince," Irina requested. "He shouldn't be traveling through the palace unaccompanied."

Caleb glanced from Irina to Erik, but when neither of them said anything further, he responded with a simple nod.

"Yes, your Highness."

Mingyue made his way through the back alleyways, moving at a quick pace. He didn't know why, but he was upset.

Erik has a fiancée…

He shook his head. That was nothing to get upset about. After all, most nobles his age were already engaged or even married. He was a notable exception.

Perhaps he was upset at Erik, for leading him on and not telling him that he was betrothed.

No. That was also nothing to get upset about. The Norden prince hadn't been lying or deceiving Mingyue in any way. Since they had met, he had simply been friendly—someone Mingyue felt completely at peace with when he was in his presence. If Mingyue had developed deeper feelings for him, that was his own fault. He already knew that the two of them could never be together. They lived in kingdoms so far apart that they may as well have been from different worlds. Mingyue was not yet engaged, but he knew that he soon would be. And it wouldn't be a marriage formed through love, but to strengthen the empire.

Suddenly, he thought of his parents. Wasn't their marriage *also* impossible? Yanlu was a foreign prince residing in Wuyue, and yet he and Huamei had married for love. No one had thought it possible, and many were resistant to the union, but it didn't matter. In the end, they did not compromise their love because of what the world wanted from them.

Still, there was one fundamental difference between his parent's relationship and the relationship between Mingyue and Erik...

IV. The Prince and the Princess

15/8/18th Year of the Golden Dragon Emperor

Year of the Wooden Goat

Erik found himself alone with Princess Irina after Caleb's departure.

"My lady…" he finally said after several moments of silence. "I am glad that you've arrived safely in Wuyue."

The Roman princess's face lit up as she threw her arms around Erik. He staggered backward in surprise but gently wrapped his hands around her waist.

"My lady…? Is everything alright?"

She pulled away from him and smiled. "I am relieved to see you again. It has been too many moons since you departed from Moskva. I wish we could've traveled together. If only my father hadn't fallen ill."

"How is he?" Erik asked.

Irina lowered her gaze. "Father passed away shortly after your departure. My sister has since been crowned as Grand Tsarina."

"Ah…I'm sorry to hear about his passing."

Irina forced a smile. "I am just happy to see you again. It has been difficult spending these last few months apart from you."

There was a moment of awkward silence before Erik spoke once again. "You wanted to see me in private? Is there something you wished to discuss?"

Irina took hold of his hand. "I just wanted to spend some time together. Alone."

Erik nodded, but his gaze flicked away from Irina and toward the ground. He couldn't bring himself to look her in the eyes.

"I apologize for not sending word sooner," Irina said softly. "I hope I did not worry you with my late arrival."

"No…it's not an issue," Erik said. "I heard that your fleet was captured in Qinglong."

The princess nodded. "It was quite frightening, but we managed to escape. That is mainly thanks to the Keliyetes and Nipponese. If it weren't for them, I'm sure we wouldn't have been able to pull off an escape on our own."

Erik managed a weak smile, "That is a relief."

Irina linked Erik's arms with hers, pulling him along a stroll through the gardens.

"I guess we won't be able to leave Wuyue until the circumstances here clear up, but that doesn't seem like such a bad thing. The city is beautiful, and the weather is much more pleasant at this time of year than it is back home. Plus, you seem well acquainted with the Second Prince. I'm sure you'll enjoy spending more time with him."

She turned to Erik, raising an eyebrow. Erik's face grew pink. He hoped it wouldn't be noticeable under the cover of darkness.

"My lady, you are mistaken. What you just saw is as the Second Prince explained—he fell on top of me while climbing over the wall."

Irina huffed. "What is a prince doing sneaking around his own palace? Doesn't he know how to use the gates? The people of the east truly are strange."

Erik spoke up sheepishly, "Did…you really mean what you said earlier…? About 'looking the other way' if the prince is pleased with me…?"

Irina's ruby-coloured eyes burned like the flames of a hearth. "What are you thinking? Of course I would never accept such a thing! But Qian Mingyue is a Yue prince. If he made such a demand of you, it would be disgracing to the House of Nylund, and also to myself. But really, what could we do about it? Wuyue is the most powerful empire in the world. If the prince wished to have you for such perverted purposes, could you really resist? I'm sure they would have your head for refusing."

Erik's face grew even redder. "My lady, I can assure you that the Second Prince is not that kind of person, and Wuyue is not that kind of place."

"He's not what kind of person? The kind who expects to have anything he demands or the kind who is interested in men?"

"The former," Erik muttered. "I'm not aware of whether he is the latter. But even if he is, what does it matter? Wuyue seems to be a much more tolerant land than back home. There are all sorts of people here."

"Oh?" Irina frowned as she glanced at her fiancé. "Erik, your face is red. If I didn't know better I would say that it was *you* who was lusting after the Yue prince, rather than the reverse."

"My lady, I would never—"

Irina pulled Erik into a tight embrace before he could finish his sentence. "I am glad to hear that. After all these months apart, I was not sure whether you would be chasing after other women...or men...on your travels. But if your heart remains with me, then I shall wish to accompany you back to your quarters this evening."

She looked up at Erik, her crimson eyes meeting the jade-green glow of his.

Erik gently pulled away. "My lady...that would be shameful. We are not yet married..."

Irina giggled, a sly smile appearing on her face. "Oh Erik, I merely asked to accompany you to your quarters. What did you *think* I meant?"

Erik carefully unwrapped himself from her. "Even this...I am not sure your father would approve of us embracing in such a way."

The princess frowned. "My father is gone. No one is here to see what we are doing."

"Perhaps no *human* is here to see us..."

Irina folded her arms and gave her fiancé a stern glance. "I doubt God is concerned with something as trivial as this. If you ask me, this just sounds like an excuse—"

"I apologize, my lady," Erik said. "But I will be returning to the festival now. I have people to meet and matters to attend to. If you would excuse me."

Irina remained motionless, staying behind in the gardens as she watched Erik slip away. She balled her fists.

"My lady?" It was Caleb, stepping back into the gardens. After failing to trail behind Mingyue, decided to return to Irina and Erik.

131

"Caleb... Irina clenched her teeth. "What must I do...? What must I do to win his approval? No matter what I have tried since the day I first met him, Erik has never been interested in me. What must I do, Caleb? What am I supposed to do?!" She turned to him, tears forming in her eyes.

"My lady, you cannot force love. You are engaged to marry him, is that not enough for you?"

Irina took a deep breath. "No. It is not. If he is not satisfied with me, he will run off with another woman. Or...even a man..."

"The prince is not that kind of person," Caleb said. "We both know that. He is loyal and devoted. Even when he doesn't get what he wants, he always makes the best of his situation. He is not the type to disobey the wishes of his parents or betray those who trust in him."

"I suppose you are right."

She gazed out into the night sky. The glow of ten thousand lights shimmered above, but one stood out among all the others—the full moon. As heavy clouds rolled in, it was obscured, and its light extinguished.

V. It Takes Two to Tango

The Norden prince slipped back into the main courtyard. Hardly anyone had noticed that he'd been absent. Agnes, of course, was an exception. She came up to the prince from behind.

"Where'd you run off to?" The fiery-haired girl asked in a low voice.

"Princess Irina asked to see me," he replied simply.

"Ah," Agnes said. "Well, there's another princess requestin' to see ya." She gestured behind her, where a young Oghuz Rumeli eunuch stood dressed in dark clothes. He was small in stature, with gentle, delicate features.

"Aysun Sultana will see you on the terrace," he said.

"Aysun Sultana?" Erik repeated in surprise. He never thought that the Oghuz Rumeli princess would ask to meet with him.

The young man led Erik to where Aysun Sultana was waiting. She stood under one of the terraces, overlooking much of the festivities in the courtyard.

"Azaria, thank you for bringing him here," she said to the eunuch.

The eunuch, Azaria, bowed to the princess.

"Aysun Sultana?" Erik said. "You asked to speak with me?"

The Oghuz Rumeli princess was accompanied by two attendants, one female and the other androgynous in appearance.

"Indeed," she replied. "I wish to discuss the peace agreement between our two empires."

Erik raised an eyebrow. "Oh?"

Aysun sighed. "I am still opposed to solidifying ties between us since my brother was killed by the Norse during the Livonian War. However, it is the Sultan's wish to move forward. And in light of recent events, I believe that is in both of our best interests."

"I don't think I follow…"

Aysun lowered her voice. "We've seen what lengths the Khorasanis have taken to eliminate their enemies. They've even dared to assassinate members of the House of Qian, the most powerful family on earth, and frame it on Karnata. Imagine what they could do elsewhere. We both know that it is only a matter of time before they attack Oghuz Rumelia or the Volga Roman Tsardom. There already exists border disputes between our three empires. Once that escalates into full-scale war, it will not bode well for any of us. Your fiancée is the Roman princess. For the sake of her people, as well as Norden, I believe it is in your best interest to work alongside rather than against the Oghuz Rumelis once Khorasan begins baring their fangs."

Erik smiled, "Aysun Sultana, I believe you are jumping to conclusions. We still don't know for certain whether or not the actions committed by Emir Abdullah are representative of Khorasan as a whole, or whether he acted individually. Plus, there is a possibility that he could have been framed and may not even be responsible for the incident."

"Oh? A double framing? Doesn't that sound a bit far-fetched?"

"Perhaps," the Norden prince admitted. "But we must acknowledge the fact we still don't know any of the identities of those who directly carried out the assassinations and kidnappings. Everyone who has been apprehended so far committed suicide, and none of them were recognized by the court or citizens. Furthermore, in the kidnapping of Second Prince Qian and the Sassanian prince, the assailants were masked, and so far none of their weapons or clothing have been found within Emir Abdullah's residence."

Aysun chuckled. "If your theory holds true, it would take a mastermind with many resources within Wuyue to carry out such a plot."

"It is still a possibility."

Aysun Sultana folded her hands together and smiled. "Indeed, it is. I just wish to warn you that should the Khorasanis attempt to expand their influence, the Roman Tsardom is likely to be their first target, as it is the weakest and least defended among Khorasan's neighbours."

"I am aware of that."

"Good. Then I would like to let you know that on behalf of my father, Sultan Osman VI of the Oghuz Rumelia, we extend our hand out to the Romans and to all those who come under threat from the Khorasanis."

Erik bowed to the princess. "On behalf of my fiancée, Princess Irina Aleksandrova of the Volga Roman Tsardom, I express my gratitude."

He soon departed, and Aysun Sultana's androgynous attendant addressed her.

"Sultana, why would you make this request to the Norden prince rather than to the Roman princess directly?"

Aysun Sultana smiled, "You see, Lusine, the Romans do not pose a threat to us. Ever since they were driven from Constantinople to the Rus, they have always been subservient to us. They offer us tribute every year and know that if the Oghuz Rumeli sincerely wished to conquer them, we would have the power to do so. The Norse, on the other hand, are different. They are a powerful empire—the most widespread naval and maritime empire in the west. They are a threat to our territories in Europe."

The female attendant raised an eyebrow in confusion. "Would the Norse really side with us against Khorasani? Is it not more likely that they would instead oppose us? After all, we pose a greater threat to them than the Khorasanis do."

"Indeed," Aysun Sultana agreed. "But as the fiancé of the Roman princess, and their closest ally, Prince Erik has an obligation to ensure their best interests as well."

The androgynous attendant, Lusine, sneered. "Would he prioritize the Romans over his own people?"

"The two are not mutually exclusive. I understand the Norden prince quite well—he wishes to preserve peace at all costs. He also knows that if the Khorasanis invade the Rus, Norden will be at risk. I think he knows where his best interests lay."

***

On the terrace of the Hall of Harmony, Sheli stared out over the square as servants waited on her. Opera performers were singing and dancing in their elaborate costumes, putting on a show for the nobles as they feasted. The current performance was a depiction of Qiantang's founding legend—King Weiyue defending Wuyue from the Shatuo invasion.

To Sheli's left, Zukang called out to his attendants enthusiastically. "More to drink! More!"

Sheli eyed her younger brother nervously. She leaned in toward Shenzhong, lowering her voice. "Has my brother had alcohol? He really shouldn't be drinking at a time like this."

Shenzhong swished the cup he was holding. "Sheli, did you not get to taste? Your fiancé brought us the finest sake from Nippon."

"*Tch*," Sheli sighed. "My brother can't hold his alcohol. You shouldn't have let him drink so much."

Shenzhong held the cup of sake to Sheli's nose. She coughed and pulled back, pushing his hand away.

Shenzhong chuckled "Too strong?"

Behind her, Zukang laughed and hiccupped as he took another sip of his drink. Sheli rolled her eyes.

"Hey! Where's A-Ming?" Zukang wondered. "He should try some of this!"

"Mingyue is busy meeting with someone at the moment," Sheli said.

Shenzhong raised an eyebrow, "Oh?"

Zukang laughed. "Meeting with someone, is he?"

Fengling giggled. "Who is he meeting with? The Sogdian dancer, perhaps?"

Zukang slammed his cup on the table. "Selah is *my* dancer! Mingyue can't meet with him without my permission!"

Shenzhong stifled a laugh. "Referring to your dancer by his name? I didn't realize how close the two of you were."

136

"I'm not a cut-sleeve!" Zukang burned bright red. It was difficult to tell whether this was out of rage, embarrassment, or perhaps just the alcohol.

Jingli rolled his eyes. "No one said you were."

"Apologies if I am interrupting a family dispute," a voice said from behind them.

They turned in surprise as the Ansei Prince approached the group. He stepped forth, bowing to his fiancée.

"Prince Hyousuke, no need to apologize," Shenzhong said.

Sheli's face became red. She hastily rose from her seat and lowered her gaze as she faced him. "Prince Hyousuke, do you require assistance?"

Hyousuke smiled softly. "Not at all. I was merely wondering what the next performance might be."

Shenzhong's gaze fell to the stage out in the square, where the performance was coming to an end. "As far as I am aware, there are no performances immediately after this one—"

Zukang sprung from his seat, cutting his cousin off, "My Sogdian dancer! I am sure your Highness would like to see my Sogdian dancer perform! They say he is the best dancer in all the west!"

"Oh?" Hyousuke raised an eyebrow, "Now I'm intrigued."

A bead of sweat rolled down Sheli's face. She cursed silently. *My brother is just making a fool of himself.*

The First Prince called out to his attendants, "Bring Selah here to perform a dance for us!"

The attendants hesitated for a moment but soon hurried off as Zukang continued pestering them.

"Hyousuke, do you have any more of that sake?" Zukang threw an arm over the other prince's shoulders.

Sheli was mortified. She froze, unable to react. Luckily, Shenzhong stepped between them, loosening his cousin's grasp from the Nipponese prince.

"Please forgive the First Prince's actions," Shenzhong smiled at Hyousuke. "He doesn't have a high tolerance for alcohol." His tone then became stern as he spoke to his younger cousin. "Zukang, I think you've had enough to drink."

Zukang giggled drunkenly, "Ah, but that sake is just *so so so* delicious…"

The Ansei Prince couldn't help but chuckle. "I understand completely, and there is no need for apologies. But First Prince Qian, perhaps you should listen to your cousin. Besides, there are many other delicacies that I've brought with me from Nippon and Tahuantinsuyu. Perhaps you would like to try some of those?"

Zukang considered his offer before nodding dramatically. "Yes. Yes! That sounds very nice!"

After the opera came to a close, Zukang's dancer stepped out into the square. Selah was dressed in loose-fitting attire, his baggy pants and draped-sleeves the typical attire of Sogdian performers. Musicians played drums and stringed instruments as he danced, gracefully swaying his body and arms. Zukang cheered as he vibed to the music. Sheli buried her face in embarrassment.

"Your brother is quite…amusing," Hyousuke noted.

"I hope he doesn't regret this," Sheli replied. She glanced at the Yi Princess, sitting with the Tahuantinsuyu prince further down the terrace.

"Yi Seo-Yeon seems to be enjoying the performance," Hyousuke remarked. "I don't think she has noticed her fiancé's drunkenness yet."

"Well, that's a relief," Sheli sighed.

Several of the Tahuantinsuyu servants approached them with platters of food.

"First Prince Qian," one of them spoke in a heavily accented voice, addressing Zukang, "we have brought some food from the Land of Heavenly Mountains for your enjoyment."

The Yue prince eyed the platters skeptically. There were strange fruits that were red, and others dark green in colour. One that particularly stood out to Sheli was an elongated vegetable in a husk, made up of yellow and purple kernels.

"Mahiz, ahuacatl, tomatl," the words slipped off Hyousuke's tongue elegantly. "The Land of the Heavenly Mountains is rich and abundant in crops. These aren't from Tahuantinsuyu itself, but one of the kingdoms to the north that we passed through on our return to Nippon."

Zukang plucked one of the red fruits from the platter—a tomatl. He spun it in his hand, eyeing it cautiously before taking a bite. The juice inside splattered all over his face. Zukang dropped the fruit onto the table in surprise.

"*Ack*! It's all over me!"

Hyousuke broke out into friendly laughter. "I apologize. You must be careful when eating these ones. If you bite down on them like that, the juice will squirt out."

Everyone else laughed as Zukang wiped the juice from his face. The prince pouted. "It's not funny."

"It's a little bit funny," Jingli muttered.

Sheli detected light footsteps approaching them from behind. It was Neili. The young eunuch rushed over and leaned down next to her.

"Your Highness, apologies for disturbing you, but I've lost track of Prince Mingyue. Wu Liqing will kill me if I don't find him!"

Sheli's gaze softened as her eyes met his face. His eyes were full of worry, not just because he might get into trouble, but out of genuine concern for the prince.

"Don't worry," assured Sheli. "He has retreated to the Palace of Lunar Serenity for the evening."

"Alone?" Neili wondered anxiously. "It's not safe for him to be traveling alone in the palace, especially at night!"

"You needn't worry."

Out in the square, Selah had finished one of his dances, leading to an outbreak of applause and cheers. Zukang cheered the loudest.

"For my next dance, I would like a volunteer from the audience," Selah spoke with a heavy accent.

Neili and Sheli were still engaged in conversation.

139

"I will head over to the Palace of Lunar Serenity to ensure that he's returned safely," Neili said.

As he stood up and began hurrying off again, Selah's voice suddenly called out. "You over there! Won't you join me?"

Neili froze in place. He turned, meeting the gaze of the golden-haired dancer. His face flushed red.

"M-me…?"

Selah extended his hand to him.

Sheli smiled at Neili, "Ao Neili, you wouldn't turn down a dance from such a handsome man, would you? Don't worry, I will send someone else to check on Mingyue."

"B-but…I can't dance!" Neili stammered.

Selah was suddenly behind him, wrapping his arm around the young eunuch's shoulders. "You don't need to do anything. You're the perfect size and height for me to twirl and spin you around effortlessly. There is nothing you need to do."

Neili's face was beet red. He wanted to object but knew that he couldn't refuse an order from the First Princess. The next thing he knew, he was in the square. Like Selah had said, he was able to swirl both of them around without Neili even knowing where to step or which direction to move in. The two whirled around gracefully to the music.

"What an exciting dance," Hyousuke remarked with a smile, clasping his hands together.

"Indeed!" Amaru exclaimed. "In Tahuantinsuyu, we don't have dances that are so…"

"Intimate?" Hyousuke offered.

"Yes!" The prince agreed enthusiastically. "Intimate…"

"Such dances are not common here either," Shenzhong noted. "This style seems to be of Mediterranean origin, but the dancer is Sogdian. I wonder how he became so skillful in a foreign dance."

Fengling piped up. "He is the best dancer in the west! It makes sense that he would have mastered many different dance forms."

Selah dipped Neili backward as the dance came to a close. The crowd erupted into applause. Neili gasped for air as he and Selah remained in that pose for a few moments longer. His face was flushed red out of embarrassment and exhaustion as he glared at Sheli.

Sheli couldn't help but smile.

VI. Bright Moon Over the Waters

15/8/18th Year of the Golden Dragon Emperor

Year of the Wooden Goat

Hansini hurried down the dark alleyways of the Palace of Lunar Serenity. After Neili had been called up by Selah to dance, Sheli had sent Hansini in his place to locate Mingyue and ensure that he made it back to his quarters safely. She found his residence empty and sighed as she decided to head to the infirmary to check there instead.

"These nobles," she grumbled to herself. "They think they can do whatever they want and that their servants will take care of them if anything goes wrong."

Pushing the doors of the infirmary open, she discovered that it too was empty. At this point, she was growing frustrated, but also worried. If the prince was neither in his quarters nor the infirmary, where could he be?

She caught a glimpse of a shadow at the other end of the room. A figure was silently seated on the terrace outside, overlooking the garden. Hansini quietly drew a dagger from her side as she cautiously approached.

"A lovely evening, isn't it?" The man on the terrace said.

Hansini drew a breath of relief as she sheathed the dagger. "Indeed, your Highness."

Qian Jinyu's hands were folded in his lap as he gazed up at the night sky. The elderly brother of Emperor Jinlong resided near the infirmary due to his ailing body and mind. Often, he would come down here and simply spend hours staring out at the gardens, as if he were seeing things that no one else could. Perhaps he was reminiscing over old memories.

"Your Highness," Hansini said softly. "If I may ask, have you seen Prince Mingyue around here this evening?"

Jinyu thought deeply. "Prince Mingyue...?"

He pointed to his right, where the terrace led to another building south of them. Hansini heard voices coming from within.

"Thank you, your Highness."

Jinyu watched her as she departed. He gazed back up at the sky as thick clouds moved in, blocking out the light from the moon and stars.

"Mingyue…" he whispered to himself. "The Bright Moon.[25]"

Hansini pushed open the red wooden doors of the building to the south, revealing a large room beyond. The far end of the room was open to the evening air. To the south was the Lake of Tranquility, a large body of water enclosed on all sides by the sub-palaces within the Imperial Palace. An island sat in the middle of the lake, covered in lush trees with a majestic pagoda protruding above the canopy. As the night was darkened by a blanket of clouds, only the dim lanternlight illuminated the room. Mingyue sat at a low-lying table on the floor as he sipped a cup of tea. Prince Sundar sat to his right while the physician named Kanen was to his left. Mingyue's eyes met Hansini as she entered the room.

Hansini sighed. "Your Highness, what are you doing here?"

Instead of him responding, Kanen spoke in the prince's place. "I saw the Second Prince returning to his quarters. His breathing was heavy and erratic, so I asked him to come inside so I could give him medicine."

"Kanen says that the best view of the floating lanterns is from this terrace, so we decided to come here and watch it together," Sundar added.

Hansini raised an eyebrow at Mingyue. "Your Highness, I thought you had already recovered from your injuries."

Kanen nodded. "He has. His current state of erratic breathing is not from those injuries. It is as if he was struck by a blunt force in the chest."

Mingyue gently rested his teacup on the table. "No such thing. I am merely tired."

"Perhaps you've suffered another fall?" Kanen suggested. "That would be an explanation for your shortness of breath."

---

[25] Bright Moon: In Chinese, Mingyue's name is written as 明月, which literally means "Bright Moon."

Mingyue thought back to early that night when he had fallen off the wall and collided with Erik. His grip tightened around the cup.

"Nothing happened," he insisted. "I just need to rest."

Hansini eyed the prince's exposed leg. "Then could you perhaps explain why your robes are torn?"

Mingyue self-consciously rearranged his robes to cover his legs. In his rush to return to his quarters, he had completely forgotten about the tear.

"Fine," the prince admitted reluctantly. "I fell."

Hansini shook her head. "Your Highness, you must be more careful. Besides, you should be at the festival right now. There is no excuse for you to be sneaking away. Don't you know better? It's dangerous for a prince to be traveling through the palace alone at night, especially given recent events."

Mingyue lowered his gaze. "I know. I apologize."

Kanen eyed Hansini, "It is best if we don't push the prince too far. It has only been a short while since Princess Huamei and Prince Yanlu left us. Given Prince Mingyue's experience during the previous festival, it is probably best for him to not be around too many people at the moment."

"I'm fine," Mingyue said sternly. He found it quite annoying that they were speaking about him as if he wasn't there.

"Fine," Hansini sighed as she turned toward the door. "But don't run off on your own again."

"Miss Wei, won't you join us for the evening?" Sundar piped up.

"The First Princess asked that I check on the prince," Hansini explained. "Now that I've completed that task, I'd best return to the festival."

"The floating lanterns will be sent out soon," Kanen noted. "You wouldn't want to miss them, would you?"

Hansini rolled her eyes and sighed. She didn't want to stick around, but she also didn't want to return to the square only to be given another task to complete.

"Fine," she muttered. "I will stay to see the lanterns."

***

At the eastern end of the Lake of Tranquility, the nobles gathered on the terrace docks behind the Hall of Harmony. From here, boats could sail back and forth to the island pagoda at the center of the lake. On the night of the Moon Festival, however, the boats were drifting through the lake amidst floating lanterns.

Erik approached the edge of the water with a lantern in hand. He stood at the shore, looking out at the waves as dozens of lanterns floated through the air and across the surface of the water. Because the sky was obscured by a layer of clouds, the lanterns were the only source of light. They bobbed across the rippling water like stars dancing in the sky.

"Will you be making a wish on the lanterns?" Arivesto inquired. The Merinan noblewoman stepped up beside the Norden prince.

"Lady Ramanantsoa…?" Erik said in surprise.

"Your Highness," Arivesto smiled. "Are you alright? You seem disoriented."

Erik shook his head and smiled lightly. "I am fine. I wanted to thank you for the ointment you gave me the other day."

"Oh, no need to thank me."

Erik nodded slightly, his gaze drifting off. "Lady Ramanantsoa, may I ask you something? Is it true what you said that day? That Prince Mingyue has taken a liking to me?"

A slight smiled tugged at Arivesto's lips. "Why do you ask? Anyone can tell that the Second Prince is fond of you. Even though you've only been acquainted for a short while, he seems able to tolerate spending time with you individually. Perhaps you haven't noticed, but even with members of his own family, the Second Prince prefers to avoid interaction with others one on one."

Erik thought back to the times he'd encountered Mingyue. Their meeting earlier that night returned to him. His back still hurt from the force of the impact after the Yue Prince had landed on top of him. He blushed as he thought about the awkwardness of that situation.

145

"Prince Erik?" Arivesto said, snapping him back to reality. "There you go dazing off again. You're gripping that lantern as if your life depended on it. Why don't you release it already? Are you waiting for someone to come along and cast them out as a pair?"

Erik's face was flushed. It was a common practice for couples, especially those who were engaged, to release their lanterns out into the sky together. Nearby, he caught sight of Prince Hyousyke and Princess Sheli doing exactly that. Sheli's cheeks glowed a rosy-pink as she watched the two lanterns floating away to join the others. Hyousuke smiled.

Erik turned to Arivesto quickly. "Not at all! I wasn't waiting for anybody. It's just...I haven't made a wish yet."

A young woman hurried up behind the two of them. Erik recognized her as Keiy, one of Arivesto's associates. "My lady, I have prepared a boat for us."

Arivesto smiled, turning to Erik. "I would invite you to join us, but I believe these boats are only large enough to accommodate two people. Will you be sailing with anyone tonight?"

Erik thought for a moment. He shook his head.

"Well then, your Highness, I bid you goodnight."

Out on the water, many boats were already setting sail. Prince Zukang sat together with his fiancée, Princess Seo-Yeon, while Shenzhong was with a young maiden—Lady Alaneya, niece of the Doge of Venesia. On the docks, Hyousuke extended his hand out to Sheli. Erik smiled wistfully as he watched Sheli take Hyousuke's hand and join him on the boat.

"Your Highness, perhaps you should make an invitation to Princess Irina."

To Erik's right, Caleb stepped out of the shadows.

"Invitation?"

Caleb gestured to the boats, "An invitation to sail out on the lake with you."

146

Erik glanced at the Roman princess. She was standing on the docks alongside Prince Narsieh, Aysun Sultana, and Prince Amaru. As the others were engaged in conversation, Irina was off to the side, staring distantly at the sky. Erik followed her gaze. The glow of the full moon dimly shone through the thick layer of clouds. As the clouds shifted across the sky, the full light of the moon was finally unveiled. Erik's eyes lit up. Finally, he knew what he would wish for. He hurried to find a brush so he could inscribe his wish on the lantern.

"You aren't going to write in Tang characters?" Caleb peeked over Erik's shoulder.

"H-hey!" Erik hurried to cover up his brushstrokes. "You're not supposed to look!"

"Too late, I've already seen what you've written. Is that really your wish? It doesn't make much sense…"

"Ah!" Erik buried his face in his arms as he lay his head down on the table. "You still haven't taught me every character, so it's best I write in Norse instead. Forget you saw anything!"

"Here," Caleb offered, plopping down next to him, and taking Erik's hand in his. "May I?"

He began guiding Erik's hand along the strip of paper fastened to the lantern, leading him in the brushstrokes.

"There."

"Are you sure it says the same thing?" Erik wondered. His gaze was still lowered, his face burning red in embarrassment that Caleb had seen his wish.

"It's a direct translation of what you wrote," Caleb said. "Though, I'm not sure if it makes sense in Wuyueyu."

"Ah, good enough!" Erik snatched the lantern.

Kneeling next to the shore, he gazed across the surface of the lake. The glowing light of hundreds of lanterns danced through the sky and across the water alongside the reflection of ten thousand stars burning brightly above as the clouds began to clear. He cast his lantern up, losing sight of it as joined the others.

Erik nodded to Caleb as he slowly headed off in Irina's direction.

Caleb sighed once the prince was out of earshot. "It seems he's getting better."

"It was good for him to be away from Norden for a while," a voice spoke from the shadows. Agnes was leaning against a pole, completely obscured by the darkness. "He likes to travel. I don't think it's healthy for him to be tied down in one place for too long."

"It's not just that," Caleb shook his head. "I haven't seen the prince smile the way he has these past few weeks ever since his parents and Princess Anna died."

Agnes nodded. "He and his sister were always close."

"Perhaps the Second Prince reminds him of Princess Anna…"

Agnus snorted a laugh, "Are you jokin'? The Yue prince and Princess Anna hardly have anythin' in common."

"That's true," Caleb said in agreement. "Then…perhaps he reminds the prince of someone else…"

VII. The Moon Festival

"Tomatl…" Aysun pronounced the word carefully. In her hand, she observed the red fruit that she spun around between her fingers. "And you say this is from the land called…Tlaxcala?"

"*Mhm!*" Amaru nodded enthusiastically. "It's far to the north of Tahuantinsuyu, but we sailed past it on the way to Wuyue."

"Interesting…" mused the Sultana. "I have seen these before. They were brought back across the Atlantic from the lands beyond."

"Oh!" Amaru went wide-eyed. "I didn't know that it grew in other countries!"

"Tlaxcala…Tlaxcala…" Aysun continued mumbling. "Perhaps they *aren't* different countries…"

Nearby, Irina stood at the edge of the water, staring out at the dozens of lanterns dancing across the lake. Despite the conversation between Aysun Sultana and the Sassanian and Tahuantinsuyu princes, Irina wasn't listening. Instead, she was focused on one of the boats out on the lake. Seated within were Prince Shenzhong and Lady Alaneya. As he steered them through the sea of light, the prince said something to the Venesian noblewoman. Irina couldn't hear his words from this distance, but whatever he had said caused Alaneya to blush and giggle. Shenzhong smiled warmly at the young woman as the two stared intimately into each other's eyes.

"Alaneya Fatima Maria," Irina muttered.

The Roman princess had met the young women on several occasions back in Constantinople. She felt a sharp pain in her chest. Watching the young couple with such a passionate, loving relationship, she couldn't help but feel a pang of jealousy in her heart. Why couldn't she have that?

She was so consumed in her thoughts that she didn't notice a hand outstretched toward her until the Tahuantinsuyu prince brought it to her attention.

Amaru cocked his head. "Princess Irina?"

The Roman princess snapped back to reality. Prince Narsieh, Prince Amaru, and Aysun Sultana were all looking at her expectantly. It was only then that she noticed a boat had pulled up next to them—it was Erik who had his hand outstretched toward her.

Irina paused, gazing up at him. Their eyes met—those glowing, jade- green eyes. Those were the same eyes that she had fallen in love with the first time she stared into them as a young girl.

"My lady, may I?" Erik asked.

Irina's expression was blank. She thought about her encounter with the prince earlier that night—how he had become upset and left her behind in the gardens. She was angry at him. They had spent many months apart, and after having been taken hostage in Qinglong, she wasn't even sure if she'd be able to see him again. After their capture, there was only one thing she had wished for—to see him again one last time. Upon arriving safely in Qiantang, she had hoped he would be happy to see him again. He said that he was, but all that Irina felt from him was indifference.

Now here he was before her, offering out his hand. She couldn't remember the last time he'd done that. Her heart fluttered. She took hold of him.

As the two of them drifted across the lake, neither spoke any words. Nevertheless, Irina was content. Though other boats surrounded them, at that moment, she felt as if the two of them were the only people in the world. She wished Erik would say something to her—there were a thousand things she wanted to say to him. But neither of them did. Both remained silent as they drifted along the surface of the lake.

***

Mingyue stepped out onto the terrace just as the lanterns were released. Dozens turned into hundreds as more and more people gathered along the edges of the water.

"It's beautiful," Sundar remarked.

Kanen and Hansini joined them on the terrace, carrying four lanterns between them.

Kanen extended one to Mingyue and another to Sundar. "Shall we make our wishes?"

"That sounds like a lovely idea," the Karnatan prince nodded.

After a few minutes, each of them finished writing their wishes, tying the strips of paper onto their lanterns, and casting them over the lake one by one. For Mingyue, however, nothing came to mind as to what he should put down.

What do I wish for? What do I want?

"Your Highness, have you finished?" Hansini inquired.

"*Mnn*," Mingyue nodded. "I have."

He lied.

Perhaps there is nothing for me to wish for. Besides, making wishes is silly.

He cast the wish-less lantern onto the water. As it drifted out to join the others, one lantern from the other shore had fallen onto the lake and was pushed toward them by the waves. Mingyue reached down and scooped it up.

"What does it say?" Sundar wondered.

Hansini sighed. "You're not supposed to read other people's wishes."

Before she had even finished her sentence, Mingyue had already begun reading. "'To see the dark side of the moon.'"

"*Tch*," Hansini stifled a laugh. "What a silly thing to write. What does that even mean?"

"Don't be so quick to judge," Kanen said wistfully. "Perhaps it's metaphoric."

Mingyue ignored the two as his finger traced over the character for 'moon'—*Yue*. The same character was part of his name.

He gazed up at the night sky, but it had become obscured by the thick mountain fog once again. The earth shone brightly with the hundreds of lanterns dancing across the Lake of Tranquility, but tonight, the heavens were dark. The moon had been swallowed up by the clouds and was nowhere to be found.

Part IV
Song of Heaven

I. Hashishiyya

More than a month passed before life started to get back to normal for Mingyue. He had fallen ill after the Moon Festival, spending most of his time back and forth between his quarters and the infirmary.

"Your Highness, your medicine." Kanen knelt alongside his bed with a cup of tea in hand.

Mingyue nodded, taking a sip. By the door, Olekina, Neili, and Hansini stood side by side, awaiting him.

"Your Highness, it's been over a month since you've attended your classes with Mister Zhang," Hansini said.

"*Mnn*," Mingyue nodded.

"He is sick," Olekina replied. "He must be given time to recover."

"It's been a month!" Hansini shook her head. "That is more than enough time."

Kanen nodded, "Your Highness, I think your condition is stable enough to attend classes."

"I'll go," Mingyue muttered.

"Good, good," Hansini gestured to Neili. "Please get him dressed."

Neili nodded, rushing over with the prince's robes. He stripped Mingyue of his sleeping attire and began dressing him.

Mingyue turned to Sundar. The Karnatan prince sat at the windowsill, gazing into the distance outside.

"Prince Sundar?" Mingyue asked. "Is everything alright?"

Sundar's attention was drawn back to the room. "Yes, your Highness. I'm fine."

Mingyue eyed him skeptically.

After a moment of silence, he added. "A ship arrived today from Karnata."

Mingyue put his arms through the sleeves of his robe, "A ship? How did it get past Qinglong?"

"It was granted safe passage," Hansini explained.

Sundar nodded, "The Qinglong governor has good reason to let them pass through. They likely have information regarding Karnata's state. This will be the first news we will be receiving from the outside world since the events of last month. I will be meeting with the envoy shortly."

"I want to come with you," Mingyue insisted.

Hansini glanced at him in disapproval. "Your Highness, do not concern yourself with these matters. You need to be attending class."

Mingyue clenched his jaw in frustration. He was desperate to know the state of affairs of the outside world. He particularly wanted news of the Khorasanis. Had they really been behind the assassinations of his parents? And if so, why? He wanted to bring those who had harmed his family to justice. There had been no more attacks since the attempted kidnapping of himself and Narsieh. On top of that, Mingyue found the events regarding their kidnapping suspicious. Why had the kidnappers brought him to Emir Abdullah's residence in such a reckless manner that they were tracked down almost immediately? He had brought this up with Narsieh, who expressed similar suspicions.

Unfortunately, for the time being, all evidence seemed to point to Emir Abdullah. Mingyue desperately wanted to believe that it had been the Khorasanis behind the deaths of his parents. If not them, he didn't know who else could be responsible. It would mean that there was a much more sinister plot going on within the palace.

Mingyue was the last to arrive in the study hall. As he took a seat at his desk, Zukang, Shenzhong, and Narsieh were already copying characters as Mister Zhang spoke. Ansei Hyousuke and Jiao Jingli were also present, sitting in on the class.

Mister Zhang smiled. "Second Prince Qian, it is good to see you again."

Mingyue nodded, taking his seat in silence.

Mister Zhang continued his lesson. "The Land of the Heavenly Mountains is a land of mystery and wonder on the far side of the Taiping Ocean. First discovered by the Nipponese three hundred years ago by sailing north and east along the shoreline of lands made of ice and snow. Ansei Hyousuke, since you have first-hand experience there, why don't you share with us some of the stories of your travels?"

Mingyue's attention was elsewhere as Mister Zhang spoke. He usually enjoyed listening to lectures on history, but today he couldn't focus. He wanted to hear news of the outside world from the Karnatan envoy that Sundar was meeting with. After a while of fiddling in his seat and only half listening to Mister Zhang and Hyousuke speak, he decided to excuse himself.

"Pardon me, I wish to use the toilet."

Once outside, he took a deep breath of fresh air. He felt as if he were suffocating as he anticipated what news the Karnatan envoy would bring.

"Your Highness?"

Mingyue had been so consumed in his thoughts that he hadn't noticed Olekina approach him from behind. "Your Highness, you should be in class."

Mingyue eyed his guard. Olekina held his spear in his right hand, always prepared to strike at a moment's notice if needed. That was the very spear that had saved him on the night of the Qiantang Festival.

"Wu Liqing, hand me your weapon."

The young guard froze. "Your Highness?"

Mingyue gripped the spear just above where Olekina was holding it. "I would like you to teach me to fight."

Olekina hesitated. He couldn't tell if the prince was being serious. Then again, Mingyue hardly ever joked around.

"Your Highness, a weapon is not something that a prince should lay his hands on. You do not need to know how to fight. That is my job."

Mingyue thought back to that night. If he'd known how to fight, maybe he could've protected himself and saved his mother. He thought of how Erik had stepped in with his sword in hand to defend him. He hated feeling so weak, putting everyone else at risk when he was unable to do anything.

"I don't want to rely on anyone to protect me."

Mingyue felt a hand on his shoulder. He turned to see a thin blade slicing through the air toward him. Instinctively, he ducked. The blade slipped past, barely missing his face. The person wielding the sword suddenly swooped the weapon around, knocking Mingyue in the chest with the hilt of the sword. He fell on his back, with the tip of the sword pressed against his neck.

"Your Highness!" Olekina shouted. He barely had a chance to react. The guard thrust his spear forward toward the chest of the man with the sword.

"I can kill him before you have the chance to strike," the man with the sword warned. Olekina froze at his words. He knew it was true.

Mingyue coughed for air as he lay in the dirt. He struggled to look up at the man pinning him down, but he recognized that voice.

"Prince...Hyousuke...?"

The Ansei Prince smiled, glancing up at Olekina. "Wu Liqing, was it? You must be careful to pay attention to your surroundings. If I intended to kill the Second Prince, you wouldn't have been unable to stop me."

He pulled his weapon away from Mingyue's neck, gracefully returning it to its sheath. Olekina glared at Hyousuke, his spear still pointed at the prince's chest. Hyousuke raised his arms in surrender.

"I didn't mean to cause any harm. But this is an important lesson for both of you. The Imperial Palace is a dangerous place. You must always be on guard."

Determining that Hyousuke wasn't a threat, Olekina retracted his spear. He leaned over toward Mingyue, helping him to his feet.

"You *have* harmed the Yue prince," he glared at Hyousuke. "I cannot overlook this."

"I apologize," Hyousuke chuckled. "However, if he wants to learn to fight, I mustn't go easy on him."

"He is a prince," Olekina muttered. "He doesn't need to learn how to fight."

"I am also a prince," Hyousuke pointed out. "When I was fourteen, I led an army to suppress a rebellion in Hokkaido."

"With all due respect, this is not Nippon."

"Perhaps not," Hyousuke mused. "Nevertheless, he wishes to learn. As his guard, is it not your duty to comply with your prince's orders? He has ordered that you hand over your spear."

Olekina glared at Hyousuke but knew that he was right. As he extended the weapon toward Mingyue, Hyousuke swiped it away instead.

"A fine weapon," he smiled.

Olekina watched with frustration as Hyousuke inspected the spear. "It is made from the most durable metals from across the empire. Even your sword would not be able to break it."

"Excellent," Hyousuke tossed the spear to Mingyue. "Is this your weapon of choice?"

Mingyue caught the weapon with surprise, staring back at Hyousuke blankly.

"What is it?" Hyousuke asked. "You wished to learn, did you not?"

"I...I don't know how to handle a weapon..."

Hyousuke chuckled. "That is fine. There is no better way to learn to fight than through experience!" He unsheathed his sword again. "Besides, this is a wonderful way of bonding with my soon-to-be brother-in-law!"

Mingyue raised the spear in front of him as Hyousuke struck down. The spear flung sideways through the air, and Mingyue fell backward into Olekina's arms.

"Your Highness!"

"Huh," Hyousuke chuckled. "We'll have to work on that. Perhaps Prince Amaru would be a better teacher for you; he's skilled in wielding polearms. I could ask him to train you if you'd be interested."

Olekina narrowed his gaze, "I don't think—"

"I would like to," Mingyue cut him off.

Olekina sighed.

"Excellent," Hyousuke clapped. "I'll send word to him."

"Your Highness, I advise against this," Olekina muttered.

Mingyue nodded thoughtfully at his guard as he reached over to return his weapon to him. "I know. But...this is my decision."

Hyousuke smiled at the two as he turned to leave. "Be sure to never let your guard down. After all, it is your duty to protect the prince. The palace is a dangerous place."

***

Sundar sat attentively in one of the palace halls as he awaited the arrival of the Karnatan envoy. Anxiously sipping his tea, his foot tapped the ground impatiently as he glanced around the room. Other than the guards standing at the door and Empress Yinfeng sitting across from him, there was no one else in sight. He found this quite strange.

"Your Majesty, will it just be the two of us?"

Yinfeng nodded, "It is best if we keep this meeting small. After what's taken place these last few weeks, it is difficult to know who to trust. I would rather have kept this meeting solely between me and the envoy. However, I assume that you have deep concern for the state of affairs in Karnata and would like to be the first to hear of recent events."

The young prince nodded. "I appreciate your consideration."

There was a knock at the door as a young Karnatan woman entered the room.

"Lady Noor!" Sundar exclaimed in relief. His eyes lightened at the sight of her.

Lady Noor folded her hands together before the prince. "Namaste."

Sundar, realizing he had not properly addressed her, returned the greeting.

"My Lord, I am relieved to see you again. May the souls of Rajah Devaiah and Princess Ahi go to a blissful place." She turned to the

160

Empress. "Your Majesty, I am sorry to hear of your losses as well. This has all happened far too suddenly."

"Indeed," Yinfeng agreed. "But we can't concern ourselves with that at the moment. Lady Noor, what news do you bring from Karnata?"

The woman's expression grew somber. "The Qiantang Festival Massacre took place on the tenth day of the eighth month. News of this tragedy and the death of Rajah Devaiah didn't reach Karnata until several weeks later. However, it was the very same day of the Qiantang Festival Massacre that Rajah Devaiah's younger brothers and the Emperor were slaughtered by the Assassins in Vijayapura.[26]"

Sundar paled. "No…"

"Who was responsible for the assassinations?" Yinfeng asked, maintaining her composure.

"Not assassins," Lady Noor asserted, "but *the* Assassins. The Hashishiyya—the Order of Assassins.[27]"

Sundar took a deep breath. "The Order of the Assassins is based in the Hindu Kush mountains…"

"Khorasani territory," Yinfeng noted.

"Indeed," Noor nodded. "But the attack was blamed on several of the court officials. Then, news arrived from Wuyue that the Rajah was killed by northern Karnatan rebels. The court officials blamed the princes in Sindh and Punjab. There were more assassinations, followed by executions of the accused. The central court in Vijayapura descended into chaos in a power struggle between the officials and various factions of the ruling dynasty. At the moment, there are numerous claims to the throne. Since I've left, the situation has likely only deteriorated. I assume that separatist movements in the north have only grown in influence since the dissolution of power."

[26] Vijayapura: The capital of the Karnatan Empire.

[27] Hashishiyya: The Order of Assassins, a name given to the Nizari Ismailis of the mountains of Persia. Founded in the 11th century, they are infamous for the assassinations of numerous caliphs, sultans, viziers, and Crusade leaders across the Middle East, Mediterranean, and Central Asia. In our timeline, they were wiped out following the Mongol conquest of Persia in the 13th century.

"It is just as we feared," Yinfeng shook her head.

"My Lord, you must return to Vijayapura with me," Noor pleaded. "Seeing as you were the husband of Princess Ahi, your title is now one of the highest in the Karnatan court. And as a prince from the northern territories, you may be able to reconcile the divisions that have arisen…"

Sundar tightened his grip on the teacup in his hand. "I…I don't know if I have the capability…"

"You are Karnata's last hope."

The room fell silent.

Sundar sighed. "Even if I could, no ships will be able to leave Wuyue until Qinglong is recaptured."

"Our troops will be launching their campaign against Qinglong tomorrow," Yinfeng announced. "If all goes well, then the region should fall back into our hands within a few weeks. I will give you the seal of the Golden Dragon Emperor to rally our armies in the Protectorates of Malabar and Ceylon to your cause, should you require it."

"Your Highness, Karnata is forever indebted to you." Sundar lowered his gaze. "If that is the case, then I will go."

II. Strings in the Garden

Mingyue strolled leisurely through the Imperial Gardens. Hyousuke had informed him to meet there with Prince Amaru so that he could learn combat with a spear, but he had arrived early, and so decided to admire the flowers and check on the vorompatra birds that Lady Ramanantsoa had gifted him. The flock sat calmly in a clearing and were being tended to by a young woman. Mingyue recognized her as Keiy, the girl who accompanied Arivesto on her travels. She bowed to him as he approached.

"Your Highness you should not step so close," Olekina spoke from behind the prince. The guard had been following him so silently that Mingyue had almost forgotten he was there.

"There's no need to worry," Keiy assured. "The vorompatra bird is typically hostile in its natural environment, but this flock is tame and docile."

Olekina eyed the birds hesitantly as Mingyue stepped toward one, gently taking its head in his hands. The creature made a gentle grumbling sound.

"Wu Liqing, no need to be anxious!" Keiy laughed. "You are also Merinan, aren't you? You should be familiar with these creatures!"

"My father was a Zanzibari[28] merchant," the guard corrected. "But I have lived in Wuyue my whole life. I've never seen creatures such as these before."

"Oh, I see," Keiy chuckled. "Maybe you just aren't good with animals."

Olekina stared blankly at the girl. Mingyue caressed the birds for a few moments before he caught sight of something in the distance. Along one of the garden paths, behind one of the cherry blossom trees, was a twenty-one-stringed wooden guzheng. The instrument was often

---

[28] *Zanzibari*: One who comes from the East African island of Zanzibar, now a colony of Wuyue. Many wealthy Zanzibari merchants travel across the world on ships carrying spices and other goods.

played during festivals and holidays, but every so often a lone performer would play in the gardens.

Mingyue took the liberty to wander over as Keiy and Olekina were engaged in conversation—it was more of a one-sided conversation, in which Olekina would merely respond to Keiy with one-word replies.

Mingyue sat next to the instrument, his delicate fingers resting over its strings. He paused. He didn't know how to play any instruments, but as a child, he often listened to his mother play the guzheng. When he was still very young, he was scared of the dark and often had nightmares. At night, the lanternlight would cast eerie shadows dancing across the walls of his bed chambers, and it was difficult for him to fall asleep. The young prince would refuse to sleep unless his mother was there with him. He wouldn't even accept any of the maids who came to tell him stories or sing lullabies. He only wanted his mother. Because of this, Huamei would have to come to his quarters, playing gentle tunes on her guzheng as he lay on her lap until he eventually dozed off.

As Mingyue grew older, he stopped having nightmares—most nights were dreamless. Though he hadn't heard his mother play the guzheng for many years now, he still remembered the rhythm of each song. He plucked one of the strings softly; a low hum reverberated through the autumn breeze. Both Keiy and Olekina's attention was drawn toward him. Mingyue gently strummed his fingers across several more strings, playing a soft melody. The rhythm was rough, but he was able to repeat one of his favourite songs that his mother used to play for him.

"What lovely music," a voice said from behind him. Leaning over him was a tall, lean figure, dressed in elegant robes adorned with jewels. The young man's golden hair glowed in the sunlight.

"Erik—?"

Through the glaring sunlight, it took a moment for Mingyue to make out the man's features. But as soon as the name escaped his lips, he knew that he was mistaken. The two young men shared many similarities in their appearance, but there was one particularly notable feature that distinguished them from one another. Instead of being greeted by the familiar jade-coloured eyes, a burning crimson glow stared back into the depths of his soul.

"It's Selah," the Sogdian dancer corrected. His warm breath blew past Mingyue's ear as he spoke with his exotic accent, tickling the young prince's neck.

Mingyue's face glowed red. He glanced away from the man's intense gaze. "Apologies. I mistook you for the Norden prince."

"I can assure you that I'm no prince," Selah smiled slyly. "Merely a dancer."

"Please do not touch the Second Prince," Olekina said from nearby.

The young guard had approached the two of them when he spotted Selah. Hyousuke's words from yesterday came echoing through the guard's mind: *After all, it is your duty to protect the prince. The palace is a dangerous place.*

"I wouldn't dare lay my hands on him," Selah assured. He was true to his word. Though he was leaning over Mingyue, breathing against his skin, the dancer did not make physical contact with the prince's body.

Nevertheless, Olekina stepped between the two of them. He couldn't take any chances.

A voice yelling in a foreign tongue suddenly caught their attention. "Ahhh! Slow down! Slow down!"

It was distant at first but grew closer and closer until a fluffy, white animal rounded the corner, speeding straight toward them. A young man sat in a saddle, riding the creature's back—the Tahuantinsuyu prince.

"Look out!" He shouted. He had no control over the animal's erratic movements.

Olekina instinctively lunged forward, grabbing Mingyue by the waist and whisking him out of the way. Selah leaped sideways, gracefully spinning through the air to safety. The animal thundered past them, trampling the ground where they'd just been standing.

"Your Highness, are you okay?" Olekina asked frantically.

"*Mnn,*" Mingyue nodded, pushing against his tight grip. "You're suffocating me."

Olekina quickly loosened his grasp. "Apologies, Your Highness. I didn't mean to."

Further along the path, the crazed animal continued lumbering around with Amaru unable to stop the creature or jump to safety. The beast turned around, making a beeline toward them once again. Just as it began to charge, a rope was thrown around its snout, and the creature was yanked in the opposite direction.

"Whoa there," Keiy pulled on the other end of the rope. The woman was small in stature but was more than capable of controlling the animal. She hurried over, offering it some fruit in her outstretched hand. The animal seemed to calm down.

"Whew!" Amaru jumped from his saddle. "Thanks for your help! I was afraid I might make a mess of the gardens."

Olekina glanced back in the direction the prince had come from. Sure enough, there was a path of trampled flowers and footprints in the dirt. What did he mean by *might* make a mess? It was *already* a mess. Olekina sighed.

"My, my," Selah smiled. "What a beast. She is both beautiful and dangerous."

Amaru laughed nervously as he patted the animal's long neck. "Not dangerous. Lasta is just a bit anxious to be in a new environment."

"What kind of animal is she?" Keiy asked. "She looks like a camel, only smaller and furrier."

"A llama," the Tahuantinsuyu prince said proudly. "They are my homeland's most prized creatures. We don't have your kinds of animals in the Land of the Heavenly Mountains. There are no horses, no oxen, and none of those big ones with the snake noses."

166

"Elephants…?" Keiy cocked her head.

"Elephants!" Amaru nodded. "Nope. We've got none of those. We use our llamas for transportation and carrying supplies."

Selah mused. "That sounds rather inconvenient."

"Not at all, not at all," Amaru shook his head. "The mountain paths in Tahuantinsuyu are too narrow and dangerous for large animals anyways."

Selah slowly approached the llama, reaching out his hand to caress its face.

"Sir, I'd be careful," Amaru warned. "She's not dangerous, but—"

It was too late. The animal reared back its head and flared its lips, spewing forth a mouthful of saliva. Luckily for Selah, he was agile and had quick reflexes. He dodged the flying spit with ease. Olekina, on the other hand, wasn't so lucky. He was standing behind Selah. When the dancer dodged out of the way, Olekina's face became drenched in the llama's saliva. He was not amused.

"Ah, I apologize sir!" Amaru exclaimed.

"My, my, Wu Liqing, you seem to be covered in saliva," Selah smirked at Olekina. "You should be more aware of your surroundings."

He produced a handkerchief from his waist and began wiping Olekina's face. The guard remained with a stoic expression on his face, pushing Selah away.

Mingyue was trying hard not to find amusement in the situation, but a small laugh escaped his lips.

Olekina turned to him in concern, "Your Highness, what's wrong?"

Keiy burst into laughter. "Nothing is wrong. He just finds this entertaining, as do I."

Olekina glared at the girl. "There is nothing funny about this."

Mingyue quickly regained his composure.

"You should wash yourself off," Amaru suggested.

"I will stay by Prince Mingyue's side," Olekina replied.

Keiy shrugged, "Suit yourself."

"Oh, that's right! I nearly forgot why I was here!" Amaru sprung over to Mingyue. "Prince Hyousuke informed me that you wished to learn spear-fighting."

"Your Highness, I still advise against this," Olekina whispered to Mingyue under his breath.

Mingyue ignored him. "Yes, I would like to learn."

"Great!" Amaru exclaimed. He removed a spear strapped to his back and tossed it to the Yue prince. "Then let's begin."

***

Mingyue was quickly worn out. He stopped counting the number of times he was knocked backward into the dirt by Amaru's strikes.

"Swing higher! Block! Dodge!" The Tahuantinsuyu prince would shout at him as they practiced. All the while, Selah sat cross-legged, observing them with a bemused grin on his face. Olekina stood nearby, expressionless.

"Ah," Amaru finally sighed, wiping sweat off his brow. "I think that's enough for today."

Mingyue gasped for breath, still clenching the spear tightly in his hands. It felt like the two of them had been training for hours, but it wasn't even noon yet. Amaru had taught him a few moves, but he would certainly require much more training if he were to defend himself in an actual attack.

"Perhaps we can continue later?" Amaru suggested.

"Your Highness, the First Princess's wedding is starting soon," Olekina stated.

"Ah! That's right!" Amaru exclaimed.

Mingyue had nearly forgotten about that. His sister and Ansei Hyousuke were having their wedding ceremony this evening.

"I should get going," Selah stretched as he pushed himself up from the ground. "I'll be performing the main dances tonight. You should probably take a bath and change into your ceremonial robes before you head over, your Highness."

Olekina nodded in agreement. "We mustn't be late."

Olekina accompanied Mingyue back toward the palace, always one step behind him. Selah spun along in a carefree manner ahead of them, humming a tune to himself. After a while, Mingyue spoke up, just loud enough for Olekina to hear.

"Wu Liqing, you don't need to follow so closely behind me."

Olekina paused. "Your Highness, it is my duty as your guard to protect you from all harm."

"I understand, and I appreciate your concern. But I don't want you to overexert yourself. You can switch your shift with another guard every so often. Or even Miss Wei. She knows how to wield a dagger, I'm sure she could defend me if necessary."

Olekina's voice dropped. "It's not that. It's just…I failed in my duties during the Qiantang Festival. I cannot trust anyone else with defending your life."

"Not even Miss Wei?"

Olekina said nothing.

"And can I trust you, Olekina?" Mingyue turned to him, his gaze intensifying.

The young guard froze. Mingyue was referring to him by his birth name, something he rarely did.

"Your Highness, I—" he stuttered. "Of course you can trust me. I serve you and you alone. I would never let anyone harm you!"

Mingyue smiled softly. "I will take your word for it."

They rounded a corner, coming in sight of the gate leading back into the palace. As they approached, he detected gentle whispers in the bushes to his left. He and Olekina gave each other a glance. He pushed through the bush, revealing a small clearing surrounded by a canopy of trees and flowers above and around. Resting in the clearing was a single stone bench; seated on that bench were a young man and young woman, hand in hand.

"Shenzhong?" Mingyue blinked in surprise at the sight of his elder cousin.

Shenzhong and Alaneya turned toward them in surprise. They quickly let go of each other.

169

"Mingyue!" Shenzhong exclaimed. "Ah…I apologize…"

Mingyue eyed the two of them, "For…what? There is no need to apologize." He glanced at Alaneya, lowering his gaze respectfully as he greeted her. "My lady."

Alaneya averted her gaze from him and bowed. "Your Highness, please excuse me."

Selah raised an eyebrow and smirked. "My, my, what is such a lovely young maiden doing with a Yue prince in the Imperial Gardens?"

Alaneya's face flushed red. "N-nothing! You have the wrong idea, sir!"

Shenzhong smiled bashfully. "I just wanted to show Lady Alaneya the places we used to hide out when we were young."

Mingyue glanced around the clearing. At first, he wasn't sure what Shenzhong was referring to, but then he began to recognize it. When he was still quite young, he and the others would often hide out in this clearing when they played hide-and-seek. That had been a long time ago, perhaps six or seven years, back when Shenzhong still resided within the palace.

"We would always make Jingli the seeker," Shenzhong reminisced.

"I remember," Olekina said blankly. "Miss Wei wasn't happy with your games. You were troublesome."

Shenzhong scratched his head sheepishly. "I wasn't that bad, was I? It was Zukang and Jingli who would always get into trouble and fight with one another."

Alaneya giggled softly. "I guess some things never change."

Olekina gave them a crooked glance. "Prince Shenzhong, you were the eldest. It was your responsibility to discipline and look out for your juniors."

Selah clapped. "Enough reminiscing. We're all going to be late for the wedding ceremony if we don't leave soon."

"The wedding!" Shenzhong exclaimed. "You're right!"

Olekina turned to Mingyue, "Your Highness, we should get going."

Mingyue's eyes met his. Olekina was only a few years older than himself, around the same age as Shenzhong. Back then, he would've been in his early teens. Mingyue hadn't realized it until now, but he couldn't imagine how difficult it was for him to deal with them as children. Suddenly, he felt a great deal of sympathy toward him. He didn't understand how the young guard always managed to remain so patient with them. He didn't want to cause any more trouble from him.

"Yes," Mingyue agreed. "Let's go."

III. The Unveiling

Neili's fingers ran through Mingyue's long, silky hair. Droplets of warm water trickled down the young prince's face, dripping into the bathwater.

There was a knock at the door. Hansini's head popped in. "Your Highness, I've brought your robes for the ceremony."

Mingyue glanced up. The robes she presented were deep red in colour, composed of the finest of silk, with strands of gold weaved in creating intricate designs.

Neili furrowed his brow in disapproval. "Miss Wei, the Second Prince isn't the one getting married!"

Hansini plopped the clothes onto the table and shrugged. "This is the only wedding outfit we have."

Neili sighed in frustration.

"It's fine," Mingyue assured. "I can always get a new outfit for my wedding when the time comes. I'm sure it won't be for a while anyways."

Neili glanced at Hansini. Hansini glanced at Mingyue. Mingyue stared back and forth between the two of them in confusion. After a few moments, Hansini broke the awkward silence.

"Anyways, you should be ready within two hours for the ceremony."

Neili clenched his jaw, "Understood."

Mingyue exited the basin and Neili called in two maids to take away the bathwater. The young eunuch spent the next while drying and combing out Mingyue's hair as the prince sat draped in a towel.

"Your Highness," Neili complained, "you should've come back earlier. I'm not sure if your hair will dry by the ceremony."

"It's fine. It doesn't need to be dry."

"It does, your Highness!" In frustration, Neili yanked the brush harder than usual.

"Ow."

"Ah…I apologize!" Neili said frantically. "I didn't mean to!"

Mingyue waved him aside. "Move on to the makeup."

The sun slipped behind the mountains by the time Neili finished Mingyue's hair, makeup, and outfit. Hansini returned shortly before the ceremony began and rushed him to the Hall of Harmony. He took his position next to Zukang and Jingli.

At the front of the room, an entourage of servants carried forth the royal palanquin with Emperor Jinlong seated on top. Everyone murmured among themselves as he was brought into the room.

"I wasn't aware that His Majesty would be attending the wedding," Shenzhong said.

As if in response to his question, Empress Yinfeng spoke up. "The Emperor is pleased he will be able to take part in the wedding ceremony of his eldest grandchild."

Jinlong smiled gratefully as his wife spoke in his place. The elderly man's face was pale, and he seemed too weak to form his own words. Even to be seated upright on the throne, he needed to have a pillow placed behind him to keep him in position.

Out in the square, the nobles were gathered in preparation for the ceremony. As with the Moon Festival, the number of guests was quite small compared to what would typically be expected of an imperial wedding. Soldiers lined every gate and wall, providing maximum security to ensure that the events of the Qiantang Incident weren't repeated. It wouldn't have been typical for guards to be present on the main terrace during the ceremony, however, Olekina insisted on taking position near Mingyue behind one of the pillars. He was just out of sight, but within perfect striking distance of anyone who got too close to his prince.

A deep orange glow engulfed the sky as dusk began to fall, gongs ringing out simultaneously as a deep drumbeat reverberated throughout the palace. At the far end of the square, the gates leading to the outer palace swung open. Two elaborate palanquins painted red and gold were carried through. Each was covered in a thin curtain, veiling their passengers, but Mingyue could just make out those hidden behind. On the left was the figure of a woman, and on the right was that of a man—Qian Sheli and Ansei Hyousuke.

The rows of guests kowtowed before the palanquins as they rode past. After several moments, they finally reached the base of the staircase leading up to the main terrace. Sheli emerged from behind the curtain, adorned in a flowing red silk dress that swept across the floor. She wore an elaborate headpiece of Sogdian fashion, adorned with precious jewels. Her face remained veiled in a thin cloth. Ansei Hyousuke was also dressed in red and gold, in an elegant Nipponese kimono.

The young couple stopped at the top of the terrace before the Emperor, Empress, and High Priestess Si Lu. It was customary for the parents of both the bride and groom to be present during the tea ceremony, but Jinlong and Yinfeng would stand in their place.

The High Priestess spoke up, "Pay respects to Heaven and Earth."

Sheli and Hyousuke prostrated themselves on the floor.

"Pay respects to the Father and the Mother."

Mingyue flinched at those words. The couple kowtowed once again in unison to the Emperor and Empress.

"Pay respects to the Husband and Wife."

The pair turned to face one another. Although her face was obscured, Mingyue could sense his sister blushing beneath the veil. The bride and groom bowed. They then knelt before the table at the center of the terrace, gently pouring the tea for Jinlong and Yinfeng.

It was time to unveil the bride. With a golden rod in hand, Hyousuke lifted the red cloth covering Sheli's face. The princess blushed as Hyousuke gazed upon her. The Ansei Prince smiled.

Next, they each took a small cup of alcohol, crossing their arms with each other and taking a sip.

Gongs and drums rang out and the crowd erupted into applause. Flowers and confetti rained down from the balconies above. The thundering roar of fireworks echoed across the sky. Mingyue quivered at the sound.

"Mingyue?" Shenzhong noticed his discomfort. "Are you alright?"

Mingyue glanced at him. "It's nothing."

Shenzhong eyed him worriedly. The last time they heard fireworks was during the Qiantang Festival—fireworks had exploded in one of the towers on the wall surrounding the central square. It was from that tower that the shadowed figure had appeared, firing the arrow which had killed his parents and injured the Emperor.

Mingyue glanced up at that very same tower. It was still badly damaged from that night but was under repairs. His gaze traced down to the foot of the palace steps, where he had fallen after the explosion knocked him off his feet. That was the spot his mother had died. The floor had since been wiped clean of blood, but Mingyue felt as if he could still see red stains tainting the pure white marble.

He tore his eyes away. He didn't want to think about that. Not right now. It was his sister's wedding; this was supposed to be a happy occasion.

His attention turned to Sheli. Amidst the celebration, she smiled at her youngest brother. He managed to weakly smile back. But in the depths of each other's eyes, they could sense the other's pain.

"Let us feast!" Yinfeng exclaimed.

Mingyue stared blankly at the platter of food brought over to his table by one of the servants.

"Perhaps the two of you will be uncles soon!" Fengling addressed Zukang and Mingyue excitedly.

"*Ugh,*" Zukang sighed. "I'm not ready for that."

"It's only a matter of time," Shenzhong mused.

"Can we not talk about this right now?" Zukang glared at their eldest cousin.

"Don't tell me you're jealous," Jingli snorted.

"Jealous?!" Zukang grew defensive. "Who are you calling jealous? Why would I be jealous?!"

Shenzhong stifled a laugh. "A-Kang, I didn't realize that the Ansei Prince was your type."

Jingli dodged as Zukang hurled a spoon across the table. The porcelain utensil smacked against Shenzhong's shoulder, landing in his lap.

"Whoa!" Shenzhong exclaimed. "No need for violence!"

"I meant jealous that Sheli is married before you," Jingli huffed. "Please don't tell me the Ansei Prince is your type…"

Zukang seemed ready to throw more tableware. "Of course not! I'm not a cut-sleeve!"

Mingyue quietly slipped away from his table. He had only eaten a few dumplings but didn't have much of an appetite. The others were too busy teasing Zukang and arguing with one another to notice his absence.

He ascended the staircase to the back of the terrace, making his way behind the other guests as they feasted without noticing him. He found being within the Hall of Harmony to be unbearable. There were too many memories associated with this place. He wanted to step outside for a moment for some fresh air.

From behind, a shadow loomed over him.

"Your Highness," Olekina bowed his head. "Miss Wei will be upset if she finds out you've wandered off again."

Mingyue glanced at the guests on the terrace, spotting the Sassanian prince.

"I wish to speak with Li Niexia."

Olekina sighed. "Very well."

It was an excuse, of course, but it worked. As he rounded a pillar, pretending to make his way over to Narsieh, Mingyue ran straight into another individual.

"Steady there," Erik said, grabbing Mingyue's wrist to prevent him from falling.

Their eyes met. The last time they had really spoken to one another was the night of the Moon Festival a month earlier, during their awkward encounter after Mingyue fell from the wall onto the Norden prince. Since then, they only saw one another during official gatherings with the other delegates, but Mingyue was often too ill to attend many of them.

Erik blushed, gently letting go of Mingyue's hand. "I apologize, Your Highness. I didn't realize it was you."

Mingyue shook his head. "It was my fault. I wasn't watching where I was going."

Erik smiled softly. "This reminds me of the very first time we met."

It was Mingyue's turn to blush. He quickly changed the subject. "I apologize again for last time. I hope your back doesn't hurt."

Nearby, the young eunuch of the Oghuz Rumeli sultana named Azaria seemed to be listening in on their conversation. His face flushed red as he eavesdropped on them. He quickly turned away, as if he'd heard something he shouldn't have.

"Your Highness," Olekina quickly hushed Mingyue. "Don't speak in such a way here. People may get the wrong idea if you use such language."

Both Erik and Mingyue's faces instantly turned bright red.

Mingyue, "I didn't mean—"

Erik, "That's not what he meant—"

The two looked at one another before glancing away in embarrassment.

"Is everything alright?" Irina wondered, coming up to them from behind Erik.

"Everything is fine," Erik said quickly.

Irina nodded. Her gaze met Mingyue as she bowed to him. "Your Highness."

"Your Highness," Mingyue returned the greeting.

There was a moment of awkward silence between them.

Olekina took hold of Mingyue's sleeve and began leading him away. "If you'd excuse us."

Erik nodded, smiling one last time at Mingyue before departing with Irina. Mingyue's eyes followed them as they made their way back to their tables.

"Your Highness?" Olekina's voice was filled with concern. "Is something wrong?"

"It's nothing."

He was about to continue on his way when Empress Yinfeng suddenly spoke up. "His Majesty has an important announcement to make."

Everyone paused their conversations and meals, turning to the Emperor's throne. Jinlong was leaning forward in his seat, seeming to use every bit of his strength to speak.

"I am overjoyed to be celebrating the wedding of my eldest grandchild today…" he took a deep breath. "As you all are aware, the tragic events of the Qiantang Festival took place only a short while ago. My daughter, Princess Huamei, and son-in-law, Prince Yanlu, were both killed that evening."

The mood of the terrace became somber. Everyone seemed to be holding their breaths.

Jinlong continued. "We are still unaware of the perpetrators of the attack, but we assume that they are linked to Emir Abdullah of the Khorasan, as well as the Governor of Qinglong. We have also been made aware of a similar plot which was carried out in the Karnatan capital, leading to many casualties."

Mingyue felt his heart drop. He glanced over to Prince Sundar. The Karnatan Prince had a blank, unreadable expression in his eyes.

"Whoever is responsible for this attack will be brought to justice. Earlier today, our soldiers launched an assault on Qinglong. We will reclaim the city and punish the governor for treason against Wuyue."

Mingyue couldn't help but think that his grandfather's words sounded like a direct threat, as if he was addressing someone in their very presence. He scanned the guests—the envoys from Norden and the Roman Tsardom, the Oghuz Rumelis and Karnata, the Keliyete

Khanate, and delegates from Ansei Nippon and Tahuantinsuyu. He eyed his family members and subjects: Xi Chengxin, Governor of Suzhou; Qian Zemao, Dowager Empress of the Xin Dynasty; Xi Yanggui, Princess of the Ailao Empire; Prince Narsieh Sasan, head of the House of Sasan. Was it possible that there were individuals among them conspiring with those who killed his parents?

"However, I must soon pass on this throne to a successor," the Emperor continued. "Due to my injuries, I will likely be unable to attend another festival or ceremony after this. Therefore, I would like to announce today, before my subjects and the world, that the successor to the throne of Wuyue will be my eldest grandson, Qian Zukang."

All eyes turned to the First Prince. Out of everyone, he seemed to be the most surprised by the news.

"I have a second announcement to make," the Emperor said, drawing everyone's attention back to him. "At the Qiantang Festival, Princess Huamei wished to announce the betrothal of her youngest son. Unfortunately, she was unable to do so. But here today, I will announce my daughter's decision."

Mingyue's heart skipped a beat.

"Qian Mingyue shall be wed to the niece of the Doge of Venesia, Lady Alaneya Fatima Maria of Oghuz Rumelia."

IV. Strings of the Heart

Crimson lanternlight danced across the walls as the cool autumn breeze drifted through the open windows. Fireworks rippled across the sky, reflected in the Lake of Tranquility below.

Sheli's maids guided her and Ansei Hyousuke into the room. Upon checking that everything was in place, the maids hurried out, leaving the young couple alone in the bridal chamber. The linens and pillows were deep red, matching the rest of the room.

Hyousuke glanced at the bed. "A bit excessive, don't you think?"

Sheli blushed. As a newlywed, she was expected to consummate her marriage in this very room but was completely dumbstruck as to what she was supposed to do.

Hyousuke produced a small jar from his sleeve, dipping two fingers inside. "I brought this, though I suppose it won't even be noticeable with these sheets."

He lifted the blanket, rubbing his fingers against a small area of the bed sheets. An even darker red stain from his fingers was smeared on the bed.

Sheli grew concerned. "What are you doing?"

The Ansei Prince paused, glancing up at his new wife. "They'll think we've consummated the marriage if we put a fake blood stain here."

Sheli blinked in confusion, taking a seat at the foot of the bed. "I…it's part of the ceremony to consummate the marriage on the night of the wedding. We can't lie about it…"

Hyousuke leaned over the princess, removing the heavy decorative crown from her head. "I apologize, my lady. I was under the impression that perhaps this was too soon for you." He bowed his head. "But if your Highness thinks otherwise…"

Sheli flushed bright pink and took Hyousuke's hand. "No, no. It's not that. It's just…I don't want to lie…"

Hyousuke smiled warmly. "My lady, you mustn't always do what others want, simply because it is expected of you."

Sheli's eyes met his as he gestured to the bed, "As long as they see the stain in the morning, no one will ask any questions."

Sheli blushed. "How do you know about all that...? You came well-prepared."

"I am well-educated."

Sheli coughed. "And what exactly does that mean?"

Hyousuke immediately realized the fault with his words. He laughed bashfully. "I didn't mean to imply that I've been with another woman. Of course not, my lady. We have been engaged for a long time. Even though we had never met before I arrived in Qiantang, I had vowed to remain faithful only to you, my future bride."

"I...I see..." Sheli was too flustered to say anything else. Instead, she simply leaned forward, planting a gentle kiss on his face. "I...appreciate your consideration. I'll be heading to sleep now."

Hyousuke smiled. "Goodnight, my lady."

***

Mingyue hurried down the alleyways of the palace. After the wedding festivities had ended for the night, he'd departed the square immediately, not even giving Olekina a chance to catch up with him.

His mind was racing. He was to be wed to Lady Alaneya Fatima Maria, niece of the Doge of Venesia. He knew it was only a matter of time before a marriage was arranged, but he still hadn't expected it so suddenly.

He stepped through the doors of the infirmary, hoping not to make any sound. Of course, he couldn't escape the attention of Kanen.

"Your Highness," the young physician bowed. "Can I assist you?"

Mingyue paused for a moment, glancing over at the herbs on Kanen's table. "I have a headache."

"I will prepare tea and some medicine."

Mingyue slumped onto the bed.

"Your Highness, is everything alright?" Kanen sprinkled some leaves into the tea before approaching the prince and handing him the cup.

Before Mingyue could respond, there were voices at the door. It slid open, revealing five people.

"There he is!" Arivesto exclaimed.

Sundar sighed, "I told you he'd be here."

"I'm not surprised," Neili crossed his arms.

"Your Highness," Hansini said in a scolding tone. "I told you not to run off on your own."

Olekina simply stared back expressionlessly.

"He has a headache," Kanen stated. "Let him rest."

"A headache?" Arivesto cocked her head. "Too much to drink?"

Neili scoffed. "Yeah right. His Highness doesn't drink."

"Perhaps he is just overwhelmed at news of his engagement," Sundar suggested.

"Oh?" Kanen's ears perked up, turning to the prince. "Your Highness, are you engaged?"

Mingyue said nothing.

Arivesto nodded. "To Lady Alaneya Fatima Maria of Venesia."

A confused expression grew on Kanen's face. "Lady Alaneya…? I've never heard of her."

"Exactly," Neili sighed. "I don't understand why they chose a nobody from the other side of the world—"

"Watch your tongue," Hansini warned. "This 'nobody' was chosen by Princess Huamei herself. Plus, she comes from one of the most prominent families of Oghuz Rumelia and is a relative of Aysun Sultana herself."

Neili crossed his arms, "Still. Prince Zukang and Princess Sheli were both engaged to nobility."

"Nobility isn't everything," Arivesto pointed out. "The Oghuz Rumelis have risen to prominence in the west. They rival only Wuyue itself in global power and influence. Even marrying into the extended family of the Younanoglu Dynasty may prove to be of greater asset to Wuyue than either the Yi Princess or Ansei Prince."

"Lady Alaneya seems like a fine and noble woman," Sundar added. "I'm sure she'd make an excellent wife."

Once again, Mingyue felt like everyone was talking about him as if he weren't even present. "I will be retiring to my quarters this evening."

"I will accompany you," Olekina said.

Neili piped up, "I'll prepare a bath."

"I will get a change of clothing," added Hansini.

Mingyue waved them aside. "Olekina may accompany me back to my quarters. The rest of you are dismissed for tonight."

Once he was finally alone upon returning to his quarters, Mingyue shed the heavy outer layers of his outfit and pulled out the pins keeping his hair up. He sighed deeply, collapsing into the sheets, and attempting to fall asleep. He couldn't. Too many thoughts flowed through his head.

He knew he shouldn't have been upset about his engagement to Alaneya. As Sundar had said, she seemed like a noble woman who would make a good wife. But did his parents have his best interests in mind when they chose her for him to wed? Or were Wuyue's affairs a priority to them?

He thought that it was unfair. His parents had been lucky to marry for love; since Yanlu was of noble birth, his engagement to Huamei had been accepted. For Mingyue, however, things were different. He didn't wish to marry. Or at least, he didn't wish for a wife.

The thought of Prince Erik came to mind—his silky golden hair, jade-green eyes, and warm smile. Mingyue had never felt anything toward someone the way he did for Erik. He didn't know why, but despite having only met the Norden prince recently, he felt as if he'd known him for a lifetime...

He closed his eyes but couldn't fall asleep. A gentle melody hummed outside. For the last month, he'd heard that same melody every single night, but could never tell where exactly it was coming from. It would always play at the same time—a stringed instrument lulling him to sleep.

He stepped out onto the terrace, gazing out over the roofs of the palace. The song was coming from the east somewhere, but he couldn't tell how far its origin was. Beside him was a guzheng. After encountering one of the instruments in the gardens earlier, Mingyue asked that one be brought to his quarters. He lowered himself beside it, fingers gently resting above the strings.

Strum.

A simple note rang out, intertwining with the rhythm of the other stringed instrument. For a moment, the other musician paused. The air fell silent. Then, they continued playing the soft melody. Mingyue tuned in with his own rhythm, blending the two songs together. He didn't know how much time passed. The two songs continued, each gradually growing softer as their fingers became tired. After a while, he rested his hands on the instrument, strumming the last string to finish off the song. The other musician continued playing his own melody one last time, and Mingyue's eyelids finally began to fall heavy. He dozed off to sleep.

***

Erik lowered his violin after finishing the song, letting out a sigh. Each night for the past month, he had retreated to this quiet garden in the palace, softly playing out this tune amidst the silence. He hadn't realized that the sound of his song was being carried by the winds beyond the walls surrounding him, or that someone had been listening to him play, until he was joined by another melody.

"Your Highness," Caleb's voice broke the silence. "I will accompany you back to your quarters if you are finished for the night."

The Norden prince looked up over the tiled-roofed buildings one last time, in the direction where the song of the guzheng had come from. He smiled softly.

"Yes. We are finished."

Only the sound of crickets chirping accompanied the two as they returned to Erik's quarters. The air was still. Shadows danced across the gardens as clouds drifted past the moon.

"I suppose I should congratulate the prince," Erik whispered.

Caleb gave him a confused glance. "Your Highness?"

Erik turned to him. "Second Prince Qian. He's been engaged."

"I am aware. I had assumed you had already congratulated him at the wedding."

"No," Erik's eyes grew distant. "He seemed overwhelmed. I didn't want to bother him while everyone was still around. I was going to approach him after the celebrations were over, but by then he had already departed."

"When will you congratulate him? Today is the first opportunity you've had to speak with him since the Moon Festival. You may not get the chance to see him again before our return to Norden."

The prince felt his heart sink. "Norden? When are we leaving?"

"We would've already left by now, had it not been for the rebellion in Qinglong. As soon as Wuyue regains control of that city, we should depart. You and Princess Irina are expected back in Moskva by summer for your wedding."

Erik said nothing. Instead, his attention shifted in the direction of a soft coo from the branches above him. Perched among the leaves sat two silky-feathered doves, one white and one black. They nestled together, looking down at him curiously.

"Those!" He pointed at them excitedly. "I'll gift them to Prince Mingyue! He seems to take a liking to animals, especially birds. It would be perfect, don't you think?"

Caleb raised an eyebrow. "My lord, you can't just capture wild birds to give to the prince."

"Then we will find domesticated ones," Erik smiled.

Caleb shook his head. "Your Highness, doves are a symbol of marriage. I'm not sure how well it will be received."

Erik cocked his head, "Why not? It's a wedding gift after all."

"But *you're* not the one marrying him. Typically, the groom would present such a gift to his bride. You giving doves to him is…strange."

Erik smiled awkwardly. "Ah…I see…"

185

"If you insist on giving him a gift, let me be the one to pick it out."

Erik chuckled, throwing an arm over Caleb's shoulders. "I can always count on you for things like that, can't I."

"Of course," Caleb buckled under the weight of the prince's body leaning on him. He shook his head. "Now if you wouldn't mind getting off me."

V. Tumultuous Departure

Sheli sat on the terrace sipping her tea. Out in the gardens, many of the trees had begun to change gold and red, turning the Imperial Palace into a beautiful pattern of colour resembling the silk robes of a noble. It was for that reason that this was always her favourite time of year.

"So how was it?" Seo-Yeon inquired.

Seated at the tea table with them were Princess Fengling, Lady Arivesto Ramanantsoa, Aysun Sultana, and Princess Irina Aleksandrova.

Sheli cocked her head. "How was what?"

Seo-Yeon poured herself another cup of tea. "The consummation of your marriage with the Ansei Prince."

"P-pardon...?" Sheli's face flushed red. "Ah...um..."

Aysun Sultana lowered her cup from her mouth. Her eyes narrowed. "Can we not speak about such things while eating?"

Seo-Yeon lowered her gaze, "I apologize. It's common to discuss such topics in the north. I forgot that it's taboo in other places."

Fengling made a face, "Princess Seo-Yeon, does that mean you have already experienced..."

Seo-Yeon's lips seemed to twitch in disgust. "Of course not. Even if it's the cultural norm among the Keliyetes to lose one's virginity before marriage, I am still a Hanguk princess. A noble of my lineage would never dream of doing such a thing."

"Oh," Fengling nodded. "I see."

Seo-Yeon turned back to Sheli. "So, you being the only one to have experienced it, what is it like? How about Ansei Hyousuke? Is he—?"

Sheli threw her hands up and waved the Yi Princess aside. "We don't need to talk about this. You can see for yourselves when you are married."

Seo-Yeon perked up, "Speaking of which, my wedding to your brother is only a few months away."

"Ooh how exciting," Fengling exclaimed. She took hold of both Seo-Yeon's and Sheli's hands. "We will all be family then!"

Sheli smiled softly.

"How about you, Princess Fengling?" Irina inquired. "Are you also engaged?"

"Ah…no," she smiled bashfully. "My mother has tried to arrange an engagement for me many times, but I always turned them down. I really don't think that is the path for me."

"What a shame," Seo-Yeon said. "There are many Keliyete princes seeking a bride. I'm sure our Khan would be delighted to form an alliance with the Crimson Emperor."

Fengling politely declined. "I think I would rather become a nun or something. Like how Uncle Jinxin renounced his noble titles and became a monk."

Arivesto nearly spit out her tea in laughter. "A nun?! I'm not sure the Empress Dowager would be happy hearing that!"

Fengling smiled nervously, "I know…"

Seo-Yeon turned her attention to the Merinan noblewoman. "And yourself, Lady Ramanantsoa?"

"Me?" Arivesto said in surprise. "I'm far too busy to think about marriage. If I *did* marry, it would have to be someone who I can travel the world with."

"Will you be leaving Qiantang soon?"

She nodded, "Once Qinglong is reclaimed, I'll be making a voyage south along the trade routes. I'm thinking of Melaya, or perhaps Ayutthaya."

"I'll be departing as well," Aysun Sultana added. "I must return to Constantinople by spring."

"That's right!" Arivesto chimed in. "I've heard news that you've been engaged!"

"Engaged?" Seo-Yeon raised an eyebrow. "Who's the lucky gentleman?"

"Asada ibn Yuhana ibn Nabil, Crown Prince of Isbaniya," Aysun Sultana replied simply.

"The Sultanate of Isbaniya," Seo-Yeon stated. "That is rather interesting."

"Oh?" Aysun said. She and the Yi Princess stared intensely into one another's eyes. "Is it?"

"Indeed," Seo-Yeon smiled slyly. "I was under the impression that Isbaniya and the Oghuz Rumelis were in an intense rivalry over control of the Mediterranean."

"My father wishes to wipe the slate clean between our two empires," Aysun replied. "Do you take issue with that, Princess Seo-Yeon?"

Seo-Yeon grinned, lowering her teacup. "Not at all, Sultana. Not at all."

An awkward silence descended on the terrace. After a few moments, it was finally broken by a knock at the door.

"Princess Fengling, you've been summoned to the Empress Dowager's quarters," a eunuch announced.

Fengling rose quickly from the table, bowing to the other. "Excuse me."

The eunuch continued, "And First Princess Qian, you have a visitor."

Sheli gave him a confused look. She hadn't had any meetings scheduled for today. Who could be asking to see her?

Irina smirked. "The Ansei Prince, perhaps?"

Sheli shot her a glance. The two cousins left the others on the terrace and quickly parted ways—Fengling to her mother's quarters and Sheli following the eunuch to the gardens.

"I will let you two speak," the eunuch said, disappearing back down the way they'd come.

Sheli spotted someone standing out in the gardens with his back facing her. The young man's golden blond hair waved gently in the breeze.

"Prince Erik?"

The Norden prince turned and bowed. "First Princess Qian."

"You asked to see me?"

"Ah, yes," he held out a large cylindrical object in front of him, covered in a dark cloth. "For your brother. A gift, to congratulate him on his engagement."

Sheli's eyes lit up in surprise. "Your Highness, I'm sure my brother will appreciate this very much."

The prince smiled, handing the object to her.

Sheli blinked in surprise. "Oh…would you like me to give it to him?"

"If it isn't too much trouble, your Highness."

"You know, I think Mingyue would be much happier to receive this gift directly from you."

"I…" the prince paused.

Sheli laughed. "Of course, I'd be willing to. But I must wonder what it is my brother has done to earn your affection. After all, I don't recall you directly presenting a wedding gift to me. What makes Mingyue special?"

Erik bowed quickly. "Your Highness, I meant no offense by this. I shall present you with a gift as well—"

Sheli laughed, "I am only joking."

"I apologize, your Highness. It was rude of me to show favour to your brother over you…"

The Yue princess smiled nostalgically, "You remind me of someone I once knew…"

"Oh?" Erik stared at her in confusion, "Who, if I may ask?"

Sheli thought for a long moment as if trying to retrieve some long-forgotten memory. She shook her head.

"I…I'm not sure exactly. It's as if I have met you somewhere before. But I know that's impossible. This is the first time you've visited Qiantang, and I have never left Wuyue."

Erik smiled, a warm expression of understanding in his eyes. "Likewise, perhaps your brother reminds me of someone I once knew as well. Maybe that's why I feel a fondness toward him."

"I see..." Sheli nodded. "Just remember that Mingyue isn't whoever he reminds you of. If you treat him as such, I'm afraid you may end up hurting both of you."

"Yes, your Highness. I know."

"Would you still like me to deliver that gift?"

The Norden prince hesitated for a moment. "On second thought, perhaps I will give it to him myself."

***

Fengling stepped over the threshold into her mother's quarters. By the time she arrived, Jingli was already present, seated at the table and sipping his tea in silence as his mother frantically directed orders to the maids and eunuchs in the room.

"Pack the linens as well. And make sure to fold my silk robes! I don't want them to get creased. Somebody fetch me some tea."

Fengling cautiously approached. "Mother? What is going on here?"

Zemao didn't even seem to notice her daughter's presence. She continued directing the servants. Amidst the tense atmosphere, Jingli sat in the center of the room like a calm in the storm.

"Mother is returning to Kaifeng."

A confused expression grew on Fengling's face. "Kaifeng? Why?"

Zemao turned toward her daughter, finally seeming to notice her presence. "Fengling! Where have you been? I am returning to Kaifeng, and you can't even find the time to see me off when I summon you?"

"I apologize, I was not aware. Why are you returning?"

Zemao hesitated for a moment. She waved her daughter aside. "Something has come up. It is nothing that concerns you, but I must return immediately."

"We will come with you—"

"You will stay here," Zemao said firmly. "It will be safer for you here. Both you and your brother will remain in Qiantang until you receive further notice from me."

"But—"

"Understood?" The sharp gaze in Zemao's eyes stared down at Fengling.

"Understood," Jingli replied in his sister's place. He set his cup on the table, turning toward his sister. The twins locked eyes with one another.

"Good," the Empress Dowager smiled, but there was no emotion behind her expression. "Tell His Majesty and Empress Yinfeng that I apologize for not being able to give an official farewell."

"Understood."

Fengling watched on in silence as the servants finished packing and began moving the luggage outside to transport it back to Kaifeng. She couldn't imagine what could possibly cause her mother to return to the Xin capital in such a rush. Perhaps something happened to the Crimson Emperor?

She didn't understand what was going on, but she knew for certain that something wasn't right.

***

"Deploy archers," Commander Yao shouted.

A thousand soldiers heeded his order, drawing back their bowstrings and releasing fire. A volley of a thousand flaming arrows rained down on the walls of Qinglong, sending the rebel troops into a panicked frenzy.

"Canons," the commander demanded.

Canons rolled into place, taking aim at the city's outer gates, and blasting them with an explosive force. The gates shook in their hinges but remained firmly in place.

"Again!"

Between Wuyue's Imperial Army and the rebel forces holding the gates of Qinglong lay several dozen meters of lifeless corpses—corpses of the Qinglong governor's loyalists. Wuyue had pushed back the rebel forces to the walls of Qinglong and was preparing to retake the city. That was when a sudden shout of panic came from behind the Wuyue line.

"Commander Yao! The river!"

Commander Yao whipped around; his eyes were fixed on the south past the forces of his army—the river. The waves of the Qiantang River were racing directly toward them. Impossible. The Qiantang River didn't flow in this direction. And yet, before his very eyes, Commander Yao could see the waves sweeping over the plain toward his army.

"Retreat!" He ordered.

As soon as the order escaped his lips, he realized that retreat was futile. His troops were trapped between the river and the city walls of Qinglong. Running toward either would seal one's fate. The soldiers panicked. Scrambling over one another to escape.

Commander Yao watched on in horror as his army was engulfed by the river. How could this have happened? How had the river surrounded them? There was only one possibility—it had been diverted.

We've been led into a trap, the commander realized in horror. He too was soon lost to the waves.

VI. Little Bird

"You may not pass," Olekina stood firmly in front of the door to Mingyue's quarters.

The Norden prince stood face to face with him, holding the cylindrical object covered in dark cloth in his hand. "Princess Sheli gave me permission to see the prince."

"It doesn't matter. The First Princess is not the one who runs the Palace of Lunar Serenity, Miss Wei is. If you would like to see Prince Mingyue, please consult her."

Erik frowned. "I don't think Miss Wei likes me very much. We both know that she won't grant me permission."

"I'm afraid I can't help you."

Hearing the commotion outside, Mingyue pushed open the door and stepped out of his quarters alongside Neili.

"Wu Liqing, is everything alright—?"

His gaze met the soft jade eyes of the Norden prince. Mingyue's expression immeadiately shifted.

"Prince Erik…?"

Erik grinned bashfully. "I came to see you, but Wu Liqing won't let me pass."

Olekina turned to the Yue prince, "Your Highness—"

Mingyue quickly waved him aside. "Wu Liqing, you recall what the Emperor said when the Norden envoy arrived in Qiantang, don't you?"

Olekina gave him a confused glance. "Your Highness—?"

"The Norden prince has permission to visit the Palace of Lunar Serenity whenever he wishes to."

Olekina said nothing.

Neili spoke up, "Your Highness, I'm sure Wu Liqing only thought that this was perhaps a bad time to receive guests since you are heading to the Imperial Gardens now. Plus, he didn't want to interrupt you while you were dressing…"

Erik's face flushed red. "No, of course not! I didn't realize this was a bad time. I'll come back later—"

"There is still time," Mingyue said. He gestured to Olekina and Neili. "You are dismissed. I will summon you when I leave for the gardens."

They both hesitated momentarily before bowing and hurrying off. "Of course, your Highness."

That left the two young princes alone together.

"Ah...your Highness. I...um...brought you a gift...to celebrate your engagement."

Mingyue stood in silence for several moments. "I appreciate the gesture."

Erik handed him the cylinder, pulling the dark cloth from it. Mingyue blinked in surprise. Beneath the cloth was a golden birdcage, and within the birdcage sat...

"What is it...?"

"A duniao[29]!" Erik exclaimed excitedly. "Newly hatched. Lady Ramanantsoa brought specimens back from her voyages in the Southern Ocean, and I asked her for one to give to you. Do you like it?"

Mingyue leaned down, putting his hand in the cage, and gently stroking the bird's soft neck. The chick had grayish blue down and was larger than any bird hatchling he'd seen before, too big to fit in the palm of his hand.

He smiled. "It is very cute. Thank you. But how did you know I liked birds?"

Erik scratched his head, "Uh...lucky guess?"

The duniao squawked, cocking its head as it gazed up at him curiously.

Mingyue chuckled softly. "It looks like you."

"It...looks like me—?"

---

[29] Dùniǎo (渡鳥): A large, flightless bird native to a remote island in the middle of the Southern Ocean.

"*Mhm*," Mingyue nodded.

"Uh," Erik laughed nervously. "Are you saying I am cute…?"

Mingyue's eyes flicked toward him. "When did I say that?"

"Well, you said it was cute, and you also said it looks like me. Therefore, you are saying that I am also cute—"

"I didn't mean it in that way," Mingyue quickly said. "I meant that you resemble its clueless qualities, like the way it cocks its head and stares at me."

The chick continued staring up at him in confusion.

Erik glanced from Mingyue to the bird, and then back to Mingyue. His face flushed red. "What do you mean by '*clueless*'?"

Mingyue raised the birdcage to Erik's face, comparing the two of them.

The Norden prince crossed his arms and made an exaggerated pouting face. "Prince Mingyue, I take back what I said before. I think that underneath your '*alluring*' surface, you just like to make fun of me."

Mingyue's face lit up. He couldn't help but laugh lightheartedly.

Erik's expression softened. "Your Highness, I don't think I've ever seen you smile like this! Now I know, the only thing that makes you laugh is my cluelessness."

Mingyue quickly wiped away his smile.

"Am I really that funny-looking?" The Norden prince asked self-consciously. "Is that really what people think?"

Mingyue studied him closely—his chiseled jawline, golden silky locks, sparkling jade-green eyes, and the smooth ridge of his nose. His features were handsomely beautiful, like that of an Immortal or an Adonis. He seemed so perfect as if shaped by the divine hands of Heaven itself. From a distance, his regal, princely features were almost intimidating. Few dared to approach. But Mingyue had never seen his cold, icy exterior. All he knew was the prince's warm smile and the soft glow in his eyes. Before coming to Wuyue, it had been a long, long time since Erik had smiled in such a way.

"I wouldn't know," Mingyue responded. "All that I had heard of you before your arrival was that you are the most handsome prince in all the west."

"Ah…" Erik smiled bashfully. "I think such a title is meaningless. One should be judged on their character, not their appearance. It's shallow, don't you think? After all, I did not choose the way I look."

"*Mnn…*" Mingyue nodded in agreement. "Then perhaps you are the *least* handsome prince in all the west."

"Hey!" Erik protested.

Mingyue smiled softly again. "Seeing as you are the only prince from the west whom I have met, there is no one else I can compare you against. Therefore, from my perspective, you are both the *most* handsome and the *least*."

Erik furrowed his brow. "Who would've thought that the Yue prince could be as beautiful as an orchid yet speak words as sharp as daggers."

"As you said," Mingyue replied. "One should not judge by appearances."

Erik giggled. "I knew from the moment we met that beneath that cold expression was a sense of humour."

Mingyue stared back blankly. "What sense of humour?"

Erik laughed. "And who would've guessed that the Second Prince also knows how to flirt! I'll have to keep that secret to myself."

It was Mingyue's turn to blush. He crossed his arms averting his gaze away from Erik. "Who's flirting?!"

The Norden prince laughed even harder.

"Your Highness," Olekina peeked us head out the terrace. "Prince Amaru will be expecting us soon."

Mingyue nodded, facing Erik once again. "Please excuse me, I must be on my way."

"Prince Amaru?" Erik asked. "What are you seeing him for?"

"He is teaching me to wield a spear."

Erik's eyes lit up. "Ooh, exciting! May I join you?"

"Would the Roman Princess approve?"

Erik shrugged. "Does it matter whether she approves?"

Mingyue fell silent.

"What's wrong with two friends spending time with one another? If she has a problem with that, let her get upset."

Mingyue smiled weakly. "Two friends?"

Erik frowned. "What? Do you not consider me a friend?"

"No, no, of course."

Erik threw an arm over Mingyue's shoulders, catching the Yue prince off guard. "Haha! Let's get going then! We don't want to keep Prince Amaru waiting."

***

"Making progress," Amaru said, helping Mingyue off the ground for what must have been the tenth time that morning.

Mingyue struggled to catch his breath. He didn't see how being knocked to the dirt after only a few moments of sparring was 'progress.'

"Your Highness!" Erik hurried over. His reaction was the same each time Mingyue was beaten down.

The Yue prince brushed him aside. "I'm fine."

Erik wasn't convinced. "Prince Amaru, there really must be a better way to train than this. Prince Mingyue has no experience with fighting yet."

The Tahuantinsuyu prince scratched his head in confusion. "This is how I was taught back home…"

"May I try?" Erik offered.

Amaru smiled, "Go on ahead."

All the while, Olekina and Caleb stood by silently on the sidelines. Selah lounged lazily nearby, peeling loquats as he played with the duniao hatchling.

Mingyue drew his spear and Erik unsheathed his sword as both took their stances.

Selah clapped, "Fight!"

Erik was the first to strike, bringing his sword down in a clear, precise strike. Mingyue quickly raised his spear, blocking the attack. The two weapons clanged against each other.

"Ooh," Amaru applauded. "Nice defense!"

"This is how we train beginners in Norden," Erik explained. "One clear, straightforward strike and defend. Now you try."

Mingyue retracted his spear, aimed, and struck. Erik blocked the attack, his eyes lighting up.

"See? Now once you get a hang of a few moves we can speed up the pace."

Amaru watched on with excitement, shouting words of encouragement as the two sparred.

"Not bad," Selah smiled in amusement as Mingyue swiftly dodged a blow from the sword.

Olekina winced.

"No need to worry," assured Caleb. "My lord will show restraint if he doesn't feel like the prince can defend the attack."

Olekina remained unconvinced.

Erik dealt another strike, this time launching forward with the weight of his body. Mingyue blocked the sword, but he underestimated the force of Erik's momentum. Erik collided with him, and Mingyue was knocked backward off his feet. His body hit the ground with a thud, with Erik landing on top of him.

"Your Highness!" Olekina shouted.

Mingyue groaned.

"Ah, I apologize," Erik laughed nervously. "I shouldn't have gone so hard."

Selah smirked, "That's quite an awkward position you're in."

Erik laughed nervously as he pushed himself up. "It's not the first time."

Selah raised an eyebrow, "Oh?"

Caleb shook his head. "Let's not discuss this…"

After being helped to his feet by Amaru, Erik extended a hand to Mingyue.

"Perhaps we should call it a day," suggested the Tahuantinsuyu prince.

Erik frowned, "We were just getting started."

"Your Highness," interrupted Caleb. "Princess Irina is expecting you for tea at noon."

"Yes. I am aware."

"You should go then," Mingyue said. "You don't want to be late."

"I—" the Norden prince trailed off. "I guess I'll see you later then. Tomorrow?"

"*Mnn*," Mingyue nodded. "Tomorrow."

VII. Lurking in the Shadows

14/10/18ᵗʰ Year of the Golden Dragon Emperor

Year of the Wooden Goat

Xi Yanggui crossed the threshold into Empress Yinfeng's quarters.

"Yanggui," the Empress addressed her niece, gesturing to the seat beside her. "Sit."

Yanggui took her place next to her aunt as a servant rushed over to pour them some tea. "Your Majesty, you asked to see me?"

Yinfeng nodded. "I received a message from Qinglong yesterday. Our forces were wiped out."

Yanggui froze, "That's...impossible...!"

"The Qiantang River was diverted from upstream," Yinfeng explained. "The battlefield was flooded."

"But the reports stated that the rebel army had been pushed back to the east!" Yanggui pointed out. "Who could've been upstream to divert the river?"

"That is what I'd like to know. Now, is there something you wanted to say? You said you had news."

"Ah," Yanggui nodded, "it is off topic. But Fengling informed me that Zemao had returned to Kaifeng."

"Oh?" Yinfeng raised an eyebrow. "She has already departed? Without even informing us?"

"She left two days ago."

"That was the same day as the events in Qinglong," Yinfeng nodded. "And what route would she have taken to return home, I wonder?"

The room fell silent. The only sound to be heard was the repetitive dripping of dew from the orchids onto the windowsill.

Yanggui finally dared to speak. "Your Majesty, you don't think that Zemao is involved...?"

"I have never trusted that woman," Yinfeng admitted. "Even as a child, she was always troublesome. She was always jealous of her sister, always envious that Huamei was heir to the throne. Now, as Empress Dowager over the Xin Dynasty, I fear that her power may even rival that of Jinlong."

"Nonsense," Yanggui brushed that comment aside. "Wuyue is the most powerful empire in the world. The Xin cannot compete."

"That may have been true in the past. However, the Crimson Emperor's reputation and influence have been growing ever since he came to power. There is prosperity in both the countryside and the cities, stability and peace in the court."

"Is that a bad thing?" Yanggui inquired.

Yinfeng paused for a moment. "For the Xin's subjects? Not at all. For Wuyue, however..." her voice trailed off as she gazed out the window. "The Crimson Emperor has not kept secret his intention of one day reunifying the Tang Realms. His wish is for Wuyue, Nanyue, and the Xin to restore the former glory of the Tang Dynasty and bring the Tang Realms under one banner once again. Of course, he hopes this can be achieved through peaceful, cooperative means. However, wouldn't it be much more convenient if Wuyue was weakened, plagued by rebellion, with the Xin Dynasty providing the only hope for peace and stability to reign once again?"

Yanggui tried to take in what the Empress was saying. "Do you really think that Zemao would be capable of such a thing?"

"Do not underestimate her," Yinfeng warned. "She is cunning and deceitful. It is only through her influence that Jiao Hongli ascended to the throne without opposition. However, she must have ulterior motives. No doubt she had wished for Jingli, her own son, to succeed the previous Xin Emperor. There must be a reason why she supported Jiao Hongli instead."

"We shouldn't speculate," Yanggui spoke up. "Speculation will only lead to concern; concern will only lead to anxiety. What is important right now is how we will proceed with Qinglong."

"But in order to do that, we must know who they are working with," Yinfeng said in frustration. "If not Zemao, then we must find out who. To divert the flow of the Qiantang River one would require a large number of workers to dig up the ground in a short period of time, yet at the same time not draw suspicion from those around them. That portion of the Qiantang River is too far south in Wuyue's territory for Xin forces to have infiltrated the region unnoticed."

"Then it could not have been Zemao," Yanggui concluded.

"That does not rule out the possibility that she may have had a hand in the matter," Yinfeng thought carefully. "She still maintains ties to nobles in and around Qinglong. In fact, the Emperor once considered marrying her off to the Duke of Jiaxing."

"The Duke of Jiaxing..." Yanggui's eyes widened. "He presides over the domain upstream from Qinglong."

"Indeed," Yingfeng nodded. "But regardless of whether he is responsible, the fact remains that this ambush on our troops would've been impossible without ties to someone in the Yue Court. The Duke of Jiaxing could not have been aware of the location or time at which Commander Yao was going to attack Qinglong. Only a high-ranking individual within the Yue court or military could've informed him of that."

Yanggui lowered her voice. "Then there is a traitor within the palace...?"

"At least one. We have already discovered Emir Abdullah's treachery in his plot to capture Mingyue and Prince Niexia. We can also assume that he was the mastermind behind the Qiantang Festival Incident. However, he could not have been the one responsible for Qinglong. For one, he would not have been made aware of our internal matters in the first place. And secondly, he is in prison."

"Are they connected?" Yanggui asked hesitantly. "The Qiantang Incident, the Qinglong Rebellion, the plot to kidnap Mingyue...?"

"And the Karnatan Coup," Yinfeng nodded. "The Karnatan Coup and the Qiantang Incident were staged simultaneously, attacking both Wuyue and our closest allies in an attempt to overthrow the leadership of both nations. The Qinglong Rebellion broke out at the same time. Ansei Hyousuke and Yi Seo-Yeon, both of whom were engaged to marry into the House of Qian, were taken hostage. Finally, the plot to kidnap Mingyue was a further attempt to destabilize the country. I'm afraid that at the moment, Zemao is our primary suspect."

"What should be done about it?"

Yinfeng took a deep breath. "Keep an eye on Jingli and Fengling. I do not want to suspect them of being involved in their mother's treachery. However, she left them behind while returning to Kaifeng. There are only two reasons she would have done that. One, she fears for their safety if they return with her to Kaifeng. Or two, she has a purpose for leaving them here."

"I will ask someone to keep them under surveillance," Yanggui bowed. "And what of the engagements? Zukang and Mingyue?"

"Zukang's wedding ceremony will remain as scheduled in the New Year, three months from now. As for Mingyue, his marriage shall take place on the fifteenth day of the eleventh moon."

"So soon? That is within a month!"

Yinfeng nodded, "Indeed. Since Mingyue is engaged to an Oghuz Rumeli noble, your father has requested Aysun Sultana's presence at the ceremony. It will be a historic occasion, marking the first union between East and West. Aysun Sultana is returning to Constantinople in the New Year, therefore we have decided to hold Mingyue's wedding before her departure."

"Will it be too soon for Mingyue? I am not sure how well he has been doing after just recently losing both parents."

"I understand that it is not ideal to hold a wedding during the mourning period," Yinfeng acknowledged. "However, Sheli went ahead with her marriage without issue. I am sure that Mingyue will also be fine."

"Is he aware?"

Yinfeng nodded. "We will also be hosting a Venesian Ball on the eve of the wedding, at the request of Lady Alaneya's father."

"A ball?" Yanggui wondered curiously. "Does he know how to dance?"

"Do not concern yourself with that. I have someone to teach him. All I need you to do is to keep an eye on Jingli and Fengling. I do not want anything else to go wrong between now and the wedding."

204

Yanggui bowed, "Of course, your Majesty."

As the Ailao princess turned to leave, someone came to mind who she thought would be a good choice for monitoring the Jiao twins for the next month. He was someone she could trust, and someone whom no one would expect either. The perfect candidate for the job. She smiled in satisfaction as she made her way back toward her quarters.

Clip, clip, clip.

The sound of light feet pattering against the ground echoed behind her. Yanggui paused. She glanced back over her shoulder down the terrace. It was empty. She continued on her way. The soft footsteps picked up once again.

Yanggui halted. "Who's there?!"

No response.

She whipped around, flinging forth a thin dagger hidden within her sleeve. The blade sliced cleanly through the air, impaling the wall at the end of the terrace with a deep thud. Once again, there was no one. However, Yanggui spotted a small black shape pinned between the knife and the wall. She approached.

As the princess retrieved the dagger, the black object fluttered to the ground. A feather. Yanggui swiped it out of the air. She cautiously eyed her surroundings. Still, no one in sight. The feather was large, longer than the palm of her hand, its bristles thick and sturdy. It seemed to be from a crow, or perhaps a raven.

Where did it come from? Yanggui had never seen any large, black birds within the palace. Besides, the terrace was covered with a roof, and there was no wind blowing at the moment. Where could this feather have come from? She turned it over in her hands.

"Your Highness!" Two soldiers came down the terrace from behind Yanggui.

"Where were you?" She scolded. "Why were you not guarding the Empress's quarters?"

"Ah…" one of the soldiers stuttered. "We were changing shifts—"

"The Empress's quarters must never be left unguarded! Even for a moment!"

The guards bowed frantically. "Apologies, your Highness!"

She waved them aside. "Fix that hole in the wall," she gestured to where she had thrown the dagger. "And don't leave Her Majesty's quarters unguarded again."

"Yes, your Highness!"

Yanggui turned to leave, clenching the black feather tightly in her hand. Something didn't seem right to her.

***

Lady Alaneya Fatima Maria froze in front of the red wooden doors of the palace. She nervously adjusted the clips in her brunette hair, brushing the stray strands out of her face.

"No need to be nervous," Azaria assured. The young eunuch stood next to the Venesian lady. His frame and height were significantly smaller than Alaneya, despite being around the same age as her.

Alaneya smiled anxiously. "I will try. It's just that this is my first time meeting with Her Highness."

"Oh," Azaria nodded. "I'm surprised you haven't met before, considering you are cousins. It's nothing to worry about! Aysun Sultana has an icy exterior, but she's really not as scary as she seems."

Alaneya gave him an unconvincing glance.

"Aha…" Azaria laughed. "You'll be fine."

The doors swung open. Aysun Sultana was seated on the terrace, overlooking the gardens and the Lake of Tranquility below. One of her servants, Dalia, stood silently at her side.

"Sultana," Alaneya hastily greeted the Oghuz Rumeli princess with a bow.

"Lady Alaneya Fatima Maria," Aysun Sultana said, "a pleasure to meet you."

"The pleasure is all mine."

At Aysun's invitation, she took a seat next to her cousin.

"I am pleased to announce that I will be attending your wedding celebrations later next month," Aysun smiled.

"Oh…" the Venesian feigned a weak smile. "I…express my gratitude. It will truly be an honour to have you present at such an occasion."

"A momentous occasion!" Aysun exclaimed. "A union which will mark the ties between Constantinople and Qiantang, one which shall solidify the alliance between our two great empires. With the East and the West bound together by the vows of marriage, who can dare oppose us?"

Alaneya laughed nervously.

"Are you not in agreement with this arrangement, Lady Alaneya?"

"Nothing of the sort," Alaneya answered quickly. "Whatever decision has been made between Constantinople and the Yue Dynasty, I will honour it. I swear my loyalty to the throne of your father, Sultan Osman VI, and none other than him."

Aysun smiled in amusement. "That is not what I meant. What I was implying was that perhaps you did not wish to wed Mingyue. Perhaps you have fallen for someone else…?"

"Of course not, Sultana—!"

"Xi Shenzhong," Aysun said simply.

Alaneya paled at the mention of his name. "Sultana, I think you are mistaken—"

"Do not take me as a fool," Aysun smiled gently. "I do not appreciate being lied to."

"I…I apologize, Sultana. I did not want you to be angry—"

"Nonsense. Why would I be angry? We cannot control who we fall for, can we?"

"I…suppose not, Sultana…"

"However, we still must recognize our responsibilities. Peasants marry for love, but nobles marry for something greater than themselves."

Alaneya nodded slowly. "I understand, Sultana."

"Good, good. I am happy to hear that."

There was a light tap at the entrance to the terrace. Azaria peeked his face out. "Sultana, someone has summoned Lady Alaneya to the gardens."

"It seems you are popular today," Aysun raised an eyebrow at her younger cousin. "Well? What are you waiting for?"

"Ah…yes. Of course," Alaneya bowed politely. "Please excuse me."

"What a strange girl," Aysun smiled in amusement after she had left. "It's hard for me to see that the two of us are related."

Azaria laughed nervously. "She is a lot like her mother."

Aysun nodded. "Indeed. Indeed, she is."

VIII. Unity and Separation

Alaneya stepped out into the gardens, a gentle breeze greeting her as it rustled through the crisp autumn air, sending leaves swirling to the ground. She couldn't imagine who could be asking to see her until she felt someone place a crown of twigs fashioned together on her head.

"Your Highness," Shenzhong flashed a smile.

"A-Shen!" Alaneya gasped in surprise. She quickly removed the crown from her head, nervously scanning the area to make sure no one was watching them. "What are you doing here?!"

Shenzhong gave her a quizzical glance, taking hold of her hand. "What's the matter? Am I not allowed to see you?"

She took a step back, putting some distance between the two of them. "I don't want to get in trouble…"

Shenzhong smiled softly, letting go of her hand. "If you're worried about Mingyue, don't be. He isn't crazy about the idea of marrying you either. He also wouldn't be angry with us talking to each other. After all, I've known you much longer than he has."

"It's not the Second Prince that I'm worried about. Aysun Sultana…"

Shenzhong sighed. "What? The Sultana won't let you speak to other men?"

"She knows."

"Knows what?"

Alaneya's face flushed bright pink. "That you…and me…"

Shenzhong laughed awkwardly, scratching the back of his head. "What? There is nothing between us. Why would she have anything to worry about?"

"Ah…never mind…" Alaneya grew silent. Her voice at this point was barely more than a whisper.

Shenzhong smiled, "My lady, you have nothing to worry about. If you get into trouble with Aysun Sultana, I will speak with her."

All that Alaneya managed was a slight nod.

Shenzhong's tone grew serious. "I know that neither you nor Mingyue expected this marriage, especially so soon. But I can assure you that there is nothing to be afraid of. Mingyue might seem a bit intimidating and distant at first, but once you get past all that he's very kind-hearted. He's a lot like you, in many ways."

"You think I'm…intimidating…?" Alaneya retreated backward in embarrassment.

"Ah, that's not what I meant," Shenzhong assured. "What I meant is that you might seem that way at first."

"I seem intimidating…" She repeated in a softer voice.

"No, no, at least not to me," the prince added quickly. "I've never seen you that way."

They both grew silent for several moments before Alaneya decided to change the conversation. "You asked to see me here?"

Shenzhong nodded. "I did."

"For what reason?"

Shenzhong seemed confused by her question. "My lady, do I need to have a reason to see you?"

Alaneya paused. Something was off. She sensed the presence of a third person in their midst. Glancing past Shenzhong, she caught sight of a figure leaning against one of the terrace pillars. The individual's face was shrouded in darkness, and from their slim build, it was difficult to tell whether it was a man or a woman. However, one thing was clear—from their high collar and buttoned-up attire, Alaneya knew for certain that it was an Oghuz Rumeli subject. How long had they been standing there?

Alaneya lowered her voice. "Don't look now, but we are being watched."

Of course, Shenzhong's first instinct was to whip around. But the shadowed figure moved quicker, slipping into the darkness before Shenzhong could catch a good glimpse of them.

"Spying on a Yue prince," Shenzhong mused.

There was no response.

"A-Shen…" Alaneya whispered nervously. "Perhaps I should leave…"

Shenzhong ignored her. "Need I remind you that this is the Imperial Palace of Wuyue? Who dares to lurk in the shadows and listen to a private conversation?"

"Shenzhong, it's an Oghuz Rumeli subject," Alaneya cautioned.

"I don't care who it is," the prince's tone grew harsher. "Even if it is Aysun Sultana herself."

There was still no response. Whoever had been there had already disappeared.

"Shenzhong, we should leave—"

Shenzhong took Alaneya's hand and began leading her in the opposite direction. "Yes, perhaps we should."

"I meant separately," the Venesian noblewoman clarified, halting in her tracks.

Shenzhong stared at her. "Why?"

"It's best for both of us," though it pained her to admit that fact, she knew it was true.

Shenzhong paused, glancing at the shadows and then at Alaneya. He forced a weak smile. "If that is what you wish for, my lady."

Without another word, he headed off on his own. Alaneya held back tears as she watched him go. Shenzhong's words from earlier came back to her: *There is nothing between us.*

Was that really true? Did he really see her as nothing more than a friend? She couldn't think about that. Not anymore. She was engaged to marry someone else, regardless of how she felt toward Shenzhong or how he felt in return.

Peasants marry for love, but nobles marry for something greater than themselves.

***

A light knock at the door interrupted Mingyue as he strummed his fingers across the guzheng.

"*Mnn*," the prince nodded. "Come in."

211

Hansini's face peeked through the door. "Your Highness, there is someone to see you."

"Who?"

"Lady Ramanantsoa. She's waiting in the southern garden."

Mingyue, accompanied by Hansini and Olekina, arrived in the gardens a few minutes later to find not only Lady Ramanantsoa but also Selah and Neili.

Olekina locked eyes with the Sogdian dancer. "Why is he here?" He glared.

"Wu Liqing," Selah smiled. "Good to see you again."

"Selah…" Mingyue said. "Lady Ramanantsoa…what are you doing here?"

Arivesto clapped her hands together. "The Empress has requested that I teach you ballroom dancing for the Venesian ball that is scheduled for the night before the wedding ceremony."

"No," Mingyue said without hesitation.

Neili sighed. "Told you he'd say that."

Arivesto smiled, "It's the Empress's decision, not mine."

"It is not customary for Yue nobility to dance," Olekina pointed out. "Especially not men."

"Exactly," Mingyue nodded in agreement.

"However, you also cannot disobey the Empress's orders," Olekina added.

Mingyue stared at him in disbelief. "You agree with this—?"

The young guard bowed. "I apologize, your Highness. I must obey the Empress's will over yours. Lady Ramanantsoa, you may teach him."

"My pleasure!"

Mingyue froze, standing awkwardly in place as Arivesto approached. "What are you doing—?"

The next thing he knew, his right hand was clasped in Lady Ramanantsoa's left, and his right hand was held down by her waist.

The Merinan noblewoman spun them around in a slow and steady circle.

"Lovely, lovely," Selah clapped.

Arivesto continued spinning the two of them around, gradually picking up the pace. Mingyue, however, wasn't used to moving in such a manner. The edge of his robes was caught underfoot, and the next thing he knew he was falling. The Second Prince landed hard on the ground. Arivesto attempted in vain to stifle her laughter.

"Your Highness!" Olekina rushed over.

"This could take a while," sighed Neili.

"If I may point something out," Selah interrupted. "The Second Prince seems to have no skill at either dancing or sparring."

Hansini rolled her eyes. "No need to state the obvious."

Selah continued. "But I believe I may have found the culprit!" His hand shot forward, pointing an accusatory finger at Mingyue's legs. "Your robes!"

Everyone turned to him in confusion.

"You see, these robes are no good for dancing, nor are they adequate attire for sparring in," Selah explained. "No wonder you're tripping and falling over all the time!"

Hansini crossed her arms, "Then what do you suggest?"

Selah spun around, gesturing to his own outfit. "Perhaps something like this? Trousers are much more maneuverable and efficient when it comes to dancing and fighting."

Mingyue winced. He didn't want to imagine himself dressed in such a fashion.

Hansini shook her head. "I don't think such attire is suitable for the prince to wear."

"Perhaps not this style specifically, but something similar. Besides, my clothing may be a few sizes off for the Second Prince."

"Indeed," Arivesto nodded in agreement. "Prince Mingyue has a thin frame but a tall figure." She snapped her finger. "Aha! I know exactly where we can find the perfect outfit for you!"

Mingyue let out a sigh. "And where is that?"

"The Norden prince!"

IX. One, Two, Three

14/10/18th Year of the Golden Dragon Emperor

Year of the Wooden Goat

"It's too tight," Mingyue complained.

Neili took hold of the prince's collar, fixing the last button into place.

"It's not," Arivesto assured. "This is how it's supposed to be. You're just not used to it."

Hansini held up a mirror in front of the prince's face. Glancing up and down at his reflection, his face flushed red in embarrassment.

"I look ridiculous."

He was dressed in a black suit lined with golden hems and buttons. The black pants he wore weren't tight fitting but also weren't as loose as what he was used to wearing underneath his robes.

"I can't wear this," he complained quietly to himself.

"May I see?" Erik's voice called out from the courtyard.

Just as Arivesto had suggested, they had gone to the Norden prince's quarters in search of adequate attire that Mingyue could wear for ballroom dancing. Erik had been more than happy to lend his outfits for the Yue prince to try on.

Mingyue frantically rushed to block the entrance, "Don't come in—"

Erik had already pushed open the doors, stepping into the room alongside Caleb. His eyes lit up.

"Your Highness, it looks good on you!"

Mingyue wanted to disappear at that moment. "Please don't look." He held up the robes he'd been wearing earlier, covering himself with them so that Erik couldn't see.

"Embarrassed?" The Norden prince chuckled, lowering Mingyue's arms. "No need to be."

Mingyue's eyes remained downcast. His face flushed red. "I feel…naked…"

Arivesto burst into laughter. Erik gave Mingyue a crooked smile.

Neili spoke up. "With all due respect, your Highness, perhaps black is not the best colour."

Mingyue muttered. "I like black—"

"Ah, yes!" Arivesto shouted in agreement. "After all, red and gold are the colours of marriage!"

"How about that one?" Hansini suggested. She pointed toward a red and gold outfit hanging in the Norden prince's wardrobe.

Erik turned to Mingyue expectantly. Well?"

Mingyue's expression fell blank. "Fine."

"Great!" Erik smiled. "Then take this off and we'll get you changed into that."

He reached forward, beginning to unbutton the top of Mingyue's suit.

"W-what are you doing?" The Yue prince took a nervous step back.

"*Hmm?* You can't try on the other outfit until you take this one off first."

Mingyue's face burned red in embarrassment. "I...I know that. But not with you here!"

Erik glanced around the room at everyone else in confusion. "What about them?"

Caleb sighed. "That's different, my lord. These are Prince Mingyue's servants."

"I'm not a servant," Arivesto pointed out. "But I've known Prince Mingyue a long time." She nudged Erik. "Once he's more comfortable around you, I'm sure he won't be embarrassed having you see him undress either!"

Mingyue fumed. "You—!"

"Alright, that's enough," Hansini took Arivesto by the arms, leading her to the door. "You're not helping."

"Hey!" The noblewoman protested.

Mingyue breathed a sigh of relief as the two of them disappeared into the courtyard.

Caleb turned the Norden prince around as Neili approached Mingyue and began undoing the top of his shirt. The black suit slid off the Yue prince's thin frame. Neili hastily draped the red suit over his shoulders, fastening together the golden buttons.

"May I look now?" Erik inquired.

Mingyue glanced at his reflection in the mirror. This outfit wasn't as tight as the last, but still wasn't as loose as the robes he was used to wearing.

"Ready!" Neili announced.

Erik slowly turned to face them.

Mingyue shifted around uncomfortably. "Stop staring."

Erik took a step forward, raising his hand and gently resting it against Mingyue's forehead.

Neili stood awkwardly beside the two, blushing furiously as he glanced back and forth between them. "Y-your Highness...what are you doing...?"

Erik carefully combed the loose strands of hair out of Mingyue's face. He then reached behind the boy's neck, brushing his long dark hair over his left shoulder.

"There," he smiled, satisfied. "Oh, one more thing. Caleb, bring it over."

The brunette boy approached with a suitcase in hand. Clicking it open, Erik revealed a wide-brimmed hat matching Mingyue's outfit, adorned with a single black feather draping down over the rim. He carefully adjusted it onto Mingyue's head.

Mingyue blinked. "What is this?"

He couldn't bring himself to observe his reflection in the mirror. He felt ridiculous and probably appeared that way as well.

"Venesian nobles wear these sorts of hats," Erik explained. "It goes with the style of the outfit."

"Your Highness, I know you think it looks strange, but I believe this attire is fitting for you," Caleb said. "It suits you better than it does Prince Erik. Perhaps you could even pass off as a Venesian nobleman."

Erik crossed his arms and pouted. "Hey! Are you saying I don't look good in that outfit?"

"I didn't say that," Caleb assured. "I simply said that it suits Prince Mingyue better. And as a final touch," he knelt before the prince, presenting him with a pair of folded white gloves.

"Gloves?" Mingyue asked. "It's not winter."

"It is customary for Venesians to wear gloves when engaged in formal events," Caleb said. "Plus, Lady Alaneya is related to Aysun Sultana. I am not sure how strict they will be in having the bride and groom abstain from physical contact before the wedding ceremony."

"I see," Mingyue nodded, slipping the gloves over his hands.

"So," Erik interrupted. He extended a hand to Mingyue. "Are you ready to dance?"

***

"One, two, three. One, two, three." Selah clapped rhythmically as Mingyue and Arivesto carefully shifted their feet, weaving in and out as they circled the courtyard. "That's it!"

Mingyue was growing dizzy as they spun. However, he did admit that it was much easier to dance in the Venesian outfit than in his regular attire. He no longer had to worry about the baggy sleeves or flowing length of the robe getting in his way. Just as he thought he was getting the hang of it, he rolled his ankle, stumbling forward into Arivesto and sending the two of them sprawling through the air. Luckily for Lady Ramanantsoa, Selah was quick to react. The Sogdian dancer swept toward them, scooping up the noblewoman before she hit the ground. Unfortunately, for Mingyue, Selah didn't catch him. The Yue prince quickly found himself face-first in the dust.

"Your Highness!" Neili called out.

At the same time, Erik shouted, "Mingyue!"

They rushed over, helping him up. Mingyue brushed the dirt from his suit, narrowing his eyes at Selah.

"What?" Selah smiled innocently. "It was either you or Lady Ramanantsoa. I wasn't about to let a lady get herself dirty because of your clumsiness."

Arivesto laughed. "I appreciate it, but it's more important to preserve Prince Mingyue's dignity than mine."

"Oh?" Selah raised an eyebrow. "Is it dignified for me to be coming to the prince's rescue like he's some damsel in distress? I think what Prince Mingyue needs is for me to demonstrate how dancing is *really* done."

He let go of Lady Ramanantsoa. In the blink of an eye, one of his hands was clasping Neili's, with the other wrapped around the young eunuch's waist.

Neili's face burned brightly. "What are you doing?!"

"Demonstrating," Selah said simply. He twirled the two of them around, gracefully weaving and directing Neili with the momentum of his body. Selah's skill meant that Neili didn't even need to know where to step or which direction to move in. Selah simply swayed the two of them in such a fashion that Neili's body naturally gravitated in a manner that matched Selah's.

"Why me?" The young eunuch protested as they danced around. His face was beet-red in embarrassment.

"Lady Ramanantsoa is the Second Prince's partner," Selah explained. "Plus, you were my dance partner during the Moon Festival. I'm already familiar with your body and how it moves."

"Don't word your sentences like that!" Neili stammered.

Selah's lips curled up into a sly smirk. "I apologize. Have I said something wrong? You must excuse me, but the Wuyueyu is not my native tongue."

Neili seemed as if he wanted to smack the dancer across the face, but with his hands being held tightly in place by Selah's grasp, he was unable to move them to his will. After a few more moments, the two of them ceased their dancing. Selah bowed dramatically before the others. Neili, on the other hand, shrunk back to hide his embarrassment.

"That's how it's done." Selah pulled Neili close again just as the young eunuch attempted to slip away.

"Hey!" Neili protested as Selah's arms wrapped around his body.

"This is how you should hold your partner during a dance," the Sogdian explained.

"A bit too close," Neili sighed. He attempted in vain to push Selah away.

"*Mhm...*" Mingyue nodded in agreement. "I'm not sure if Lady Alaneya will be comfortable with such close contact."

Arivesto shrugged, taking a step toward the prince. "She's a Venesian. She would've learned ballroom dancing when she was young."

Mingyue stepped backward. "Perhaps another time..."

"Yes," Neili agreed, finally managing to break free from Selah's grasp. "Another time. His Highness still has other tasks to attend to today."

Arivesto sighed. "We'll need to practice a lot before the eve of the ceremony. We don't want you tripping in the middle of a dance and making a fool of yourself in front of the entire world!"

Selah smirked. "Now, now. No need to make him nervous."

They bowed in respect to the prince before taking their leave.

Neili then turned toward Erik and Caleb. "Allow me some time for him to change back into his robes. We will return your suit to you—"

"No need," the Norden prince smiled. "You can keep it until the ball is over."

"Ah..." Neili bowed. "Thank you, your Highness."

Erik smiled. "My pleasure."

He glanced at Mingyue. The Yue prince's attention was firmly fixed on him. He quickly lowered his gaze.

"Thank you...Erik."

"I believe that is the first time you've addressed me by name," Erik chuckled.

Mingyue went wide-eyed. "I...no..."

The jade-eyed prince chuckled. "Just Erik is fine, your Highness."

Mingyue's eyes met his. Silence. Erik cocked his head, giving the Yue prince a quizzical gaze. Mingyue gave in with a sigh.

"Qian Ming," he said in a low voice.

Erik's eyes glimmered. "Pardon?"

"Qian Ming," he repeated. The Yue prince folded his hands together, bowing before quickly turning to leave.

Erik blinked in confusion as Mingyue disappeared into the alleyway.

"Ah…" Neili nodded in understanding. "Qian Ming."

He too bowed to the Norden prince before heading off in the same direction as Mingyue.

"What does he mean by that?" Erik called out.

"He is saying you can call him by his birth name, Qian Ming," Neili paused. "I'm surprised. He never lets anyone call him by his birth name…"

"Oh…I see…"

Erik watched as Neili too disappeared down the alleyway. His gaze lingered there.

"Your Highness?" Caleb's voice interrupted the silence, snapping Erik back to reality. "They're gone. Should we depart now as well?"

"Oh, yes. Let's be on our way."

As the two left the gardens, a strange feeling fluttered in the Norden prince's chest.

"Qian Ming," he whispered to himself. A smile lit up on his face.

X. The Anointed One

"Lord of Heaven, Son of Heaven, Spirit of Heaven."

Mingyue entered through the doors of the temple just as the priests were finishing off the prayers, giving their final three bows before the altar.

"A-Ming," one of the older men greeted the prince.

"Your Highness," the others turned to him and bowed in unison.

Mingyue politely repeated the gesture.

"Uncle Jinxin," he addressed the man who had greeted him.

Qian Jinxin, the youngest brother of Emperor Jinlong, renounced his princely title many years ago in pursuit of the monastic life. Typically, he resided with the other monks in the Jingjiao Monastery in the mountains southwest of the palace.

The elderly man's face lit up with a warm smile. Though his long hair, beard, and mustache were graying, he still had a youthful aura about him. He had always been the most carefree and laid back out of his siblings, and thus it didn't come as a surprise to anyone when he renounced his titles all those years ago and became a monk. Being much loved, perhaps the favourite son of the previous emperor as some would say, his decision had been well-respected.

"A-Ming, I'm glad to see you here. It's been a while since you've visited the temple, hasn't it?"

The Temple of Heavenly Light included a seven-story pagoda towering above the temple complex. Located on the island at the center of the Lake of Tranquility, it was seated at the very heart of the Imperial Palace. One could only enter the temple by first taking a boat across the water. Only those who were granted permission were allowed to step foot on the island, and due to its isolation, it served as a quiet refuge from which one could escape from the noise and bustle of the palace.

"*Mhm*," Mingyue nodded, muttering softly. He gazed up at the enormous statue of the Son of Heaven, the one called the Highest Emperor, the Buddha of Light, and the Anointed One. His face was obscured by dark shadows that stretched up toward the ceiling of the temple high above. The flames of a thousand candles danced across the darkness of the room, illuminating ornately decorated walls covered with pale iconography and niches filled with statues of the bodhisattvas and Immortals.

Jinxin could easily read the young prince's intentions for coming here. He turned to the other monks. "Come, let us leave the prince to pray."

They nodded, hastily making their way toward the exit.

Jinxin directed Mingyue's attention to the right. "The Ancestral Hall is this way. Shrines dedicated to your parents have both been set up."

Mingyue nodded. "Thank you."

A tranquil silence descended on the hall as Jinxin departed. The two large wooden doors of the temple creaked shut, leaving Mingyue alone in the darkness. The flickering flames of hundreds of candles provided the only source of light. The thick scent of incense from the burners wafted throughout the entire temple, weighing heavily on the prince's senses, and casting him into a drowsy state.

His footsteps clip-clopped along the wooden floor as he made his way toward the Ancestral Hall. The Ancestral Hall was a series of corridors along the perimeter of the temple complex, housing hundreds of small shrines, each dedicated to a member of the House of Qian. The temple itself was established centuries ago and held shrines dedicated to every Emperor and noble of the Yue Dynasty stretching back over a thousand years to the dynasty's founding.

Mingyue soon located the shrines dedicated to his parents.

Qian Huamei, eldest daughter of the Golden Dragon Emperor
Born in the Celestial Year 5116
Died in the Celestial Year 5159

An Yanlu, prince of the House of An
Born in the Celestial Year 5115

A stylized portrait of them commissioned during life rested above each shrine.

Mingyue folded his hands together, carrying out his bows of respect. He lit the candles and took a burning stick of incense between his hands, kneeling before the two shrines. He had planned on coming to pray, but his mind went blank as he knelt alone in the corridor amidst the darkness. He didn't know what to say, so he said nothing. He simply knelt in silence, closing his eyes as he faced the two shrines. Only the drip of melting wax pierced the silence. Shadows from the flames danced across the walls.

Mingyue didn't know how long he'd been kneeling there. The potent incense muddled all sense of time. A gentle hand rested on his shoulder.

"Your Highness," Hansini's voice drew him back to reality.

"*Mnn...?*" He muttered. "How long has it been?"

"The incense stick has already burned up," she replied.

Mingyue turned his attention to the incense stick pressed between his palms. Indeed, it had already been extinguished. He buried it in the ashtray. Hansini took his arm, gently helping him to his feet as he noticed two figures approaching. As they stepped forward, the candlelight illuminated their faces. One was Lady Alaneya—she had shed the fancy attire that she typically wore as a Venesian noblewoman in place of a simple black dress. Her wavy brunette hair was covered in a loose shawl. If Mingyue hadn't recognized her, he could've mistaken her for a nun.

"Your Highness," she lowered her gaze.

"My lady," he returned the gesture, glancing at the young man standing beside his fiancée.

He donned a black robe, and had handsome, foreign features, with a similar visage to that of Alaneya. His gaze was downcast, a simple wooden cross hanging around his neck.

"Your Highness, this is my cousin," Alaneya introduced the man beside her. "Signore Lorenzo Belini, head of the Constantinian Missions in Wuyue."

Mingyue folded his hands together, about to bow before the young man, but Lorenzo suddenly caught him off guard. Pulling him into an embrace, he gently kissed Mingyue on each cheek. Mingyue's face flushed red as he pulled back. Instinctively, he brought his sleeve to his face and began wiping away at the spots where the man had kissed him.

"You——?"

"Ahaha…" Alaneya laughed nervously. "Your Highness, I apologize. This is a standard greeting in our culture. He isn't very familiar with Wuyue's customs."

"It…it is fine," Mingyue assured. He quickly changed the conversation. "Are you also a relative of Aysun Sultana?"

"No, I am not," Lorenzo chuckled. "My father is Patriarch Sergio II, High Priest of Rome. He is cousins with Alaneya's father."

Mingyue hadn't heard of a Patriarch Sergio II before, but nevertheless decided to be polite.

"It is an honour to meet you."

"Lady Alaneya and Signore Belini have come to pay respects to Princess Huamei and Prince Yanlu," Hansini explained.

Alaneya lowered her gaze. "I am greatly saddened that I was never able to meet them in person. But I am honoured that I was the one whom they chose for their son to wed."

Mingyue said nothing. He turned toward the shrine one last time, folding his hands together and bowing. The others mimicked the prince's gesture. As he lifted his head, his eyes rested on the portraits of his parents.

Huamei bore a solemn expression, but Mingyue could detect the warmth behind her eyes, even through a simple painting. Yanlu's lips were curved up, in a barely noticeable but slight smile. The Sogdian prince's long hair was neatly tied back. However, the palette didn't do justice to his eyes, painting them as cold and distant rather than clear and bright. Mingyue couldn't help but notice the similarities between his father's appearance and that of the Sogdian dancer Selah.

"This is your father?" Lorenzo inquired. "I didn't know he was a Westerner. This mustn't bode well for successorship to the throne, I would assume."

"A prince of the House of An," Hansini explained, "the ruling dynasty of the former Sogdian Kingdom. Many of the Yue Emperors took foreign wives. Why can't the Crown Princess take a foreign husband?"

"Who am I to say who the princess should've married?" Lorenzo mused. "However, it must be noted that the Yue, as with the Oghuz Rumelis, trace their lineage along the paternal line."

Hansini scoffed. "It is inevitable that this would result in controversy. But Emperor Jinlong has no sons, only daughters. The rightful heir to the throne would be one of her children. Wuyue has had female monarchs in past centuries."

"Perhaps," Lorenzo shrugged. "If Princess Huamei had succeeded her father to the throne, there would've been little concern. Her reign would've paved the way for her successor, a son or daughter whose paternal lineage was not of Tang origin. Princess Huamei's rule would've legitimized her children as her successors. But without her reign acting as an intermediary period…"

"That is why the Emperor has decided that my brother shall succeed him," Mingyue explained. "He recognizes the controversy that would ensue if my sister became Empress. Sheli's husband is a foreign prince."

"Your Highness," Hansini whispered. "We should not discuss this now."

"*Hmm*," Lorenzo smiled. "So *that* is why Prince Zukang has been chosen as heir instead. He is engaged to the Yi Princess if I am not mistaken. Yi Seo-Yeon?"

"Yes."

"And the Keliyetes trace their lineage along the maternal line, do they not?"

Hansini was growing visibly annoyed with the man's questioning. "Yi Seo-Yeon is not a Keliyete princess."

"No, but she resides in the court of the Keliyete Khan."

"Irrelevant," Mingyue said. "She will become Empress of Wuyue, but my brother will be Emperor."

Lorenzo shrugged. "Or perhaps, Your Highness, you would be more suitable to inherit the throne?"

"Lorenzo!" Alaneya scolded. She quickly turned to Mingyue and bowed. "I apologize for his words."

Mingyue blinked in confusion. "I think both of my siblings would be better candidates for succession than I. I respect the Emperor's decision."

Lorenzo smiled. "It was just a thought, your Highness. Forget I said anything."

Before departing the hall, Alaneya paused before another shrine. She folded her hands together, giving a short bow.

"My lady?" Mingyue noticed her lagging behind. He glanced at the shrine she stood before. On a plaque above the shrine was the name of the deceased in ornate golden characters. Qian Jinling—the Emperor's elder sister.

"I just wished to pay my respects," Alaneya said apologetically.

"Ah, of course," Mingyue replied.

He felt guilty. Huamei and Yanlu, the Crown Princess and her husband, had been the most prominent victims of the Qiantang Festival Massacre. But there had been others killed in the attack— Narsieh's father, Rajah Devaiah, Princess Ahi, Qian Jinling. Mingyue felt as if he hadn't given the others their due respect.

He reached for two incense sticks, igniting the tips. Then he extended his hand to Alaneya.

"Here."

Alaneya blinked, hesitating for a moment before taking one of the sticks from the prince. They folded their hands together, bowing three times to the shrine.

"Did you know Princess Jinling?" Mingyue wondered.

"Oh…yes…" Alaneya nodded. "I admired her very much. A-Shen did as well."

"A-Shen…?" Mingyue repeated softly.

"Ah…I mean Prince Shenzhong," Alaneya quickly corrected herself. "Prince Shenzhong admired her very much as well."

She turned her face away in an attempt to hide the fact that she was blushing.

Mingyue couldn't help but flash a slight smile. A-Shen was an affectionate nickname for Shenzhong, but Mingyue had never actually heard anyone outside the family refer to him as such before. He knew that Alaneya and his cousin were close, closer than they would let on to anyone else. But he didn't wish to intrude on her personal life.

Perhaps the way she felt toward Shenzhong was the same way he felt toward Erik.

***

In silence, they proceeded back to the main hall, where the giant statue of the Son of Heaven sat cross-legged on a lotus flower. With one raised hand, he pointed toward the heavens; with the other he held a smaller lotus, a simple golden cross rising from its center. At the very center of that cross was a simple orb, glowing with a crimson hue. That orb was said to be an ancient relic, containing the very blood of the Anointed One himself. It had been in the possession of the House of Qian since the very founding of the dynasty.

Mingyue and the others lined up with their hands folded. Just as they were about to bow, however, the doors to the temple swung open.

"Your Highness! There you are!" Amaru exclaimed. The Tahuantinsuyu prince hurried toward them.

Kanen followed in tow, shaking his head in embarrassment. "This is a sacred place. You shouldn't be running or shouting so loudly." His scolding tone changed to an apologetic one as he bowed to Mingyue. "Your Highness, I apologize. He insisted on coming here to see you."

"Aha," Amaru laughed nervously. "I'm sorry, I didn't realize this was a temple!" He stared at the statue of the Son of Heaven, glancing at it up and down. "Is this your god? Praise be to thee, God of Wuyue!"

Amaru threw himself to the ground, prostrating before the statue.

Lorenzo winced. "Your Highness, that is not a god."

Amaru looked up in confusion. "It's not?"

"It is a depiction of God, but is not God himself," Lorenzo explained.

"Oh, I see!" Amaru nodded. "What is he the god of? The god of Tahuantinsuyu is Inti, God of the Sun."

"The Son of Heaven is the Anointed One," Lorenzo proclaimed. "God of Healing, God of Light, the God of Forgiveness and Mercy. The God of New Life, and of Conquest over Death. He is not a god, but *the* God! God over all things seen and unseen."

"*Hmm*," Amaru thought about that. "I see. So that is why you call him the 'Son of Heaven.' Because he is the king of all the gods!"

"Indeed," Kanen said.

He folded his hands together. Amaru mimicked the gesture. In silence, the six of them bowed three times in sync toward the statue.

As they exited the temple, Amaru hurried back toward the boats. "C'mon, your Highness! You can ride in my boat. We can head straight to the gardens from here to practice your spear-wielding skills.

Hansini spoke up in response. "I apologize, your Highness. The Second Prince has a meeting with the Sassanian Prince today."

Amaru slumped in disappointment. "Aw, really? I was looking forward to training!"

Kanen raised an eyebrow. His gaze met Hansini. "A meeting? I wasn't informed of this."

Hansini narrowed her eyes. "I'm sorry. I didn't know you wished to be informed."

"Hansini, next time please inform Kanen and the others if there is a change in my schedule. We don't want to create confusion."

Hansini was surprised that the prince had referred to them by their birth names.

"Of course, Your Highness," she bowed before turning to Amaru. "Your Highness, may I request that you take Lady Alaneya and Signore Belini to the Palace of Lunar Serenity. She will be dining there with Prince Mingyue this evening."

"Of course!" Amaru smiled.

Mingyue bowed to the others one last time before parting ways. "What does Prince Niexia want to see me for?" He inquired as he stepped into his boat.

"Tea," Hansini responded. She pushed off the dock with a long, bamboo pole. "Other than that, he did not specify what he wished to discuss."

XI. Around the Tea Table

15/10/18th Year of the Golden Dragon Emperor

Year of the Wooden Goat

Their boat docked at Prince Narsieh's residence at the Palace of the Eternal Sun, at the southern shore of the Lake of Tranquility. He hadn't been to this side of the palace since before the Qiantang Incident. In the distance, he could see the tiled rooftops of Huamei's wing of the palace. He'd been purposefully avoiding coming here since that day. It was too painful to see his mother's palace now sitting empty.

"Your Highness," a servant hurried down the dock to greet Mingyue and Hansini. "This way, please."

Mingyue and Hansini followed the servant down the terrace, strolling alongside the garden complexes. A crackling sound mumbled in the distance—an eternal flame burning in the prince's private Fire Temple. They stepped through an opening and paused before the door that lay beyond.

"Prince Narsieh will be with you shortly," the servant said, taking his leave.

"I will wait for you here," Hansini said as Mingyue turned toward her. "It should only be about an hour or so. Then we need to head back to the Palace of Lunar Serenity to get you ready for your dinner with Lady Alaneya tonight."

Mingyue nodded. He pushed open the door to the room and stepped inside. To his surprise, there were already two people seated at the low tea table in the center of the room. Prince Sundar's head was downcast, his eyes closed in what seemed to be a meditative position. Xi Chengxin's gaze was fixed out the window of the room, staring longingly into the distance. Mingyue's entrance caught both of their attention.

"Uncle Chengxin, Prince Sundar," Mingyue paid his respects to his mother's cousin and the Karnatan Prince.

"Your Highness," they both folded their hands together as they held their teacups, bowing from their kneeling position.

"Prince Mingyue," Narsieh's voice spoke from behind. He entered from an adjoining room to the left. "Just in time. Come, sit."

Mingyue took his position at the foot of the table, between Chengxin and Sundar. Narsieh was seated by the window across from him. A servant hurried in to pour them some more tea. Mingyue gently blew on the cup before taking a sip.

Sundar shifted nervously. "Your Highness, I am honoured to be here, but may I ask why you've invited me?"

Indeed, Mingyue found it strange that Sundar was here. After all, he was not a member of the Yue Court like the rest of them, and Mingyue had assumed that Narsieh wished to discuss political matters.

The Sassanian Prince smiled. "The four of us all have something in common, do we not?"

Mingyue glanced at the others. It took him a moment to realize what he was talking about.

"We all lost someone in the Qiantang Incident," Narsieh said. "For me, it was my father. Prince Chengxin, you lost Princess Jinling, your mother. Prince Sundar, your father-in-law, and your wife. And Prince Mingyue, you lost both your parents."

Mingyue felt as if a fresh wound were being opened.

Narsieh continued. "It is clear to me that the events of these past few months are not unrelated. The Qiantang Incident took place simultaneously with the uprising in Qinglong. The Ansei Prince and Yi Princess, both engaged to marry into the Yue Court, were taken as captives. Luckily, they were able to escape. Additionally, the Karnatan court has descended into chaos after rumors that Rajah Devaiah and Princess Ahi's death had come at the hands of Karnatan rebels."

Chengxin traced his finger along the rim of his teacup as he addressed Narsieh. "However, it is obvious from the attempted kidnapping of both yourself and the Second Prince during your father's funeral that it was not Karnatan rebels who were responsible. They were framed."

232

"Indeed," Narsieh nodded in agreement. "And I am of the opinion that Emir Abdullah was also framed."

Sundar paused before taking a sip of his tea. "The Emir was framed? How could you say that when he was the one who kidnapped you?"

"Was he though?" Narsieh wondered. "True, we were brought to his residence, but if it really was the Emir responsible for the kidnapping, how could he be so careless as to have brought us to a place where he would be exposed had he been discovered? There are two possibilities. One, Emir Abdullah made a very unwise decision leading to us discovering him as the culprit. Or two, he was framed by someone."

"Killing two birds with one stone," Chengxin mused.

Sundar turned toward him with concern in his eyes. "Pardon? Could you elaborate?"

"If Emir Abdullah was indeed framed, it is clear that someone wished to eliminate him. But why? Well for one, Emir Abdullah has been a vocal opponent of Khorasani's expansionist policies. Therefore, the mastermind behind the Qiantang Incident accomplished two things in regard to Karnata. For one, it fractured the Karnatan court, dividing the empire and making foreign infiltration and conquest a plausible outcome. Secondly, it framed the attack on Emir Abdullah, removing the leading critic of Khorasani's policies from the equation."

Sundar took a deep breath, "So you think that the Khorasani elite framed him?"

"That seems like the most likely scenario," Narsieh nodded. "Now there is no one in the way to resist their expansion. And with Karnata now divided, they can swiftly sweep into the northern territories, taking Punjab, Gujarat, perhaps even further south."

Sundar shifted nervously in his seat. "I have to get back there as soon as possible."

"We will do our best, your Highness. Unfortunately, that will be difficult now that our forces have been wiped out in Qinglong. It will be impossible for any ships to pass through territory held by the rebels.

And over the past few days, I have heard reports that simultaneous rebellions are breaking out in the south. The capital itself remains under curfew to ensure that further violence doesn't ensue. All in all, the empire has become increasingly unstable since the Qiantang Incident. The Emperor still lives, but the fact that he was maimed in the attack showed to the people and to the world that the Yue Dynasty is not as strong as it might seem. His Majesty has been unable to participate in court affairs since his injury. Once a successor takes the throne, order can finally be restored to the empire."

"My elder brother," Mingyue stated. "Qian Zukang will be the one to succeed the Emperor."

He didn't appreciate how everyone was avoiding mentioning Zukang by name. There seemed to be a hesitation in accepting his elder brother as the Crown Prince ever since Jinlong had appointed him as successor to the throne.

Narsieh's eyes met Mingyue, "Your Highness, you look like there is something else you wish to say."

Mingyue's fingers fiddled with the teacup. "I am confused as to why you invited me here."

He didn't mean to come across as rude, but he didn't understand why he needed to participate in a discussion on Karnatan affairs.

"Ah, I apologize, your Highness," Narsieh folded his hands together and bowed. "I thought that perhaps you might be able to offer us some insight."

Mingyue glanced at the Sassanian Prince quizzically. It was rare that others asked him for insight.

"Your Highness," Chengxin's eyes lit up as he turned to Mingyue. "You are engaged to marry the cousin of Aysun Sultana. Perhaps we could use this newfound alliance to our advantage and request that the Oghuz Rumelis send their fleets to defend Karnata against a Khorasani invasion."

"Unrealistic," Mingyue shook his head. "Why would the Oghuz Rumelis put themselves at risk for our allies? If I made that request to Aysun Sultana, it would only strain our relations."

"Ah, but you forget that the Oghuz Rumelis also have border disputes with the Khorasanis," Chengxin pointed out. "They also seek to expand their territories in the Southern Ocean. Who knows? Perhaps if they are willing to assist our allies in Karnata, the Yue Court will be willing to lease them a port or two in the Malabar Protectorate or Zanzibar."

He took a sip of his tea.

Sundar chimed up. "Likewise, I would be willing to give the Oghuz Rumelis a port city on our west coast if they assisted us."

Mingyue's gaze met each of them. He knew that their offers would be too tempting for the Oghuz Rumelis to turn down. However, was that really in the best interest of Wuyue? He brought this question up.

"It's simple, really," Chengxin said matter-of-factly. "The Empress has vowed to send Wuyue's support to Karnata in an event such as this. Our fleets positioned in Malabar and Melaya are prepared for deployment immediately upon the Emperor's orders. However, if we have the Oghuz Rumelis come to our assistance, our troops in Malabar are more than sufficient to come to Karnata's aid. We can redirect the focus of our remaining fleets in Melaya to Wuyue. Thus, we will be able to besiege the rebels in Qinglong from both the west as well as the east."

Mingyue took a deep breath. He didn't like the idea of being involved at the center of such a complex diplomatic situation. But, as an imperial prince, this was his responsibility. If it was in his people's best interest to marry Lady Alaneya and form an alliance with the Oghuz Rumelis, that is what needed to be done.

"I will see what I can do."

***

The meeting finished a short while later, and Chengxin and Sundar both wished their farewells to Narsieh before departing. Mingyue was about to do the same, but Narsieh called out to him just before he stepped through the door.

"A-Ming, a word if I may?"

Mingyue paused, turning to face the Sassanian Prince as he approached. A-Ming was the name others used to address Mingyue affectionately. It was the name his parents and grandparents had called him by when he was young, and occasionally his siblings and elder relatives would use the name as well. But Narsieh? He wasn't sure if Narsieh had ever referred to him by that name before.

The Sassanian Prince lowered his voice as he leaned in toward Mingyue. "I didn't want to say this around the others, but you and I both know that Zukang is…perhaps not the best candidate to ascend to the throne."

Mingyue narrowed his eyes. "What are you suggesting?"

"Nothing, nothing," the prince assured. "But I think we can both agree that Sheli would make a more suitable Empress. Or, perhaps, you would make a more suitable Emperor."

This was the second time today that someone had brought this up. Mingyue shifted uncomfortably. He had brushed it off when Signore Lorenzo mentioned this earlier—it wasn't his place to speak on Wuyue's affairs. But it was different hearing this from Narsieh. The House of Sasan was one of the most prominent families in the Yue Court; several of the previous Emperors had taken wives and consorts from among them. The Sassanians held even greater influence over Wuyue's affairs than the family of Mingyue's father, the House of An.

"I will not question the Emperor's decision," Mingyue said simply. "Had he appointed me as his successor, I would've obliged."

"This is why I think you would make a better Emperor," Narsieh mused. "You demonstrate filial piety, integrity, loyalty, and the ability to analyze a situation with diligence. You exemplify the proper balance of Yin and Yang to enact justice yet also display mercy. That is exactly the type of leader Wuyue requires right now. Your brother is an upstanding man, but I fear that he possesses too much Yang, not enough Yin."

"If I demonstrate filial piety, then I must respect my grandfather's decision to appoint my brother as his successor."

Narsieh chuckled. "That is true. But don't you think that the next Emperor should be appointed for merit, and not birth order?"

"Sheli is the most appropriate successor based on both birth rank and merit."

"You're quite stubborn," Narsieh smirked. "Stubborn and skeptical. Always thinking, always questioning. Unlike your brother, you do not take things at face value. You do not make rash decisions."

"I am unqualified to take the throne."

"Is anyone really qualified to rule a nation?" Narsieh wondered.

Mingyue paused. "Perhaps not. But it certainly shouldn't be me."

"Just give what I said some thought, how about that?"

"*Mnn…*" the Second Prince nodded his head slightly. He closed the door behind him as he left the room, turning right down the hallway, and coming face to face with Hansini.

She folded her arms together. "What did he want to see you for?"

Mingyue paused as his eyes met hers. "Nothing much. We should get going. I can't be late for my dinner with Lady Alaneya this evening."

XII. West and East

15/10/18th Year of the Golden Dragon Emperor

Year of the Wooden Goat

Mingyue took a deep breath as he stood before wooden doors. Through the holes in the door's screen, he observed a large, rectangular table in the room beyond. One cushion sat at each of the opposite ends of the table.

"You will take your place on the left," Yanggui said to him in a hushed voice. "Once Lady Alaneya arrives, you will give one another the proper greetings. Ao Neili will be the one serving you this evening. Between courses, you will engage in conversation, following the dialogue which I have suggested for you. Do you understand?"

The prince gave a hesitant nod.

"Good."

She gestured into the room. On the wall opposite to them, there was a screen, the same as the one on the door that they were peering through to see into the room. The difference was that the other screen wasn't on a door, but rather a window. The diamond-shaped holes were too small and too far apart for Mingyue to be able to see what lay beyond. These screens were designed in such a way that one could see through them if they stood close enough. However, if one was standing further back, they wouldn't be able to see anything beyond.

"The Empress is sitting in that room," Yanggui said quietly. "She will be observing everything, ensuring that this evening goes smoothly. Your job tonight is more so about pleasing the Empress than it is about impressing Lady Alaneya. The Empress has high hopes for you. If it were up to her, she would've made you heir to the throne. You were always her favourite, you know."

Mingyue paused before pushing open the door and stepping into the dining room. This was the third time today that someone had brought up the idea of him inheriting the throne. Was he that much more favourable than his siblings? He didn't understand what they saw in him.

He took his seat on the left. The table was long enough to host a dozen people for a feast, but it would only be the two of them this evening. Behind him, the slightly ajar window let in the crisp chill of an autumn breeze from the gardens outside. On the opposite side of the room was another window in front of which Alaneya would be sitting. That one offered a view looking out over the Lake of Tranquility and beyond toward the southern end of the palace. In the middle of the lake, the glow of the island's pagoda where he had been earlier that day pierced the evening shadows.

The door to the left of that window creaked open. Mingyue sat in silence as a young man stepped through—the Oghuz Rumeli eunuch named Azaria. He bowed to Mingyue.

"Your Highness, Lady Alaneya Fatima Maria has arrived," he gestured to the door as the Venesian noblewoman entered the room.

Alaneya wore a silky light blue dress of Wuyue fashion rather than Venesian. The wide sleeves of her outfit flowed gently from the breeze blowing in over the lake. She shifted nervously as she greeted Mingyue with a bow and took her seat across from him.

"My lady, you are like a spring cloud coming down from Heaven."

Mingyue cringed as those words rolled off his tongue—they felt unnatural to him. But that was the greeting that Yanggui had provided as an example when she suggested what he should say when Alaneya entered the room. She had asked him to think of a similar phrase on his own, but his mind had fallen blank, and he was unable to find any other words. Through the wooden screen, Mingyue could sense a sigh from his grandmother.

Alaneya smiled faintly. "Good evening, your Highness."

The door to Mingyue's right swung open and Neili approached with a pot in hand.

"Tea, your Highness?"

"*Mhm*," Mingyue nodded.

As Neili began to serve them, Mingyue attempted to start conversation.

"Have you been enjoying your stay in Qiantang so far, my lady?"

239

He realized it was a stupid question as soon as he'd begun speaking. Her experience in the capital had thus far consisted of the massacre during the Qiantang Festival, the outbreak of the Qinglong Rebellion, and the curfew imposed on the city to prevent further violence. It certainly hadn't been an enjoyable couple of months.

Alaneya paused, considering Mingyue's words as if they were a trick question. Her eyes flickered nervously toward the screened window and back to the prince.

"Your Highness, Qiantang is the most beautiful city in the world. I am saddened by what has taken place…"

"*Mnn*," Mingyue nodded. "I'm sorry. I shouldn't have asked that."

He took a long sip of tea, keeping the rim of the cup pressed between his lips even after he'd already finished. He didn't know what else to say.

Neili spoke up hesitantly. "Your Highness, I will bring the first dishes, if that is alright with you."

Mingyue responded with a simple nod.

A while passed without either Mingyue or Alaneya speaking. As Neili brought the dishes and they ate in silence, Mingyue could feel the stern, disappointed gaze of the Empress radiating from that screen window on the left. With his chopsticks, he picked lazily at the rice on his plate. He knew he should say something, but he didn't know what.

The young eunuch standing by Alaneya caught his attention. Wasn't he the one who served Aysun Sultana? He asked Lady Alaneya this.

"Ah, indeed," Alaneya nodded. "Aysun Sultana assigned him to my service as a wedding gift."

"I see," Mingyue eyed the young man.

Though the boy looked to be only about twelve, he assumed that this wasn't really the case. In reality, Azaria was probably around his age but simply appeared younger due to castration stunting his growth.

"What is your name?" Mingyue inquired.

Azaria blinked in surprise. "A-Azaria Nazaryan. I am honoured to soon be serving in your court, your Highness."

"*Mnn…*" Mingyue nodded. "Mr. Nazaryan, may I ask where you are from?"

"I have lived my whole life in Constantinople, but my parents are from Hayastan…"

"And how long have you served Aysun Sultana?"

"Four years."

"You speak our tongue quite well for someone who has never been to Wuyue before," Mingyue noted with curiosity.

"My parents were merchants. They traveled widely throughout the east, and even to Wuyue. They are the ones who taught me."

"*Mnn…*" Mingyue nodded.

Something about this boy's presence put him off, but he knew he shouldn't linger on it for too long. His attention flicked toward his fiancée.

"And how long have you lived in Suzhou, my lady?"

"Nearly three years. My father leads most of the trade between Wuyue and Venesia."

"And how does it compare to back home?"

The girl's face lit up with a small smile. "It is lovely. The canals of Suzhou are just like the ones back in Venesia. In fact, they even call Suzhou the Venesia of the East back home. Or perhaps we can call Venesia the Suzhou of the West."

"It does sound lovely…" Mingyue trailed off.

"Perhaps we may visit sometime," suggested Alaneya.

The prince paused. "I have never left the capital. Even the Imperial Palace itself is a place that I rarely step foot out of."

He glanced briefly out the window. In the skies above, a soft orange glow descended on the clouds. Somewhere in the west, the sun was beginning to set, but he was unable to see it past the walls of the palace and the mountain beyond.

Alaneya blinked in surprise. "Not even to Suzhou?"

"No."

"I see."

"Can you…tell me about it?" Mingyue requested sheepishly.

"Pardon?"

"Tell me about Venesia…and Suzhou…and all the other places you've been."

The request seemed to put the Venesian noblewoman at ease. She began telling Mingyue about the two cities, where there were canals instead of streets and people traveled by boat rather than carriage. She told him about the magnificent city of Constantinople, the endless expanse of sand surrounding the Great Pyramids in Egypt, and the tropical coasts of Malabar. Mingyue said nothing as he listened intently to each tale she told.

The moon was high on the horizon by the time he had eaten his fill. Distracted by her own storytelling, Alaneya had only cleared half as much food as the prince.

"Thank you for the meal, your Highness," Azaria addressed Mingyue on behalf of his lady.

"Oh…" Mingyue said softly, his attention falling on the platters of food in front of Alaneya, many of which remained untouched. "I apologize, my lady. You didn't get the chance to eat."

"Ah, no need to apologize. This evening was rather enjoyable. I am glad that I got the chance to spend it with you."

Mingyue's face flushed pink in embarrassment. "I…was happy to have you…"

As Azaria escorted Alaneya from the room, Mingyue glanced toward the screen window in the corner of his eye. He could feel his grandmother's presence behind that screen gazing back at him, shaking her head in disapproval, yet also unable to resist a slight smile. Their evening certainly hadn't gone as she had hoped; Alaneya had spoken too much, Mingyue too little. He just hoped that he hadn't managed to disappoint her too much.

As he exited onto the terrace, a familiar tune filled the air—the hum of a lone violin reverberating through the autumn breeze. He

242

paused for a moment to appreciate the composition. Each note from the strings of the instrument tugged at his heart with a yearning passion as if searching for a lost soul. Mingyue listened on, his fingers strumming lightly through the air as he imagined himself playing along on the guzheng. The violinist finished their song in solitude, awaiting the sound of the guzheng which never came. One final note rang out as the tune concluded, fading out as a gust of wind blew through. The first signs of winter had arrived as tiny snowflakes danced across the terrace.

Part V

Eternal Night

I. Jul

3/11/18th Year of the Golden Dragon Emperor

Year of the Wooden Goat

A light blanket of snow covered the gardens in an endless expanse of white. Crystalline flakes fluttered down from the pale sky above, resting gently in the prince's silky-black hair like stars in the heavens. Mingyue sat in silence on his terrace overlooking the Palace of Lunar Serenity. His eyelids were lowered, catching a couple of snowflakes in his lashes that tickled his skin.

"Your Highness," Neili spoke softly from inside the prince's chambers. He hugged himself for warmth as the cool winter air drafted into the room.

"*Mnn…*" Mingyue replied simply.

His mind was dazed as he sat in an almost meditative trance on the terrace. Neili approached to drape a sable coat over his shoulders. Mingyue's eyes slowly fluttered open as his mind was brought back to the present.

"Your Highness, it's cold outside," Neili warned. "You're going to fall ill. Your wedding is in one week, and I'm sure the Empress will not be pleased if you are sick."

Mingyue took a deep breath. The clear winter air calmed his mind. It was not common for snow to fall in Qiantang so early in the winter season. The snow-covered scene before him, unblemished by any footprints or marks, put him at ease.

"I won't be sick," he assured. "Chu Kening is providing me with herbal tea every evening. I will be fine."

Neili sighed. As if on cue, Kanen stepped foot onto the terrace with a tray in hand. He laid it onto the snow-covered table beside the prince, pouring a steaming cup of tea.

"Drink," Kanen gently lifted the rim of the cup to the Second Prince's lips.

Mingyue took a careful sip. The warm steam emanating from the cup melted the snowflakes in his lashes.

"*Mm…*" the prince savoured the flavour of the tea, one that was unfamiliar to him. "Chu Kening, what is this?"

"Cinnamon, your Highness. There will be plenty more at the Jul Feast this evening."

"Speaking of which, we best get going soon!" Neili exclaimed.

The Jul Feast was to be hosted in the Great Hall of the Palace of Heavenly Peace, just to the east of the Palace of Lunar Serenity. It was a Norden festival—in fact, the most important holiday in the Norden calendar, and thus was to be hosted by the Norden envoy. Though Mingyue typically didn't look forward to the social gatherings held by envoys, he couldn't help but feel a bit excited this evening. Jul was not a festival he had celebrated before, and he didn't know what to expect.

He left for the Palace of Heavenly Peace a short while later, accompanied by Olekina. Night had fallen fast, and the snow grew heavier with each passing minute. Olekina lit a lantern to light their path and was forced to open an umbrella to prevent Mingyue's hair from getting wet.

"I apologize," muttered the guard. "I didn't realize it was going to be this bad, otherwise I would've requested a palanquin to transport you to the feast."

"It's fine," Mingyue assured.

He took careful steps through the snow, now piled up several inches on the ground. By the time they arrived at the Great Hall, his outer garments were soaked with melting snow.

Erik's attendant Caleb rushed over to greet them as they stepped foot into the building.

"Your Highness, I'm glad you could make it. Let me take your coat and hang it to dry."

Mingyue obliged and made his way to the center of the building. Most of the guests had already gathered and stood around chatting with one another. To his left he spotted Zukang with a cup of what was likely alcohol in hand, laughing cheerfully as he threw his arm over Shenzhong's shoulders and patted him hard on the back. To his right, Sheli and Hyousuke sat around a table with some of the foreign nobles, seeming to be having a light discussion.

"I've been informed that the Empress will be unable to attend the celebration," Caleb said as he rejoined them. "Prince Chengxin and Princess Yanggui are busy as well. I believe that makes you the final guest to arrive."

Caleb guided Mingyue to the front of the room where Erik was in conversation with Aysun Sultana. As soon as he spotted Mingyue both he and Aysun turned their attention toward him.

"Your Highness," they said in unison, bowing in respect.

"Prince Erik, Aysun Sultana, *God Jul.*"

"*God Jul,*" they repeated the greeting, a Norden expression for wishing one well on the holiday.

"Your Highness, I'm afraid that Lady Alaneya is ill this evening and will be unable to join us," Aysun said.

Before Mingyue could say anything, Olekina already responded in his stead. "That is terrible to hear! Is she doing alright?"

Aysun blinked at Olekina and turned her attention to Mingyue. "She is fine. She should be fully recovered by the wedding ceremony next week."

Mingyue nodded his head slightly. "Thank you for informing me."

"Of course," Aysun took her leave.

Mingyue felt guilty for feeling relieved that Alaneya wouldn't be there this evening. It wasn't that he had anything against her, but the closer they grew to his wedding date the more uncomfortable he'd been feeling about interacting with her in the presence of others. He felt as if all eyes were on them, and that he was forced to act in a particular manner and say certain things around her.

However, his moment of relief was short-lived, as a pale-haired girl in an ornately decorated, blue fur-lined dress approached Erik from behind. Irina flashed a small smile at Mingyue as she greeted him with a bow.

"*God Jul,* your Highness. I don't believe that Erik has properly acquainted us."

Mingyue thought back to the night he had fallen over the wall and landed on top of the Norden prince. Irina had come across them and

249

nearly slapped him for mistakenly believing that her fiancé was fooling around with someone else. It wasn't the best of first encounters. Both Erik and Mingyue blushed as they recounted the event, averting their gaze from one another.

Erik laughed nervously. "Aha, yes. I apologize. Your Highness, this is my fiancée Princess Irina Aleksandrova of the Volga Roman Tsardom. My lady, this is Prince Mingyue, Second Prince of the Yue Dynasty."

"I am aware that the two of you are…close," Irina eyed them both.

Erik's face flushed. "Ah—"

"We're not close," Mingyue asserted. He and Erik shared an awkward glance. "We have only interacted occasionally since the Norden prince arrived in Qiantang."

"Unfortunate," Irina smiled. "Perhaps you would enjoy spending more time together."

Annoyance stirred within Mingyue. Was she mocking him? He found it difficult to determine her intentions based on the way she spoke.

"I'm sure the Second Prince is quite busy," Erik said. "Especially over the coming week."

"Ah, yes, I nearly forgot," Irina exclaimed. "Your wedding is coming up. I was looking forward to meeting Lady Alaneya this evening, but I suppose that will have to wait until the Venesian Ball."

"So it would seem," Mingyue muttered.

"Lady Alaneya is a lovely young woman," Erik assured. Mingyue couldn't tell whether that was addressed to himself or Irina. Perhaps both. "I've met her on several occasions on my travels to Venesia and Constantinople."

The ringing of bells signaled that the feast was about to start. Erik politely excused himself from them as the rest of the guests began heading to their seats. Mingyue found himself seated next to Irina as their meal for the evening was brought out. The Norden servants presented him with several platters of food, mostly ham and other meats that he didn't recognize. The prince politely turned these away, instead taking the few dishes of fish and vegetables that were brought forth. When they came by with mead, he inquired as to what it was and declined this as well upon discovering that it was alcohol.

"Are you sure this is enough for you?" Caleb whispered when he noticed that the Second Prince had refused most of the courses.

"*Mnn*," Mingyue nodded. "I don't have much of an appetite this evening. Also, during the mourning period, it is not customary for one to eat meat or drink alcohol."

"Ah, I see. Would you like me to get you anything else to eat or drink?"

"This will be enough," Mingyue assured.

It was a few moments later that Irina spoke up after taking a sip of mead from her chalice. "The mourning period for your parents has already come to pass, has it not?"

Mingyue paused. He had said those words to Caleb without much thought, not thinking that anyone else was listening or that they would interrogate him regarding this.

"Indeed, it has."

"Is there perhaps another reason you've declined this meal?" Irina inquired. "Is it not to your liking?"

It was true that Mingyue had never been fond of meat, especially pork. However, he rarely declined to consume it, as this was seen as bizarre, perhaps even rude. After the incident at the Qiantang Festival, however, he had been turned off meat for good. The sight of his mother's body laying on the ground, an arrow protruding from her left shoulder, and blood pooling beneath her, came flooding back to him. The nauseating scent of blood and the sight of flesh from that night were all that came to mind every time he saw meat. His distaste for meat had since turned into revulsion.

Mingyue gave Irina a simple nod. "Alcohol is also not to my taste. You may have noticed that my brother has a low alcohol tolerance. He gets that from my father. I don't wish to make a fool of myself as he has."

Across the room from them, Zukang was visibly drunk, slurring his words, and seemed as if he might fall over. He leaned on Sheli's shoulder, laughing rowdily at almost everything that was said. Sheli gently propped up her brother and smiled softly.

"A-Kang, I think you've had enough. You should drink some water."

The prince simply laughed. "More alcohol!"

Nearby, Seo-Yeon sat in silence, a stoic expression resting on her face. She took no heed to her fiancé's condition as she sipped from her mead. She had already drunk more than Zukang had this evening yet managed to remain sober. It seemed the Keliyetes had a higher tolerance for alcohol than the rest of them.

"I think the two of them are a good match," Irina noted. "They balance out one another."

"Perhaps…"

A chorus accompanied by harps and violins set the hall in a festive mood as the feast continued. It was much more casual than any holiday celebration Mingyue was used to attending. Regardless of status or class, all the guests seemed to interact with one another as equals, and many even got up to dance around with one another between courses.

When dessert was finally brought forth, Erik stood with his cup of mead in hand to give a toast.

"Before we conclude this feast, I would like to explain the meaning of Jul and why it is celebrated, for those who aren't aware. Jul marks the day on which Norden celebrates the birth of the Anointed One. In Wuyue, you celebrate this on the same day as your New Year. However, in Norden, we celebrate this on the longest night of the year, which is tonight."

From the side of the room where Mingyue had entered from, a group of about a dozen young maidens from Norden clothed in white dresses entered through the doorway, chanting a hymn in the Norse tongue. They crossed the room to Erik in an orderly fashion, their hands folded together as if in prayer. The girl at the front of the group held a burning candle in hand, with a wreath of candles resting atop the golden locks of her head. When the procession reached Erik, they bowed before their prince and the girl passed on her candle to him. Erik accepted the candle, turning to ignite the hearth along the back wall.

"In Norden, we celebrate the Festival of Jul by commemorating the martyrdom of Sankta Lucia of Syracuse. According to tradition, under the persecution of Emperor Diocletian, Lucia wore a wreath of candles on her head to light the catacombs as she worked to help those who were persecuted. The candles of Sankta Lucia represent the Star of the East which guided the Magi to the birth of the Anointed One. On the darkest night of the year, we proclaim the entrance of Light into the world. The Light shines in the darkness, and darkness cannot overcome it."

With that, the chorus began once more. Erik extended his hand out to Irina. Just as she took hold of it, the prince's eyes rested on Mingyue for a brief moment. That gentle smile on his face was quickly swept away as the couple began to whirl around the room in dance. The other guests quickly followed suit.

Mingyue, unaccustomed to being in such a festive environment, slipped back into the shadows of the room, watching over the scene as the others twirled about in pairs. Paired dancing between a couple was not a common form of dance in Wuyue. More commonly, a single individual or a dance troupe would perform a well-coordinated dance as entertainment for others. This form of dance between pairs seemed much more leisurely, but also much more intimate, than anything he was used to.

"Your Highness," Arivesto's voice caught Mingyue's attention.

"Lady Ramanantsoa," he greeted her.

Arivesto gestured to the dancers. "Is this your first time witnessing a ballroom dance?"

He nodded.

"Then perhaps we should take this opportunity to practice your footwork? Lady Alaneya is absent this evening, and it'll be our last chance before the Venesian Ball. What do you say?"

He hesitated. Practicing his dancing in the company of a few was different than taking part in an actual dance with so many others around. He was about to turn down her offer, but before he could, she grabbed hold of his hand and dragged him toward the center of the room.

"Ah, c'mon! We may as well."

Mingyue didn't want to make a scene, so he reluctantly went along with her. As Arivesto directed their movement with careful steps, all eyes in the room soon turned toward them. Mingyue's heart rate sped up at the thought that everyone was watching them. He simply focused on Arivesto, and the motion of their bodies moving in sync with one another. If his attention was anywhere else, he was sure to mess up.

Unfortunately, his attention fell on Erik once again. That familiar, warm smile had once again appeared on the Norden prince's face as he looked upon Mingyue and Arivesto twirling about the room. Mingyue's gaze then rested upon Irina. Her expression was blank as her glowing crimson eyes stared back at him. He lost his focus, tripping over the hem of his robes. Thankfully, Arivesto instantly noticed that he had lost his balance and was able to maneuver them in such a manner that instead of falling forward onto the ground, the momentum of his fall spun them around in a circle instead. Thanks to her swiftness, the pair managed to remain standing on two feet.

The song drew to a close, and Mingyue followed Arivesto's lead in bowing before the guests as the room erupted into applause. Because Arivesto had been able to cover up Mingyue's misstep, his mistake had gone unnoticed.

II. Silent Night

As the evening concluded and everyone began returning to their residences for the night, Aysun Sultana pulled Mingyue aside just as he was departing.

"Your Highness, I have a gift for you. It's from Lady Alaneya. She would have liked to be the one to have given it to you this evening, but asked me to do so in her stead." She gestured to her attendant. "Dalia, please present my cousin's gift to the Second Prince."

Aysun's olive-skinned attendant approached with a small wooden chest in hand, kneeling before Aysun Sultana as she held it up before the princess. Aysun propped open the lid, revealing an ornately carved, crystalline dove within.

"This necklace is molded from Venesia's famous Murano glass, said to be the finest glass in the world."

Dalia passed the box to Olekina. The glass dove shimmered in the moonlight, much like the snowflakes fluttering down around them.

"It is customary to exchange gifts during this season," Aysun explained. "The Venesian equivalent for Jul is called Natale and takes place next week."

"I will be sure to give her my gratitude."

Mingyue headed back to his quarters accompanied by Olekina, who once again held up an umbrella to shield them from the torrent of snow that seemed to only grow heavier with each passing moment. Just as they were about to cross into the alleyway that led west back to the Palace of Lunar Serenity, Mingyue detected movement to his right. In the distance, a hooded figure appeared from a parallel alleyway and began heading north. Mingyue paused.

"Your Highness, is everything alright?" Olekina wondered.

Mingyue didn't know why, but there was a strange feeling stirring within him as he watched that figure disappear into the darkness. They hadn't encountered anyone else since they'd left the hall, and that individual had come from the same direction as them. There was also something familiar about him—he was quite tall, and his posture when he walked was composed, like that of a noble. Could it be the Norden prince? That didn't make sense. Erik's quarters were not this far to the west, and it was also strange for him to be traveling on his own.

He knew he shouldn't intrude, but his curiosity got the best of him. Mingyue began heading off in that direction.

"Your Highness!" Olekina called out. "Where are you going?" With no response from his prince, the young guard shook his head and hurried after him. "Your Highness, you'll get covered in snow. Your Highness, the Empress will be upset if she knows you've stayed out so long. Your Highness!"

Olekina's attempts to convince Mingyue to return to the Palace of Lunar Serenity with him were to no avail.

They rounded a corner and Mingyue halted in his tracks, holding up a hand to silence Olekina.

"Your Highness," Olekina whispered harshly. "What are we doing lurking around the palace?"

Mingyue directed his attention forward. Olekina looked ahead to see the hooded figure speaking with two other cloaked individuals. They stood next to one of the many small canals that crisscrossed their way through the palace, providing easy passage for small boats to deliver cargo and transport supplies to various quarters. A simple boat, large enough to hold a few people and supplies, was docked nearby. It seemed to already be packed with several crates.

A sudden gust of wind caught Mingyue and Olekina off guard, and their umbrella was blown forth out of Olekina's grasp, landing in the snow.

"Oh, do we have a stalker?" One of the hooded figures said in the Norse tongue. Mingyue instantly recognized her voice as that of Agnes. "Second Prince Qian, is that you?"

The other two turned their attention to where Mingyue and Olekina were standing, and Mingyue saw that the hooded man he had spotted earlier was indeed the Norden prince. The third individual was Caleb.

Erik's eyes lit up as he lifted his hood. "Qian Ming, I thought you had returned to your residence for the night."

"I could say the same of you."

Mingyue's heart stirred when he heard Erik refer to him simply as Qian Ming. When they were in the presence of others, like at the Jul Feast, he had called Mingyue by his formal titles. Now that they were in private, however, he referred to him in familiar terms.

Erik gestured to the boatload gently bobbing up and down in the canal. "We're taking the leftover food from the feast across the lake."

Olekina raised an eyebrow.

Erik smiled softly. "It is customary to give gifts on Jul. Back in Norden, Jul is a time of year when the doors of the palace are thrown open to everyone—nobles and commoners alike. They feast alongside one another as equals. The next day, the king rides out on a white horse and delivers gifts to his people, typically grain, and decrees that all the churches of the empire are to distribute to the poor in their cities and villages. This season has been harsher than usual for Wuyue. I hear that there usually isn't snow this early in the season. And given the rebellion in Qinglong, food supplies from the south have been cut off. I figured the least I could do was bring some of our leftovers to the people. I have connections in the Armenian Quarter, and was planning on heading there so they can redistribute the food."

Olekina shook his head, "I'm afraid I can't allow that. It is forbidden to leave the palace—"

"I grant permission," Mingyue interrupted.

Olekina turned to him, dumbstruck. "Your Highness—"

"Wu Liqing, I will not prevent the Norden prince from serving my people. Especially at a time like this."

Olekina took a deep breath to resist becoming frustrated. The Second Prince had never been this rebellious before. "I apologize, Your Highness. The Empress's authority is above yours. Besides, it is far too dangerous to leave the palace without an escort."

"I think we can handle it," Agnes smirked as she flashed a deadly-looking dagger.

"I will have to alert you to the guards and prevent you from leaving."

Mingyue stepped toward the boat. He leaned over to pick up the last crate of food and place it aboard.

"I will be going with them, Wu Liqing. You can report me to the Empress."

"*Tch*," Olekina shook his head. "If you insist on going, then it is my duty to accompany you. I will be at fault if anything happens to you."

Agnes laughed. "No one needs to know about this. If ya don't tell anyone, ya won't get in trouble."

"I will bear whatever punishment the Empress may inflict should she find out," Mingyue said simply.

Olekina sighed. "Fine."

It wasn't long before the five found themselves all crammed onto the small boat with the crates of leftover food. Caleb pushed them off the shore with a long pole, steering them eastwards down the narrow canal.

"The guards at the Imperial Gate won't let you pass," Olekina warned, bringing up a rather important point. "How do you expect to get through?"

"There's no need for us to pass through the main gate," Caleb said.

They neared the eastern wall of the palace where the canal veered to the southeast toward the gate. Caleb instead steered the boat to the left, down a branching canal that was even narrower than the first, barely wider than their boat.

"Where are you taking us?" Olekina questioned. "This path doesn't go anywhere."

Caleb pointed ahead, where the canal seemed to end at the wall of a building. Thick undergrowth from the shore covered most of the base of the building, even the parts of it over the canal. At first glance, it seemed to be just a wall. Upon closer inspection, however, one could make out that there was an opening in the wall that was covered by the undergrowth.

Olekina's eyes narrowed. "How do you know of this? There shouldn't be any paths here that lead outside the palace."

"On the day that the Volga Roman Princess arrived in Qiantang, my lord had me go to the docks at the front gate to greet her," Caleb explained. "I got lost along the way and passed by here. I saw a young man come through the opening here in the wall."

"You saw someone enter the palace without passing through the main gate and you didn't tell anyone?"

Caleb sighed as he shook his head, "He was wearing an imperial uniform, so I figured he was a servant in the court. Plus, that was three moons ago. It wasn't until a few days ago that I checked for myself and realized that it led to outside the palace."

"We will have to cover it up. It's dangerous to have an unguarded entrance to the palace."

Mingyue's heart sank. For a brief moment, seeing the opening in the wall sparked hope inside him that maybe he would be able to sneak out of the palace this way and visit the outside world. When he was younger, he would often scour the walls, looking for a hole or a tree that he could use to escape. His mother would reprimand him for that every time she caught him.

"Be patient," she would say. "One day I'll take you outside the palace, and we can explore the world together."

Of course, that had never happened.

"It's just one small hole," Mingyue noted. "What's the big deal?"

Olekina shook his head. "Armies can't pass through here, but all you need is a single assassin to slip through the cracks. An assassin is deadlier than an army. In fact, I wouldn't be surprised if the attackers from the Qiantang Incident entered and perhaps made their escape through here."

As they arrived at the wall, Caleb pushed aside the undergrowth and vines blocking the hole. Because of the water level, they couldn't pass through while seated upright.

"We'll have to lie down to get through."

They obeyed. Caleb crouched over as he maneuvered the boat into the hole and pushed them through. Mingyue lay there in silence as the ten thousand stars flickering in the sky above disappeared the moment their boat entered the passage. The air grew still. Mingyue exhaled. Beside him, he could hear the gentle breathing of Erik only a few inches away. The only other sound to be heard was the melodic *drip, drip* of water from the ceiling. This continued for a while as Caleb steered them through the passageway, which spanned the thickness of the palace's outer wall. Then, a gust of cool air washed over them as they were propelled forth to the other side of the wall, sailing out into the West Lake. The ten thousand stars flickering in the sky appeared overhead once again.

The night was silent as Caleb directed the small boat away from the palace walls. Behind them and to the right, Mingyue could see the main gate, from where ships that had entered the West Lake from one of the canals connecting to the Qiantang River could enter the palace from. The passage they had come from was barely visible, even when Mingyue stared directly at it. Like the side from which they had entered, it was covered by the thick layer of water lilies and lotuses that sprouted at the base of the wall.

"The Armenian Quarter is closest to us, but we will still need to pass through the causeway," Caleb explained. "Given the hour and the curfew, we are unlikely to come across anyone."

The West Lake causeway was a thin strip of land that ran through the middle of the lake, connecting the northern and southern shores. It was typically used for transportation but was also a popular scenic location. At various points along the causeway were openings under which boats could pass. They made their way through one of these with ease. As Caleb had predicted, there was no one in sight. The night remained silent as they sailed toward the city.

III. The Longest Night of the Year

A gust of wind blew over the boat, stirring up frozen droplets of water that danced through the air.

Olekina turned to Mingyue, "Your Highness, please move away from the edge. You're going to get sick."

Erik shed the outer layer of his coat and gently laid it over Mingyue's shoulders.

"What about you?" Mingyue wondered.

"I'm used to the winter," he smiled. "This isn't very cold compared to back home."

Qiantang was dark as they approached, the air still and silent. Caleb began chanting a Norse hymn. Knowing that Mingyue couldn't understand, Agnes translated the lyrics for him:

> Good King Venceslav looked out, on the Feast of Stephen,
> When the snow lay round about, deep and crisp and even;
> Brightly shone the moon that night, tho' the frost was cruel,
> When a poor man came in sight, gath'ring winter fuel.

> "Hither, page, and stand by me, if thou know'st it, telling,
> Yonder peasant, who is he? Where and what his dwelling?"
> "Sire, he lives a good league hence, underneath the mountain;
> Right against the forest fence, by Saint Agnes' fountain."

> "Sire, the night is darker now, and the wind blows stronger;
> Fails my heart, I know not how; I can go no longer."
> "Mark my footsteps, good my page. Tread thou in them boldly
> Thou shalt find the winter's rage freeze thy blood less coldly."

> In his master's steps he trod, where the snow lay dinted;
> Heat was in the very sod which the saint had printed.
> Therefore, Christian men, be sure, wealth or rank possessing,
> Ye who now will bless the poor, shall yourselves find blessing.

"My mother used to sing that carol for me every Jul when I was young," Erik explained. He gazed off into the distance, reminiscing over his childhood. "It was always my favourite."

They soon arrived in the Armenian Quarter, at the southern shore of the West Lake, and Caleb steered the boat down one of the empty canals. A thin layer of ice had begun to form over the surface of the water. This was a sight that Mingyue was unfamiliar with. It was rarely cold enough in Qiantang for ice to form on the water, and even if it was, the ice was typically broken apart by waves and boats. But this year the canals were empty. At this time of night, the Armenian Quarter would normally be bustling with festivities. The streets were still decorated with glowing lanterns and wreaths on the doorways, but because of the curfew, there was not a soul in sight.

Down the canal, a towering building stood out from among the golden-tiled rooftops. Its cone-shaped roof was architecturally foreign to Wuyue, and one could tell at first glance that this building was at the heart of the Armenian Quarter.

"Surb Grigor Monastery," Erik pointed to that building. "That is where we are heading."

"You have connections in the Surb Grigor Monastery?" Olekina inquired.

"I do," the Norden prince nodded. "One of the monks is an old friend of mine. We traveled together on our way to Wuyue, but I haven't seen him since we arrived in Qiantang. He said I could come to him whenever I needed."

As the boat docked near the monastery, two hooded figures appeared down the road and began making their way over. Agnes instantly reached for her dagger, but Erik raised a hand and signaled for her to lower her weapon. The two men each wore a golden brooch depicting a dragon on the outside of their coats.

"They are Imperial Guards," he whispered.

The guards approached. "Identify yourselves. What are you doing out at this hour? Are you not aware that there is a curfew in place?"

Erik smiled and bowed politely to the guards. "We are aware. We just need to deliver a few things to the monastery, and we will be on our way."

One guard glanced past Erik at the boat, noticing the crates. "What are you delivering? It can wait until morning."

"Food," Erik explained. "It will have gone bad by morning. I am bringing this here now so that the monastery can distribute it to the community."

The guards propped open the lids of the crates, checking to see if they were filled with food as Erik claimed. But even upon realizing that he was telling the truth, they still seemed unsatisfied.

"Where is this delivery coming from?"

Before Erik could say anything, Olekina stepped between them and spoke in his place. "It is coming from the Palace, from the Jul Feast of the Norden Prince." He flashed them his brooch under his coat, identical to theirs.

The guards' eyes went wide. "You!" One of them said. "I recognize you! You're that Kunlun[30] guard who serves the Second Prince, aren't you!"

Olekina hesitated for a moment. "You must be mistaken. Why would the Yue prince's guard be here?"

The other guard laughed. "That's true. He has more *important* responsibilities than delivering food. I still don't understand how someone like him could achieve such a high status in the Imperial Guard. He was a commoner, even a criminal according to the rumors I've heard. Yet somehow, he managed to become the primary guard of the Second Prince. What are his merits? It was only because Princess

---

[30] Kūnlún (崑崙): Referring to dark-skinned slaves who were brought to China in the Tang Dynasty. Most came from Southeast Asia, but later slaves brought to China from Africa by the Arabs were often referred to as Kunlun slaves as well. Because Wuyue had abolished slavery centuries ago, those of Kunlun descent within the empire are no longer slaves but are free persons. Most have gradually assimilated into the general population over the centuries, but many maintain their unique cultural identity, especially in Qiantang's Kunlun Quarter.

Huamei showed him favour that he received his rank. Meanwhile, those of us who have actually trained and earned our titles can never even dream of achieving what he has achieved. Heaven chooses who it will bless and who it will not."

"Watch your tongue," Mingyue warned.

The guard turned to him, surprised that he had spoken out against them.

"Am I wrong?" He then looked back at Olekina. "I'm sure you too have merit yet haven't been acknowledged for it—being sent out here to deliver food to the monastery while the royal family and their inner court are feasting safely behind the walls of the palace. The rest of us are the ones who maintain law and order in the city. We're the ones who protect and serve the people. Yet what acknowledgment do we get for it? Nothing. And what have those who sit in the court done to deserve their ranks? Nothing."

"Perhaps that is true," Olekina raised his head. "But though there are many parts, there is only one body. There is one empire, but many roles to play. I am sure that the court is doing the best they can to resolve these circumstances. And we too must play our part."

The guard laughed again and shook his head. "Maybe that's what they think. 'There is neither slave nor free, rich nor poor.' Isn't that what their god says? Then why are they in the palace while we are out here? Why are they feasting while their people are starving because the trade routes have been cut off by rebel forces?"

Mingyue was about to confront the guard and reveal his identity, but one stern glance from Olekina advised him against that. Olekina addressed the guard himself.

"I understand that you are upset. And you are correct—there are many who share your sentiment. But I would be careful what I say if I were you. As of right now, Emir Abdullah is the primary suspect in the Qiantang Incident. However, even if he truly was responsible, it is almost certain that he had inside help. Perhaps from those who share sentiments such as yours."

The guard took a nervous step back. "Hah…that is ridiculous! I haven't even been to the Imperial Palace in months! If anything, it's those in the inner court who are the biggest suspects! They have the most resources and opportunity to commit such an act! Plus, many of them are of questionable backgrounds and do not have Wuyue's best interests in mind. They only wish to maintain their power and gain more."

"I didn't accuse you of being guilty," Olekina explained. "I simply said you should be careful what you say. Your words could get you into trouble."

"*Tch*," the guard narrowed his eyes.

"Come on, Jiang Chu," the other guard sighed, placing his hands on his partner's shoulder, and beginning to lead him away. "Let them deliver what they need to and be on their way."

Before leaving, the first guard grabbed a loaf of bread from one of the crates and headed off with it. Mingyue turned to Olekina in frustration.

"Why didn't you let me say anything?"

"Because you shouldn't be here," Olekina replied simply. "We don't know who we can trust, even among the Imperial Guard. Now let's bring these crates to the monastery and return to the palace."

After knocking for a while at the gates, a weary face of an elderly bearded man finally answered. At first, he seemed hesitant, worried about who could be here at this time of night. But his eyes lit up as soon as he spotted the Norden prince.

Erik smiled. "Brother Arman!"

The monk embraced Erik without hesitation, giving him a couple of pats on the back. "Your Highness! Such a pleasure to see you again!"

Mingyue was taken aback at how casually the monk had greeted Erik. He could never imagine hugging another noble, much less a commoner.

Erik laughed. "Now, now, didn't I tell you before? No need for formalities. Just Erik is fine. It's a pleasure seeing you again too, but I'm afraid this will be a short visit."

He gestured to the crates, and the monk nodded in understanding. After a few minutes of hauling the crates to the monastery, the rest of them returned to the boat while Erik remained by the gates for a little while longer to catch up with Brother Arman.

Agnes observed them for a while before leaning in toward Olekina and addressing him in a whisper. "Is it true what that guard said? Ya have a criminal history?"

"I was young," Olekina muttered. "I did what I had to for survival."

"There's no need to be ashamed about it!" Agnes laughed, gesturing to Caleb. "We both have a criminal history as well. But that's in the past. The prince gave us a second chance!"

Olekina looked at her in surprise. "A second chance…? Did you deserve it?"

Agnes thought for a moment and then shrugged. "Does anyone really deserve a second chance? That is beside the point. The point is that we were offered another chance, regardless of whether we deserved it or not. We should be grateful for it and take it as an opportunity to do better next time."

"Our prince too was given a second chance," Caleb explained. "After his parents and sister died from the Plague, he felt so alone and isolated in Norden. But during one diplomatic visit to Constantinople, he met Brother Arman, and Brother Arman became like a father to him. Since then, we have never gone back to Norden. For the past four years, we traveled with him throughout Oghuz Rumelia and the Volga Roman realms as a diplomatic envoy. Then, when Brother Arman said he would return home to Qiantang, the prince decided to accompany him. It was like he was always meant to be here—I have never seen him as happy as he has been since he came to Wuyue. This place has given him a second chance."

Mingyue pondered on Caleb's words. Erik had always seemed so cheerful and lively ever since they'd met. It was difficult for him to imagine that the prince had not always been that way.

"Then what happens when he returns home?" Olekina wondered. "He is soon to be married to the Roman princess, but surely that is not what he desires."

"He knows the role he has been given," Caleb looked on intently as Erik and Brother Arman gave their final words to one another. "Perhaps Heaven blesses nobles with lives of prosperity and security, but that life is also a curse. His duty is first and foremost to his people, not to himself."

"Even though it may not be forever, I know that Erik will always cherish the time he spent here," Agnes smiled. "Of course, we came with the intent of establishing an embassy in Wuyue, as Norden does not yet have one here. But for the first time in his life, Erik is free from the influence of Norden. For the first time in his life, he doesn't need to be Prince Erik, but just Erik."

Their voices quieted down as Erik returned to the boat. Mingyue's gaze was drawn toward the shimmer of light in the other prince's eyes, like a glimmer of hope. All his life, Mingyue had desired nothing more than to step beyond the walls of the palace—to glimpse the sunset. But Erik was someone who had seen hundreds of sunsets, who had traveled the world, and still wasn't content until he'd come to Wuyue. Now, seeing that look in Erik's eyes, Mingyue realized that maybe he'd been searching for the wrong thing his whole life. Maybe that's not really what he needed.

"Let's return to the palace," Erik smiled. It was a genuine, heartfelt smile.

IV. Venesian Ball

Mingyue sat uncomfortably in his dressing room as he anticipated the Venesian Ball this evening. Two eunuchs combed and dried out his hair as Neili applied a thin layer of makeup on his face, outlining his eyes and powdering his cheeks. Mingyue sneezed.

Neili giggled softly. "I apologize, your Highness. This is the type of makeup that is worn by Venesian nobles." He addressed the two eunuchs. "Make sure you tie his hair back. Long hair is not the traditional style for Venesian men. Wigs are common fashion, but unfortunately, we don't have any."

"I don't want to wear a wig," the prince muttered.

There was a knock at the door. Hansini peeked her head into the room. "It is almost time. Is he ready?"

"Nearly," Neili replied. "We just need to get him dressed."

He hurried over to fetch the outfit they had borrowed from Erik and draped it over Mingyue's shoulders. Then, he handed the prince something—a mask with elaborate feathers emerging from the sides. Mingyue gave him a confused glance.

"It's a masked ball," Neili explained. "Everyone will be dancing around the room, switching partners between songs. The goal is that by the time the seventh song is finished, you and Lady Alaneya would have found one another. The objective of the other guests is to try and keep you apart. The trick is that no one will recognize each other if you're all wearing masks."

"That sounds stupid," Mingyue scoffed.

Neili sighed. "It's a Venesian custom. I think it sounds fun. I would take part if I could."

One of the eunuchs snickered. "You just want another chance to dance with that Sogdian dancer."

Neili's face went bright red. "Nonsense! Why would I want that?!"

"I permit you to partake in the dance if you wish to," Mingyue said as he made his way out the door.

"I…um…" Neili fumbled for words, "I don't think it's permissible for a servant such as myself to be dancing at the ball."

"Why not?" Mingyue wondered. "As you said, we will all be masked anyway."

Despite his secret desire to partake in the dance, Neili was hesitant to accept the invitation. But Mingyue was persistent. He gave his mask to Neili and retrieved another one from the chest that he liked better.

"I…I'm not sure about this, your Highness," he stuttered.

"No need for formalities," the prince stated. "Just 'Qian Ming' is fine."

***

As they entered the hall where the ball was taking place, Mingyue anxiously expected that he would instantly be recognized. He was surprised when no one seemed to pay him much attention. They arrived later than most of the other guests and slipped into the crowd.

"I'm still not sure about this," Neili said nervously.

Mingyue's eyes scanned the room. Before arriving, he had thought it would be simple to distinguish between the guests, especially those that he knew well. But he quickly realized that with everyone donning the Venesian style of dress and masks, not to mention that many were wearing wigs, it would be much more difficult than he initially anticipated.

There were not that many young men in attendance who had blonde hair, only Selah and Erik and perhaps a few other minor guests from Venesia and the Volga Roman Tsardom. However, as he glanced around, it was a challenge to determine who was who. He spotted one man with traces of blonde hair peeking out from beneath his wig, but from this distance couldn't determine whether it was the Norden prince, or perhaps Selah.

An ensemble at the other end of the room began playing a tune. The melodic hum of violin strings filled the room, and soon guests began pairing off with one another in dance.

"Your Highness…er…Qian Ming…what are you doing?" Neili hissed. "Stop staring around aimlessly, you have to find a partner and take part in the dance!"

Unfortunately, he'd been so distracted in trying to determine who everyone else was that by the time he came to his senses, everyone else around them had already found a partner. Neili shook his head. Seeing as he had no choice, Mingyue reacted quickly by taking Neili's hand and dragging the boy into a dance.

"W-what are you doing?!" Neili gasped in disbelief.

"Shush, you're going to draw attention to us."

They carefully weaved in and out between the other dancers, Mingyue directing them closer to the violinists, where the blonde-haired man had been earlier. He spotted him again, dancing with a young woman who seemed to be about Lady Alaneya's height.

The sooner I find her the better. Then I won't have to keep participating in this stupid game.

As they drew near, he got a good glance at the man's eyes peering back at him through the mask. Crimson. It was Selah.

The song soon came to an end. Swiftly, Mingyue maneuvered them toward Selah and the girl he was dancing with. They switched partners, Selah taking hold of Neili's hands and Mingyue taking hold of the girl. As the next song began, the two pairs parted ways.

Mingyue's attention turned to the girl whose hands he was now holding. Her wavy, dark hair flowed gracefully past her shoulders, while a set of deep brown eyes gazed back at him from behind her mask. He recognized those eyes.

"Sheli…?" He said in surprise.

Sheli blinked back at him. "A-Ming…? A-Ming! I didn't recognize you! Your hair looks very different in that style, and with that outfit, you could almost pass for a Venesian!"

Mingyue managed a slight smile. "I also thought you were a Venesian—actually, I thought you were Lady Alaneya. Your hair looks different when it's wavy."

Sheli couldn't help but laugh. She gestured to the other side of the room as they continued to spin about. "I saw a girl who looked like Lady Alaneya there. Come! Let's head over."

As they moved about, Mingyue found that he was unable to focus much attention on looking for Alaneya. Just focusing on stepping in the right place and avoiding tripping over his sister's feet was difficult enough.

As soon as the song ended, they swapped partners once again. But the girl who his sister had thought was Alaneya turned out to be someone else. The next girl he danced with wasn't her either. By this point, he was starting to give up on finding her. What did it matter whether or not they found each other?

By the time they switched to the fifth song, Mingyue had given up. He took the hand of whichever girl was nearest to him. As the new song began, he locked eyes with the girl and was startled to see a pair of crimson irises staring back at him.

"Second Prince Qian," the girl raised an eyebrow as she greeted him.

"Princess Irina…?" Mingyue replied. "You recognize me?"

He found that strange, considering they'd only met a couple of times. The only reason he'd been able to recognize her was because of her distinctly-coloured eyes.

"The outfit you're wearing is Erik's," she pointed out. "I see he's lent it to you.

"Ah…yes. He did…"

Irina smirked. "I remember the first time we met. It was four years ago, at a ball in Constantinople, very similar to this one, actually. By that point, it had already been decided that we were to be engaged."

Mingyue smiled politely at her words, turning his attention down to their feet to avoid stepping on her toes. Why was she telling him all this?

"Once you're wed, why not travel with Lady Alaneya to the West?" Irina suggested. "It would be the first time a Yue noble set foot in Europe. You could strengthen ties with the Oghuz Rumelis, Volga

Romans, and Norden, and visit Constantinople and Venesia. You've been wanting to leave the palace your whole life, haven't you? It would be the perfect opportunity!"

"Constantinople…" Mingyue whispered.

"I would also be honoured for you to attend my wedding ceremony," the princess added. "It is likely to take place in two years, in Moskva."

Mingyue nearly stepped on her foot. "I…will consider the offer…"

Nearby, Arivesto was dancing with Prince Amaru. She had been observing the two since the beginning of this song and noticed Mingyue's discomfort. Arivesto took the initiative to switch partners early, letting go of Amaru and approaching the other pair.

"Your Highness! I see your dancing skills have improved."

"Lady Ramanantsoa…?" Mingyue remarked in confusion.

"The song is not yet finished," Irina protested as Mingyue let go of her hands and took hold of Arivesto's.

Amaru swooped in and pulled Irina away from them. "It's nearly finished, Princess!" He flashed a smile and wink at Mingyue as they began moving in the other direction.

"I couldn't bear watching you any longer," Arivesto smirked. "You two were so out of sync and uncoordinated—definitely not a good pairing."

Mingyue managed a small laugh. "I agree."

Arivesto nodded in the direction over Mingyue's shoulder. "Over there, on the other hand, is someone who'd make a *fabulous* pair with you."

He couldn't see who she was referring to since they were behind him, but as they turned, he caught sight of someone who matched Alaneya's profile in that direction. But the man she was dancing with was also familiar. Tall, blonde, and dressed in the royal blue of Norden—he matched Erik's figure. Mingyue was concerned that he didn't know who Arivesto was referring to when she mentioned 'a fabulous pair.'

As they drew closer to the others, Mingyue was able to catch the other man's attention. He stared into those deep, jade-green eyes. They stared back at him. Mingyue felt embarrassed, but he didn't look away. For the remainder of the song, he looked on, mesmerized by those eyes staring back at him.

Once the song changed, they let go of their partners. Mingyue moved in to take Alaneya's hands, but Arivesto was quicker. She took hold of the confused girl and the two spun away as the next song began. She couldn't help but burst into laughter at the sight of Mingyue's face.

"What? The goal is to keep you two apart! You didn't think I'd let you win *that* easily, did you?"

Mingyue and Alaneya locked eyes as the distance between them grew greater. There was nothing that could be done about it now— Arivesto had stolen their chance at pairing up for the final dance. He should've known better than to trust her; this meant that she was referring to Erik when she mentioned 'a fabulous pair.' He didn't know how to feel about that.

Everyone else had already switched partners, leaving the two princes standing awkwardly in the center of the ballroom. Erik extended his hand to the other prince.

"Well, your Highness? Care to join me for the final dance?"

He was hesitant to accept Erik's hand. What would everyone think when they saw him dancing with another man? Or perhaps that wasn't strange in Venesian custom? He had no idea. What he *did* know was that a certain Roman Princess wouldn't be happy. Already he could see her giving him a deadly glance from across the room as she danced with Prince Narsieh.

"I told you, it's 'Qian Ming,'" Mingyue reached out and grasped Erik's hand at the precise moment that Irina locked eyes on him. They commenced the closing dance.

V. The Last Dance

The last song began with a melodic strum of violins, which were joined by a Latin soprano. It was much slower than the previous songs. As they continued, Mingyue realized that the tune was familiar.

"My mother used to always sing this song for me," Erik reminisced. "*Roma*, by the great composer Floriano. Did you know he was one of Lady Alaneya's ancestors? He composed the song to commemorate the Eternal City after the Oghuz Rumeli took the city two hundred years ago. It's still popular in Venesia to this day, though I'm not sure how Aysun Sultana will feel about having it played tonight."

They both glanced over at the Oghuz Rumeli Sultana, who wasn't taking part in the dance, but instead observed from the sidelines. Contrary to Erik's concern that she would be displeased with the choice of song, she seemed to be enjoying herself. A gentle smile rested on her face as she watched over them, the first time that Mingyue had seen her with such an expression.

"It's a fitting song for the occasion, don't you agree?" Erik inquired.

"If I was dancing with Lady Alaneya, then perhaps it would be."

"Ahaha," Erik chuckled. "I meant since we've been playing this song together these past few months."

Mingyue suddenly realized why this tune was familiar to him. Though it sounded much different when played as an ensemble and accompanied by vocals, the song was unmistakably the same as the one he had been hearing recently on the nights he spent on the terrace. He would play along to the rhythm on his guzheng, following the notes of the stringed instrument off in the distance. He suddenly became embarrassed.

"I…I didn't realize you were the other person playing."

"Aha," Erik smiled. "I see."

"How did you know that I was the one playing the guzheng?" Mingyue inquired.

"*Hm…*" Erik thought for a moment. He shrugged. "I just had a feeling that it was you."

"Well, feelings can sometimes be wrong," Mingyue pointed out.

"Sometimes they are," agreed Erik, "but sometimes not."

For some reason, that caused Mingyue to blush. He was relieved that he had a mask covering his face at the moment, otherwise it would've been quite noticeable.

So far, they had not been dancing particularly close together. Mingyue's right hand was clasped in Erik's left, and Erik's right hand barely touched the other boy's waist, while Mingyue's left hand rested on Erik's shoulder. But at that moment, Erik pulled the two of them closer together, his right hand moving further around Mingyue's waist and onto his back. Their bodies became pressed together.

Mingyue's face turned an even brighter shade of pink, and this time he was certain that Erik noticed.

"W-what are you doing?"

"One of us needs to take on the role of the lady in this dance. You're a bit shorter than me and can pass more easily as a girl."

Mingyue huffed. "Is that so?"

"It is! And we're starting to get weird glances for not dancing in proper form."

"Are you sure that's not because we're two princes dancing together?" Mingyue wondered matter-of-factly.

"Do you think the others can tell?" Erik wondered. "With your long hair and a mask covering your face, they probably assume that you're a girl."

"*Tch,*" Mingyue scoffed. "I think it's this outfit that makes me look more feminine than anything else."

Erik smiled. "Maybe to you, but in Venesia and Norden this is considered to be the attire of men."

"Then what will they think when they realize that my final dance was not with Lady Alaneya, but with the Norden prince?"

"Who cares what they think!" Erik exclaimed. "You are the Second Prince of Wuyue. Can any of them even dare to question you?"

Mingyue was unable to prevent a slight laugh from escaping his lips. Erik laughed as well. The last notes of the song rang through the air and the dance came to a close. It was time to remove their masks. Mingyue's face flushed once again when he realized that everyone nearby had begun turning their eyes toward him. The looks on their faces told him that Erik was right about everyone confusing him for a girl. They all were shocked when he removed his mask and turned out to be the prince.

"It would seem that the young couple was unable to find one another during the dance. How unfortunate!" A man who had not participated in the dance and was still masked remarked. Mingyue recognized his voice as belonging to Signore Lorenzo Belini, Alaneya's cousin.

Nearby, Arivesto sent Mingyue a cheeky grin. On the other hand, he earned a disapproving scowl from Irina.

"Your Highness, I apologize!" Erik gasped as he feigned ignorance over Mingyue's identity. "I didn't realize it was you!"

Of course, Irina would not so easily be fooled by his words. She was well aware that Erik had recognized the Yue prince before the dance began. He was wearing Erik's outfit, after all.

"No need to apologize," Mingyue went along with Erik. He then turned to Alaneya, who stood halfway across the room alongside Arivesto, and in typical Venesian fashion bowed to her with one arm folded across his chest. "My lady, *Buon Natale*."

She responded with a curtsy. "*Buon Natale*, your Highness."

It was the Eve of Natale, the day that the Venesians celebrated the birth of the Anointed One. The two slowly approached one another, meeting halfway. Mingyue raised his hand and gently felt the glass dove necklace hanging around his neck, the one which Alaneya had gifted to him for Jul. He retrieved a small box from his pocket and presented it before her, popping open the lid.

"For you, my lady…" he hesitated awkwardly as he held it out toward her. She took it. Within was a necklace similar in size to his

276

own, bearing a carefully carved jade phoenix inside. "It's the Fenghuang, my grandmother is named after it. It represents the union between yin and yang."

"It's beautiful," whispered Alaneya. "Thank you. I will wear this during the ceremony tomorrow, and I hope you will wear the dove."

Mingyue smiled slightly and nodded. "Of course."

His eye caught Shenzhong in the background. The jade phoenix had actually been his idea—Mingyue went to him asking what he should gift to Alaneya. He was reluctant to approach his cousin on the matter and was afraid Shenzhong might be offended. However, his cousin had happily assisted him.

"I was going to give her this for Natale," Shenzhong said. "That was before…well…before I knew she was to be engaged. Will you give it to her for me?"

"Are you sure you want me to?" Mingyue had wondered.

"Yes. I want her to have it."

As the two cousins maintained eye contact, Shenzhong flashed him a weak smile. Another song was beginning.

"Your Highness," Alaneya said, "since we did not get the chance to dance this evening, they will probably be expecting us to take part in one now."

"Ah, I see," the prince realized. He hesitantly extended his hand out to her. "Then…shall we dance…?"

She took his hand and smiled. The other guests stood by and watched as the pair slowly waltzed across the ballroom. Toward the rear of the crowd, Zukang grinned drunkenly as he observed his brother. He sipped another cup of alcohol but lost his balance slightly as he threw his head back, stumbling to the side. Luckily, someone was there to catch him. Selah grabbed hold of Zukang's shoulders from behind just as it seemed the prince was about to fall to the floor and make a fool of himself.

"Your Highness," Selah whispered in Zukang's ear, "I think you've had enough to drink for tonight. Shall I see you to your room?"

"*Mhm…*" Zukang nodded drunkenly.

277

Selah waved two guards over and they escorted him back to his quarters, Zukang leaning on Selah for support as they walked. Their departure caught the attention of Seo-Yeon, who quietly slipped away after them to follow her fiancé, leaving behind the other guests as the festivities continued. Navigating from the ballroom at the western edge of the Lake of Tranquility to Zukang's residence in the Palace of Lunar Serenity proved to be difficult when the prince was only able to stumble along, nearly pulling both himself and Selah over the railing and into the lake a couple of times.

Seo-Yeon sighed and shook her head as she trailed them from behind.

He really needs to learn to hold his alcohol.

They arrived at Zukang's bed chambers, and the two guards stood by the door as Selah helped the prince take a seat.

"I'll fetch a servant to bring some water and get you ready for bed," Selah suggested.

"*Mm…*" Zukang groaned. "I don't wanna sleep yet."

"You need your rest," Selah explained, "your brother's wedding ceremony is tomorrow."

"*Pfft,*" Zukang chuckled. "My little brother is getting married before me. Sad that he didn't get to enjoy his bachelorhood."

"Oh?" Selah smiled. "Are you not looking forward to your own marriage, your Highness?"

Zukang smirked. "The Yi Princess is a Keliyete noble. They are not as…conservative as the Venesians. Ha ha! I'm sure she would not mind if I took a few concubines! That's not uncommon in the Keliyete Khanate."

"*Tch,*" outside the window, Seo-Yeon rolled her eyes.

Selah chuckled. "Concubinage is also common in Sogdia." He poured a cup of tea for the prince, sprinkling in a pinch of crushed herbs before handing it over. "But if I recall correctly, polygamy was outlawed by your ancestors, under the rule of Emperor Nuxia nearly a thousand years ago. It goes against the teachings of your god, does it not?"

"*Pfft,*" the prince snorted as he took a sip of tea. "I will be Emperor soon, why do I need to follow outdated rules put in place by my ancestors or by God? The Emperor of Wuyue was once viewed as the Son of Heaven before these reforms took place. The Xin Dynasty still regards their Crimson Emperor as divine. Why can't I also be a god?"

"You are ambitious indeed, your Highness," Selah smirked.

He turned to depart, but Zukang drew his attention back.

"Dance for me…" muttered the prince in a drunken slur.

"I will fetch some dancers for you on my way out, your Highness," Selah suggested.

"*Mnn,*" the prince shook his head slightly in disapproval. "*You* are my dancer. You were gifted to me by the Xin court. So, dance for me."

Selah chuckled, "Of course, your Highness."

He shed his outer coat and began his routine performance for their viewing—both the prince and the Yi Princess. From the window, Seo-Yeon observed the two from outside, stifling a laugh.

It would seem he has a taste for both men and women.

Of course, that wasn't something that was uncommon or even frowned upon among the Keliyetes or Sogdians. In Wuyue, however, it wasn't as acceptable.

Seo-Yeon was hesitant as to whether she should stay or return to the dance. As she stepped back from the window, a dark shadow fell over her, and she sensed someone's presence from behind. She turned to see a dark, hooded figure standing there.

VI. The Maiden of Venesia

The young Venesian noblewoman sat attentively in the bridal chambers, waiting for the procession to begin. A couple of bridesmaids attended to the final details of her outfit. She was dressed in silky red attire, with intricate golden embroidery. Her hair was done up and decorated with flowers and a crown, her face powdered with makeup and complete with a vermillion mark in the center of her forehead.

"Just like a Tang princess," Aysun Sultana commented as she waited patiently in the doorway.

"Sultana," Alaneya bowed her head upon noticing her enter the room.

Aysun took the Venesian noblewoman's chin gently in her hand and lifted her face. Their eyes met. "Cousin, this marriage marks one of the most important unions in the history of the world. The power you will wield will be equal to, perhaps even surpassing my own."

A nervous smile crept across Alaneya's face. Her whole life, she'd always been overshadowed by her more reputable relatives—Signore Lorenzo Bellini, son of the High Priest of Rome, and Aysun Sultana, daughter of the Oghuz Rumeli Sultan. Alaneya was simply the daughter of a merchant, niece of the Doge of Venesia. When she had arrived in Suzhou alongside her father a year ago, she never would have imagined that she would soon be engaged to a prince of the House of Qian.

She remembered the day that word of the Oghuz Rumeli envoy's arrival in Wuyue reached Suzhou. Aysun's servant Lusine presented a letter to Alaneya's father. After a few moments of glancing over it, his eyes lit up.

"Alaneya! It's a message from your cousin!"

Alaneya was completely taken aback when she learned she was to marry Mingyue. After her mother had died of the Plague a few years ago, she left Venesia with her father and set sail for a new life in Suzhou. With the brother of the Doge of Venesia overseeing all Oghuz Rumeli maritime trade in the East, their empire would quickly ascend to become unmatched by any of their rivals in the West. She never realized that she would have a role to play in facilitating this, perhaps more important than any other, by solidifying the alliance between Constantinople and Qiantang.

The young eunuch Azaria popped his head into the room, his eyes lighting up as he glanced upon the bride. "My lady, the procession is beginning shortly."

Alaneya reached out and took hold of his extended hand, slowly rising to her shaky feet.

"My lady…? Are you alright?"

Alaneya forced a smile. Her heart was racing, and beads of perspiration appeared on her forehead. She was glad that her face was obscured by a veil.

"Yes, I'm fine," she assured, inhaling a deep breath.

The foreign envoys, nobles, and the court were gathered before the Hall of Harmony as dusk descended. Security was ramped up, with three times the normal number of guards stationed along every stretch of the wall and every exit from the square. Besides those already present, no one else was getting in, and no one would be able to leave. All the guests had been checked for weapons to ensure that there would be no repeat of the Qiantang Festival Incident. Even if they were all trusted envoys and members of the court, there was a looming suspicion that someone within the palace was tied to the massacre. One couldn't be too cautious given the circumstances.

Twin palanquins sat just before the gate, the left for the bride and the right for the groom. Alaneya was seated inside on the plush, red cushions. Thin, translucent drapes covered her on all sides, allowing only a silhouette of her figure to be seen from the outside.

She sensed movement as another person entered the right palanquin. Beyond the drapes, she couldn't make out his face, but from the figure of his silhouette, she could tell it was Mingyue. As soon as both bride and groom had taken their positions, trumpets rang out from the top of the gate. The escorts hoisted the two palanquins onto their shoulders and the gate creaked open.

Between the main gate of the square and the Hall of Harmony was a line of Oghuz Rumeli soldiers flanking either side of the path that the palanquins traveled down on their way to the pavilion. They began playing a lively tune, accompanied by the deep reverberation of drums from along the walls. Dozens of flag bearers went ahead of them, as flower petals that were tossed from the walls drifted down with the wind. Each row of people turned and bowed, falling to their knees once the palanquins passed them by. The setting sun cast a deep orange glow above, beautiful yet haunting, as long shadows danced across the ground.

The palanquins stopped once they reached the steps leading up to the Hall of Harmony. The bearers lifted the curtains for Alaneya to step out. On her right, Mingyue exited the other palanquin. He was dressed in deep red robes, his long hair flowing down his back and draping over his shoulders. It was a bit unexpected to see his hair not tied up. Though Mingyue normally wore his hair open, and this was an acceptable custom for men in Wuyue, on important celebrations such as this it was typically expected that his hair would be tied up. She didn't look directly at him as they slowly made their way up the steps but glanced at him out of the corner of her eye. His face was also covered in a thin veil, as it was customary among the Sogdians for the groom to cover his face with a veil alongside the bride if his parents were deceased. With the dimming light, it was difficult to make out his features. However, one thing that was obvious was his blank expression—the slight downward curve of his lips was a clear indication that he was not particularly enjoying this evening.

Alaneya was careful not to trip over her long dress, which dragged across the ground and flowed elegantly down the steps like a gentle waterfall as she ascended. In the Hall of Harmony, the members of the House of Qian and the Venesian and Oghuz Rumeli envoys were lined up on the sides. An elaborate tea table sat in the center of the pavilion, ready for the ceremony to begin. Behind the table were her father, Empress Yinfeng, and Emperor Jinlong of Wuyue himself. He looked better than he had during his last public appearance less than two months prior, at the wedding ceremony of Sheli and Hyousuke.

Si Lu, the High Priestess of Qiantang, accompanied by two attendants, approached from the back. Each wore long, red robes and had their faces obscured by veils, only their eyes showing.

Alaneya and Mingyue took their positions on either side of the table, kneeling before the Emperor and Alaneya's father, and bowing three times. Typically, the parents of both bride and groom would be present, but of their four parents, only Alaneya's father remained alive. Emperor Jinlong and Empress Yinfeng substituted for Mingyue's parents.

The bride and groom were each given a pot of tea from the attendants. They went around the hall, Alaneya pouring tea for the Yue nobles, and Mingyue pouring it for the Oghuz Rumelis. Alaneya tried to recall the names of every face she knelt before. After presenting a cup to Emperor Jinlong and Empress Yinfeng, she moved on to Mingyue's extended family. There was Yanggui, Shenzhong's aunt, and Jinxin, the youngest brother of the Emperor. Jingli and Fengling, the twin cousins of Mingyue and children of Empress Dowager Qian Zemao of Xin. There was Mingyue's elder sister Sheli, and her new husband, Hyousuke. She could hardly keep track of everyone. Finally, she approached Chengxin and Shenzhong.

Her hand trembled slightly as she poured tea for Mingyue's eldest cousin. She couldn't bring herself to make eye contact with him and was unable to steady herself. Beginning to swoon, she feared she might pass out. Tea started spilling over the rim, but Shenzhong suddenly took a gentle hold of her hand. It was as if everything became clear again for her.

She forced her eyes to meet his gaze, and all her fears melted away as a warm smile crept across his lips.

I am here, she could hear him saying. *There's no reason to be afraid.*

Her heart felt as if it were being squeezed. For the past year, she and Shenzhong had grown close. When they had first met, Alaneya hardly knew any Wuyueyu. She was introduced to him at the Xi

Residence in Suzhou and was embarrassed that she couldn't speak to anyone. He had been friendly toward her, and they would spend a lot of time together. Even if it was difficult for them to communicate at first, that never inhibited their ability to understand one another. They played board games, strolled along the city canals, and would sit in silence together in the gardens. She had learned most of what she knew of Wuyueyu from him, and in turn, he had picked up some Venesian, Latin, and Oghuzi from her. She may have never spoken the words out loud, but deep down she knew that she had fallen in love with the prince.

After delivering tea to the family, Alaneya and Mingyue returned to the table. Alaneya hesitated before taking her seat. Something seemed off, as if someone was missing from the ceremony. She glanced back at the members of House of Qian gathered behind her. For most of them, she had only met them on a few occasions. Qian Zemao had returned to Kaifeng. Huamei, Yanlu, and the Emperor's eldest sibling Princess Qian Jinling had all passed away during the Qiantang Incident, thus their absences were notable. Yet there was still someone missing, wasn't there? She just couldn't place a finger on who it was.

"Pay respects to Heaven and Earth," Si Lu announced.

Alaneya and Mingyue obliged, prostrating themselves onto the floor.

"Pay respects to the Father and the Mother."

As with at Sheli's wedding, those words struck a chord, but both bride and groom bowed once again.

"Pay respects to the Husband and the Wife."

Alaneya and Mingyue turned to face one another from across the table. They bowed. Then Mingyue slowly raised his hands to lift his veil. In the dimmed pavilion, his removal of the veil didn't make his face any clearer. He reached forward to uncover his bride. His hands were noticeably shaking as the fingers brushed against Alaneya's cheeks. The veil was lifted.

From the throne, the Emperor spoke up in a weak voice. "Both bride and groom will now take their cups and serve them to one another."

He lifted his cup to his lips and took the first sip.

Mingyue took his cup, raising it toward Alaneya. Alaneya did likewise, their arms crossing one another as they prepared to seal the ceremony with a drink from the other's cup. As Mingyue tilted his head back, his attention caught that of one of the priestess's attendants. Standing toward the rear of the pavilion, the attendant stared back at him intensely. He would not look away. There was something about those eyes, something which Mingyue immediately knew was off. Just as the liquid from the cup grazed his lips, he froze.

Alaneya jumped back as the sound of shattering ceramic pierced the silence. She didn't know what had just happened. A moment earlier, Mingyue had been holding his cup to her lips, and the next he had flung it off to the side. Everyone stared on in shock and confusion as the teacup cracked against the steps of the pavilion, bouncing off to the square below.

"Your Highness…?" Alaneya inquired.

Her eyes had since adjusted to the light after having removed the veil. For the first time, she got a good look at the groom's face. He was wide-eyed in fear, his breathing heavy. But that wasn't what surprised Alaneya the most. Something about his features were off…

A flash of light appeared from his chest as a necklace slipped out from under his robes. It was a silver crescent.

Her mind went back to the previous evening when Mingyue had gifted her the jade phoenix pendant.

I will wear this during the ceremony tomorrow, she had said to him, *and I hope you will wear the dove.*

Of course, he had replied.

She instinctively raised her hand to her chest. Indeed, the jade phoenix was hanging around her neck. But Mingyue was not wearing the glass dove, but a silver crescent. She had noticed that crescent the night before, worn by one of the men she danced with at the ball. She turned back to look upon the members of the House of Qian once again.

That is who was missing!

How could she not have realized that the Crown Prince himself wasn't present at the ceremony?!

"Prince Zukang...?" She said in surprise.

The man sitting across from her wasn't Mingyue, but his elder brother.

VII. Who Has Seen the Groom?

"Prince Zukang…?" Alaneya whispered in confusion.

If Zukang had been the one taking part in the wedding ceremony this whole time, where was Mingyue?

"A-Kang…!" Sheli gasped in surprise; her eyes went wide in confusion as she gazed upon her brother. "We were wondering where you were, why you were late to the ceremony! What are you doing taking A-Ming's place? Where is he?"

The Crown Prince, who seemed to be dazed since he had thrown away his teacup, snapped back to his senses. He whipped his attention toward the back of the pavilion once again, where the veiled attendant of the High Priestess had been standing. There was no one there. Where did that attendant go?

"A-Kang…?" Sheli said in a gentle tone, stepping toward her younger brother and placing her hand on his shoulder. "What is going on?"

Zukang didn't acknowledge her. Instead, his gaze fell toward the teacup still clenched tightly in Alaneya's grasp. He swiped his hand, startling the poor girl as the cup went flying, sending spilled tea all over the floor.

"Don't drink it!" He shouted frantically. "Put your cups away! Don't drink it!"

Everyone was shocked at his outburst—it was as if the prince had gone mad. But hesitantly, most of them obeyed and put down their cups.

Empress Yinfeng arose from her seat, brows furrowed in frustration. "Zukang, what is this about? Explain!"

Though she loved them all, it was well-known that the Empress favoured Mingyue out of all her grandchildren. She was understandably infuriated that Zukang had ruined the wedding ceremony.

Zukang brought his attention in the direction of his grandmother, but his eyes fell on the Emperor instead. Clasped tightly in Jinlong's hand was a teacup. The Emperor had already drunk his tea before the rest of them! Jinlong's face was pale, but since everyone's attention was focused on Zukang, no one had noticed yet—no one except Zukang. His eyes went wide in horror upon realizing what was taking place, but he was too shocked to react.

A phlegmy cough escaped Jinlong's lips as the Emperor stumbled forward out of his seat. The teacup slipped from his grasp and rolled across the ground. It was then that everyone turned to him.

"Your Majesty!" Sheli exclaimed. She rushed forward just as her grandfather hit the floor.

Yinfeng stepped back in surprise, falling speechless at the sight of her husband's body on the ground. The reactions of everyone else was a mix of those two, with some hurrying over and others fearfully pulling away. In the square below, it was difficult for most of the guests to see what was going on, but murmurs could be heard as they wondered just what was happening.

Zukang simply stood in the middle of the pavilion, eyes wide as he froze in fear. He frantically scanned the back of the room, to the spot where the attendant of the High Priestess had been watching him earlier, but the masked figure was no longer present. He whipped his head around, searching the rest of the hall, but among the confused and frantic faces of the Oghuz Rumeli envoy, guards, priests, and his own family, he couldn't locate that masked attendant.

It was then that he felt a presence behind him. Before he had the chance to turn around, a firm grasp pulled his arm behind his back, and he felt the chill of a blade about to slit his throat. As the blade dug into his flesh, he knew there were only moments before he would be bleeding out on the floor. He wouldn't even know who killed him.

"A-Kang!" His sister shrieked from behind.

At the precise moment that those words escaped her lips, the blade froze, remaining pressed against his neck.

"Qian...Zukang...?" Whispered the man about to take his life. There was something vaguely familiar about his voice, but Zukang couldn't put a finger on it. He had heard this voice somewhere before. But where?

The man pulled Zukang's hair to tilt his head back. The prince strained his neck to glance at who it was, but all he could see was a set of deep brown eyes gazing back at him from behind the veil.

"The Crown Prince…?" Whispered the masked figure. "But how…? Where is your brother…?"

Zukang wanted to shout, but with a blade pressed against his neck he thought it unwise to startle his captor. Instead, he let out his words in a harsh, bitter tone.

"How the hell am I supposed to know?! I barely have any memories of what happened last night. I just remember waking up after being held hostage and being threatened to take on A-Ming's role in the ceremony. I haven't seen my brother since the ball. I assumed whoever kidnapped me must have done the same to him as well. The one responsible is you, isn't it?! So *you* tell *me* where he is?!"

The masked figure fell silent, but from the confused glimmer in his eyes, Zukang could tell that this man had no idea what he was referring to.

How could it be that the person who had plotted to kill him during the ceremony didn't know that his brother had been switched out for him? Then he realized that the masked man had been planning to slit Mingyue's throat, not his own. It was only after discovering that the prince he held before him was not Mingyue, but Zukang, that this would-be assassin froze. This masked man had expected to discover Mingyue at the ceremony, thus, whoever had put Zukang in this situation must have been unconnected with the man now standing behind him.

Sensing movement, the masked figure pulled Zukang around. Several guards had been attempting to creep up on the pair from behind, but the masked figure was quicker and pressed his blade harder against Zukang's throat.

"Do not come closer. Do you know who this is? This is your Crown Prince, Qian Zukang! If any of you make a single move, I will slit his throat!"

You won't kill me, Zukang thought hopefully to himself. *You wanted to kill my brother, not me. If you wanted me dead, you would have done it by now.*

"Stand down," Yinfeng said reluctantly. Although her husband lay motionless on the floor beside her, and her eldest grandson had a knife at his throat, the Empress remained cool and collected.

Slowly, Zukang was forced to walk back as the masked figure held him hostage, inching their way toward the edge of the pavilion. He turned around and hovered above the top step, out above the square for everyone below to see.

"The Emperor is dead," the masked man announced in a resounding voice.

The murmurs of concern among the crowd turned into gasps of shock upon hearing those words and realizing that the prince was being held captive.

The masked man hesitated as he considered his next words carefully. "I demand the immediate release of Emir Abdullah in exchange for the prince. Tomorrow morning, at dawn, there will be a boat at the gates of the palace. I will bring the Crown Prince to be exchanged for the Emir. If these demands are not met, I will slit the prince's throat and cast his body into the West Lake."

A whizzing arrow suddenly sliced through the air, but Zukang couldn't discern which direction it was fired from. The masked man, however, sensed immediately and maneuvered himself slightly to the side. This all took place in the blink of an eye, the arrow barely missing him. Had the man failed to react in time, the arrow would have made its mark, and struck the hostage prince rather than the hostage-taker himself. The masked man whipped out a small sachet hanging from his waist and flung it forward, and a thick powder dissipated into the air, a dark curtain of smoke spreading out from the top of the stairs. There were gasps of shock and confusion, but by the time the diversion had settled, both the masked man and the Crown Prince were gone.

VIII. Distrust

"Who fired that arrow from the wall?!" Yinfeng fumed.

It had only been an hour since Zukang's kidnapping. The physicians hastily arrived at the Hall of Harmony as guests were cleared out and it was confirmed that the Emperor was indeed deceased. But Yinfeng had no time to mourn the death of her husband. By cutting off the head of the empire, the assassin had one goal in mind—to sow as much chaos, confusion, and discord as possible. If Wuyue did not have a strong leader at its darkest hour, the empire might completely shatter like Karnata had only months earlier. An assassination of this scale, infiltrating the marriage ceremony, poisoning the Emperor to death, and escaping the scene with such ease when there were guards at every exit, was a covert plot that had been nearly perfectly executed by the perpetrators. The physicians examined each teacup and discovered that all of those which had been poured for the House of Qian had been poisoned with the same substance that had killed the Emperor. However, those which had been poured for the Oghuz Rumeli envoy were not contaminated. Alaneya had been the one to pour the tea for the imperial family, thus she and the Oghuz Rumelis were suspects in the assassination. Of course, the one who had handed that contaminated teapot to the Venesian lady had been the veiled man, and his identity remained unknown after he escaped the pavilion with the Crown Prince.

Yinfeng hastily placed the palace on lockdown following Jinlong's passing. The guests were all instructed to return to their quarters to be put under house arrest, partially for their own safety, and partially because the Empress didn't know who could be trusted. She took the reins of control from her husband—after all, someone had to, lest a power vacuum open and another step in to try and assert their influence. Yinfeng ordered that all guards who had been present at the ceremony return to the palace garrison and headed immediately there to interrogate them. Alongside them, she brought the rest of those who had been present in the pavilion, including the members of the House of Qian, the Oghuz Rumeli envoy, and the High Priestess.

"Who fired that arrow?!" She raged once again. "It nearly struck the Crown Prince! Were you trying to kill the assassin or my grandson?!"

There was a deafening silence among the guards, who stood solemnly before the Empress, none daring to speak. Then one of the guards broke down and fell on his knees, crying out in a wavering voice as he folded his hands together.

"Your Majesty it was me! I fired the arrow! I was trying to kill the assassin, but my aim was off! I apologize! Forgive me, your Majesty! Forgive me!"

He knocked his head against the ground several times.

"Fool!" Yinfeng spat. "Had that man not moved, the arrow would have pierced Zukang! Take him away!"

"Your Majesty! Have mercy! Have mercy! I was trying to kill the assassin, I swear! Have mercy!" He cried out in vain as the other guards removed him from the area.

Yinfeng then turned to the High Priestess and her remaining attendant, who lay prostrate on the floor before her feet.

"Who was the other attendant present at the ceremony?"

Si Lu spoke in a calm voice but didn't dare to raise her head. "Your Majesty, the deacon named Ma Xiu was supposed to take part in the ceremony this evening…"

"Ma Xiu is dead!" Several deacons and monks from the palace temple rushed into the square and threw themselves onto the floor.

"Dead?" Yinfeng said. "Has he been caught? Where is my grandson?"

One of the deacons hesitantly raised his head. "Um…no. We found Ma Xiu's body in his quarters. His throat had been slit and his body was cold. He must have been dead since this morning at least…"

"Ma Xiu is dead?" Si Lu said in a soft voice. "Then…someone killed him to take his place in the ceremony…?"

At the mention of 'take his place' the Empress was immediately reminded of Mingyue. If Mingyue's place had been taken by Zukang during the ceremony, then where was he? She turned and whispered to her closest guards.

"Take me to the Palace of Lunar Serenity."

"Your Majesty..." one of them hesitated. "It's been a long evening. I suggest you return to your chambers for the night. We will get someone else to search for the Second Prince."

She glanced at everyone gathered in the garrison square and her voice fell even lower. "I cannot trust anyone to do this. Not even them. It must be me."

The guard paused but then nodded in understanding. He raised his voice to address those present. "Under the Empress's orders, everyone is to return to their quarters for the evening."

There were some eyebrows raised among the Oghuz Rumelis and the Empress's own family members, but none dared question her decision. As they departed the square, Chengxin whispered under his breath.

"The Empress is acting as if she cannot trust us, but how do we know we can trust *her*?"

This was said just loud enough for nearby Jingli and Fengling to hear. The twins glanced in their uncle's direction, saying nothing as they parted ways. As soon as they were alone, Fengling spoke up in a hushed voice.

"Jingli...do you think...?"

"I have a bad feeling about this," was all he said to his sister. "I think we should return to Kaifeng and join Mother as soon as we can. It's not safe here, and there is clearly someone within the palace who is responsible for this. I don't want us to get caught up in this mess."

Meanwhile, Yinfeng headed to Mingyue's residence. She flung open the doors to his bed chambers.

Squawk!

The duniao hatchling raced over to Yinfeng as she stepped foot into the room. The Empress recoiled.

"What is this?"

"I heard the Second Prince was gifted this creature by the Norden prince a short while ago," one of her guards said.

Yinfeng glanced around the room, surprised to find that everything was in place. There hadn't been any break-in or intrusion—it seemed like no one had even stepped foot in this room for more than a day. If that was the case, then where had the prince stayed the night? When exactly had he gone missing? She thought back to the previous night. The last time she had seen Mingyue was as he departed the ball.

After he had finished his dance with Alaneya, there had been a few more songs that were played before he retired for the evening. Yinfeng sat at the front of the room near the musicians, sipping on tea for most of the night as she observed the guests dancing. Mingyue didn't dance after that and instead disappeared into the crowd. A while later, he approached her as she spoke with Yanggui, informing her that he was going to return to his chambers for the night. She nodded and dismissed him without much thought, watching as he departed with Hansini.

"Where are his attendants?" Yinfeng asked out loud. She turned to her two most trusted guards, who had both accompanied her to the Palace of Lunar Serenity. "Where are his guards? I want to know where my grandson went after leaving the ball last night and why no one reported his absence."

IX. Islands Amidst Mist

Mingyue's eyes grew heavy as he stared aimlessly out across the Lake of Tranquility. The atmosphere was foggy, and the sun had long since set. The only light came from the glowing, golden lanterns of the palace in the distance, seeming to be hovering hauntingly over the waters. Nearby, Hansini sat next to the prince, fingers fidgeting anxiously as her eyes darted about.

"Something isn't right," she whispered. "The ceremony would have started a while ago and is probably finished by now. I don't understand why no one has come to retrieve us yet."

Mingyue thought back to the previous night. Upon departing the ballroom, Hansini had been the one to guide Mingyue back to the Palace of Lunar Serenity. However, once they arrived at the complex, they were approached by two guards who rushed up from behind. These were no ordinary palace guards—each wore a brooch of the Golden Dragon. They were the Emperor's guards.

They bowed. "Second Prince Qian, the Emperor has requested that you stay at the Northern Island Residence this evening."

Mingyue didn't know what they were referring to and gazed silently at them before turning to Hansini expectantly.

"Northern Island Residence…?" Hansini raised an eyebrow. "I've never heard of such a place."

"It is in the Lake of Tranquility, halfway between here and the temple. Princess Huamei used to spend time there to escape the bustle of palace life."

Hansini was reluctant to agree. "The wedding ceremony is taking place tomorrow. I must get the prince ready…"

"It is customary for nobles to stay at the island on the eve of their marriage," the guards noted. "The Emperor has requested it. Everything you need to prepare the prince will be brought to the island tomorrow."

"There is already a boat waiting at the docks," added the other guard. "Come."

Mingyue had known then that something was off, yet they went along with the guards anyway. After all, how could they refuse a request by the Emperor? Even if they had attempted to resist, the two men were armed with weapons. They wouldn't be able to escape.

Mingyue recognized the island as they approached. Though the temple island at the center of the Lake of Tranquility stood out the most, there were dozens of smaller islands scattered about across the lake—most only contained trees or other flora, but a few did have buildings on them. The Northern Island Residence had always stood out to Mingyue, as he could see it from the balcony which overlooked the lake at the Palace of Lunar Serenity. He had always wondered what the buildings were for, assuming they were simply garden pavilions for leisure. He hadn't realized that one of them was an entire residential complex.

The guards departed once they had delivered Hansini and the prince to the island. Mingyue expected to find other servants or guards present on the island to attend to them but was surprised to discover that it was eerily deserted.

"They've taken the boat with them," Hansini muttered simply.

"*Hm?*" Mingyue inquired.

Hansini nodded in the direction of the boat as the two guards sailed away, disappearing into the foggy night.

"We are alone on this island and have no way of getting back without a boat."

Indeed, they were trapped here until someone else came to pick them up—their presence on the island seemed more like confinement than anything else. The garden outside the complex was overgrown, and the floors creaked as they entered the residence. It was evident that no one had stepped foot on this island for months, if not years.

"I am sure the Emperor has reason to send us here," Mingyue noted. "But Wei Hanxi, I have a question. Did my sister stay on this island before her wedding ceremony? And did my mother really spend time here?"

Hansini's eyes met his and fell dark. "Not that I am aware of, your Highness."

***

By midday, Mingyue knew that something was wrong. The guards who brought them here had never returned, as they should have by now if he was to be ready for the wedding ceremony that evening. Hansini was agitated, cursing silently for having gone along with them to the island. She had known something was off when they approached but hadn't considered that perhaps those men had impersonated the Emperor's guard. But if not sent by the Emperor, then by who? And what were their intentions in trapping the prince on this island?

"We have to get back or we'll miss the ceremony," Hansini fumed.

Mingyue knew that she would get into a lot more trouble than he would if they missed the wedding. After all, she was his attendant and was supposed to ensure that he was always safe, and always punctual.

"Someone must have noticed by now that you were missing," she continued. "Olekina arrives at your quarters early every morning, so I am sure the Imperial Guard would have already been sent out to search for you. But they'll never find us here."

She began to scavenge through the complex, searching for anything they could use as a raft. The rooms were mostly empty, stripped of most of their furniture, with a thin layer of dust settled atop everything. There wasn't even anything to eat. As Hansini continued scouring the rooms, Mingyue slipped outside and headed down to the water. Like the previous night, a heavy layer of fog rested above the lake, obscuring the shore and even nearby islands from view. Unfortunately, Mingyue did not know how to swim. Even if he did, the distance to the shore was too far—he would certainly freeze long before then.

The prince knelt by the lake and scooped some water into his hands. He brought it to his lips and shivered as it poured into his mouth.

"Your Highness, what are you doing?!" Hansini gasped as she came running out of the building.

"I'm thirsty," he said simply as he turned to her. "There's nothing to drink here."

Hansini fumed. "You can't drink lake water! It's filthy! And drinking freezing cold water isn't healthy either!"

"Well, we don't have any other choice until we get back to the palace," Mingyue pointed out. He noticed Hansini was carrying what looked to be a couple of lanterns. "What are those for?"

"I found these in the courtyard," she explained. "They must have landed on the island when they were released over the lake during the Moon Festival. I thought perhaps we could use them to send a message back to the palace. They should still be able to float in the air, as long as we can start a fire."

They found some ink and brushes in one of the rooms and wrote out a simple message on several slips of paper to attach to the lanterns: *The Second Prince is stranded on an island in the north of the Lake of Tranquility.*

They had four lanterns and decided it would be best to send all four toward the northeast since this was the closest shore as well as the direction in which the wind was currently blowing. Based on this, the lanterns should end up either in the Palace of Lunar Serenity or the Palace of Heavenly Peace.

As they tied the slips of paper to the bases of the lanterns and prepared a fire to send them off, a thought crossed Mingyue's mind.

"If these lanterns were from the Moon Festival, why are there no wishes attached to them?"

Hansini considered this question. Indeed, it was strange that none of these lanterns had any slips of paper already attached to them, considering it was customary to send a lantern off with a wish, and the vast majority of lanterns would have had wishes tied to them. She shrugged and brushed aside that question.

"Perhaps I was wrong, and they were not from the Moon Festival."

Mingyue shook his head. "Everything here is covered in a layer of dust as if it hasn't been touched in years, but these lanterns are not, meaning they haven't been here as long. They must have come from the Moon Festival then, meaning that they would have had wishes on them, but someone took them off. But why would they do that?"

Hansini nodded slightly and pointed to the other end of the courtyard. "I found them all in that corner. I didn't think much of it, but someone must have put them there—they wouldn't all have coincidentally landed there on their own. I suppose whoever gathered them must be the one who took the wishes off."

This puzzled Mingyue. He didn't know why, but he felt slightly disturbed by this. Hansini noticed the discomfort in his face and tried to reassure him.

"I wouldn't worry about this too much, your Highness. Let's just focus on sending off these lanterns."

Once they had finished, they watched the lanterns disappear into the dark sky. For the remainder of the day, they waited, hoping that someone would find one of the lanterns. Hours passed, and the sun eventually set. Hansini became increasingly anxious as the day progressed, keeping track of the time, and noting when the ceremony would have begun. As they sat on the terrace, gazing out across the lake in silence, the possibility that they may be trapped here indefinitely finally began to settle in. A deep sense of uneasiness washed over Mingyue at the thought of this. Though still within the grounds of the palace, he felt completely isolated, as if they were trapped in another world. Even if they screamed, their voices wouldn't be loud enough to reach the shore.

Having not eaten since the ball the previous night, the prince found himself growing lightheaded and on the verge of passing out.

"Hungry?" Hansini wondered.

"*Mnn,*" Mingyue nodded.

Hansini sighed. "Get some rest. You didn't sleep much last night. I'll search around again and see if I can find anything to eat."

"How about you?" Mingyue wondered. "You didn't sleep much either."

"*Tch*," she scoffed. "Nothing I'm not already used to."

"You sleep," Mingyue said. "I'll stand watch."

Hansini blinked in surprise before shaking her head. "What if those men come back? I need to be awake to protect you."

"Prince Amaru taught me to fight," Mingyue persisted.

He reached down and grabbed a fallen branch off the ground, clasping it in his hands like it was a spear. He jabbed it toward Hansini, who intercepted it with an unconvinced expression on her face. She yanked it away and snapped it in two.

"Not that I doubt your abilities, but you'd better leave the fighting to me."

"I'll wake you if anyone draws near the island," Mingyue promised.

Hansini crossed her arms, a doubtful look appearing in her eyes. "It's *my* job to watch *you*."

"And you've done a fantastic job at that, for so many years," Mingyue noted. "But you need time to rest too."

Hansini chuckled. "This is hardly the time for that."

However, seeing how persistent he was, and how he wouldn't take no for an answer, she finally gave in, retreating inside the residence to find a comfortable place to lie down.

"Keep your eyes on the lake," she said, "and wake me if you see anything."

Dusk turned to night, and as the thick layer of fog that had descended grew increasingly dense, the other islands of the lake soon disappeared from view. Shapes began to appear in the mist, and after a while, Mingyue could no longer tell if he was still seeing reality, or if he was simply growing tired. It was then that he noticed a shape in the water, emerging out of the fog. It began drifting closer and closer to the island. Was he hallucinating?

"Someone is coming," Hansini whispered.

She approached quietly from behind. It hadn't been long since she'd gone off to sleep, yet she had already been roused from her slumber.

"It's a boat. They're coming in this direction."

X. Red Moon

As the boat drew nearer, it was clear that they were intent on docking on the island. Hansini took hold of Mingyue's arm and pulled him back into the building. She slipped a thin blade out from her sleeve.

"What are you doing?" Mingyue hissed. "You're not going to kill them, are you?"

"We don't know who they are or why they're here," Hansini replied. "It could be those men who brought us here yesterday. If so, I want to know what their intentions are and what they plan on doing with you. Come. We should take cover. If we catch them off guard, we'll have the upper hand."

She took hold of the prince, pulling him into the residence. Mingyue peeked his head out the window. As the boat drew nearer, he could see that there were three figures aboard, one rowing and two others that were seated. Although all three were hooded, he spotted the familiar, curly red locks of one of the seated figures. It could be none other than Agnes, meaning that the other two must have been Erik and Caleb. He broke free from Hansini's grasp and hurried outside to greet them.

"Your Highness!" Hansini fumed, chasing after him. "We don't know that we can trust them!"

Mingyue was already on the dock to greet the arrivals. When Erik spotted him, he threw back his hood and smiled in relief, his jade-green eyes like glowing beacons of light amidst the darkness.

"Qian Ming! You're alright!"

Hansini emerged from the shadows with a gaze of suspicion on her face. "Prince Erik…what a surprise to see you here. Why were you the ones sent to retrieve us? I would have expected them to send Olekina, or perhaps some of the other guards."

"The Empress has locked down the entire palace," Caleb explained. "Technically we shouldn't be here either, but my lord insisted."

Erik reached back in the boat and produced one of the lanterns which they'd sent out earlier. "This landed on the balcony at my quarters. We would've reported it to someone else but—"

"We didn't know who to trust," Agnes interrupted, stepping forward.

The red-haired girl hopped off the boat and stood between Mingyue and Hansini, crossing her arms. She narrowed her eyes at the Yue prince's attendant, eyeing the dagger that was clenched between the other woman's fingers.

Sensing tension and mistrust between the two, Mingyue hastily spoke up.

"Wei Hanxi, put that away. I apologize. Two men brought us here last night and we thought you might be them. Wei Hanxi was simply concerned for my safety."

"Last night?" Agnes repeated. "So, you've been here this whole time? Huh, guess that explains why yer still in Erik's outfit."

Mingyue quickly glanced down at himself, realizing that indeed, he still was in Erik's outfit from the ball the previous day.

"You said the Empress locked down the palace?" Hansini inquired. "What exactly is going on?"

The three arrivals exchanged nervous glances with one another. Their faces fell dark.

"There is a lot to explain," Erik said softly. "I can tell you on the way back."

Before stepping foot on the boat, Mingyue's eye was drawn to something he hadn't noticed before—in the lower branches of one of the nearby trees rested a lantern caught between the branches. He didn't know why, but he felt drawn toward it. Erik seemed to notice this and quickly volunteered to retrieve it for him. The Norden prince hurried over and hoisted himself up from the bottom branches, earning disapproval from Caleb who was worried he'd fall.

Erik soon returned with the lantern, handing it over to Mingyue, who placed his hand through the opening at the bottom. Sure enough, there was a slip of paper tied inside. He pulled it forth, but it was impossible for him to decipher what it said in the darkness.

They boarded the ship and set off back to the Palace of Lunar Serenity, the Northern Island Residence soon disappearing into the fog. Everyone held their breath as Erik began to recount the day's events to Mingyue. Mingyue sat in silence, staring blankly out over the lake as he was told of the Emperor's death and the kidnapping of Zukang by a mysterious masked figure.

"We still can't be sure of the Emperor's fate," Erik said hopefully. "From where I stood in the square, it was difficult to tell exactly what happened. But I did see the Emperor collapse and that masked man declared that he was dead."

Mingyue felt his chest tighten up, but he shed no tears. He didn't know what he was supposed to feel right now—after having already lost his parents so recently right in front of his eyes, he was just relieved that he didn't have to witness another death himself.

"Qian Ming?" Erik whispered. He reached out and put his hand on the other prince's shoulder. "I'm...I'm sorry..."

Mingyue pulled his gaze away from the water and toward the Norden prince.

"You don't have to apologize for anything. Actually...I'm glad that you're the one who came today. Thank you for being here."

Erik was taken off guard by his reply but managed a weak smile as their eyes locked together. For a moment, it was as if they were the only two in the boat. Overhead, the looming tiled roofs of the Palace of Serenity started to come into view as they neared the shore. The fog began to thin, and the light of the moon up above came into view.

"We're almost there," Caleb said.

Before reaching the shore, Mingyue pulled forth the slip of paper from the lantern resting in his lap. As the fog cleared, he was able to make out the characters written on it.

The raven will paint the bright moon red.[31]

---

[31] The characters for "bright moon" can be written as 明月, transliterated as "Ming Yue."

These are the same characters in Mingyue's name (錢明月). Thus, when reading this, Mingyue could interpret it as referring to the literal moon or himself.

XI. Under the Cover of Night

"What does it say?" Erik poked his head over Mingyue's shoulder and glanced down at the slip of paper between his fingers.

Mingyue hastily folded up the slip and tucked it away into his sleeve. "Ah…nothing…"

Erik chuckled. "You know I can't read Tang characters, right? Well, Caleb tried to teach me a few, but they're difficult to pick up."

Mingyue internally rebuked himself for being so stupid. He didn't want anyone to see that note, and so had instinctively pulled away. But now he realized that would probably make Erik want to know what it said even more.

"Everythin' alright?" Agnes inquired, glancing back at the two.

"Yes," Erik smiled at her as the boat bumped against the dock. "Oh, we're back!"

He hopped onto the shore, extending his hand out to Mingyue. The other prince took hold and disembarked.

"We need to inform the Empress that the Second Prince is safe," Hansini said. Her gaze shifted from Erik to Caleb to Agnes.

"*Hm*?" Agnes tilted her head. "Ya want *us* to tell the Empress?"

Hansini sighed, "I have to escort the prince back to his quarters."

"I can escort him," Erik piped up.

"You seem awfully eager to do so," Hansini raised an eyebrow in suspicion.

"Aha…no…" Erik scratched his head. "Well, yes…well I mean…I wouldn't mind doing so. But also, since you're the only one among us other than Qian Ming who is qualified to speak with the Empress, shouldn't you be the one to go?"

Hansini was struck that Erik had referred to the prince simply as 'Qian Ming' and not by his title, or even courtesy name. She crossed her arms.

"I'm not qualified to speak to the Empress either, but that's beside the point."

"We're already back at the Palace of Lunar Serenity," Mingyue pointed out. "My quarters aren't far from here. I can return there on my own."

Of course, after what had happened that day no one else thought that was a good idea.

"Not that I don't trust you, but—"

"I trust them, Hansini," Mingyue said, "please inform the Empress of our situation."

Once again, the young woman was speechless—Mingyue hardly ever referred to her by her birth name, typically preferring her courtesy name of Wei Hanxi. She paused for a moment before bowing to the prince.

"Of course, your Highness. I'll be on my way. Rest well tonight, and I will see you in the morning."

"No need to worry bout if you can trust us!" Agnes assured. "If somethin' happens to the prince we'll take full responsibility."

Hansini scoffed and hurried off in the direction of the Empress's palace.

"Your attendant doesn't seem to like us very much," Erik noted.

He popped open an umbrella to shield them from the light flurries of snow which had begun fluttering down from the sky. As the two of them walked ahead, Caleb and Agnes gave them some space, trailing behind.

"She doesn't dislike you," assured Mingyue. "Wei Hanxi has been with me since I was young; she practically raised me. She may not always show it, but she's quite protective of me. That's why she is unsure whether she can trust leaving me with you."

"You two are similar then," Erik noted.

Mingyue cocked his head, "What do you mean?"

"You don't trust others easily."

"*Mnn.* Maybe you're right. But how can you trust anyone when the world is such a misgiving place."

"You said you trusted me," the Norden prince pointed out.

Mingyue said nothing.

"Why is that?"

Mingyue thought for a moment. He didn't know why, but he had a sense of familiarity with Erik since they first met, as if he had always known the Norden prince.

"I trust you. Does there have to be a reason for that?"

Erik shrugged. "I suppose not."

They rounded the corner, coming into view of Mingyue's residence. Along the way here, they hadn't encountered anyone else—the alleyways and complexes were far quieter than usual, as everyone remained inside under the Empress's curfew. The only noise came from the gentle breeze, their shoes crunching in the freshly fallen snow, and Caleb rebuking Agnes in frustration behind them as the red-haired girl flung snowballs at him. However, as the lantern light from the residence up ahead illuminated their pathway, they sensed someone scurrying down a nearby alley. A figure's shadow appeared on the ground as this unknown individual hurried in their direction.

XII. Midnight

16/11/18th Year of the Golden Dragon Emperor

Year of the Wooden Goat

Erik took hold of Mingyue's hand and pulled him into a doorway.

"Who is it?" Whispered the Yue prince.

Erik shook his head and held a finger to his lips. "I don't know, but no one else should be out right now. They're defying the Empress's orders."

"So did you."

"Aha…yes. That is true."

Though the two kept a low profile as they huddled in the doorway, Agnes and Caleb hadn't yet realized that someone was coming. The two rounded the corner from the right at the same time as the unidentified figure came from the left, both parties startling the other. Agnes instinctively whipped out a small blade and hurled it at the newcomer, who swiftly dodged and moved in for an attack.

Luckily, Mingyue could see all three of them now and recognized who the newcomer was.

"Chu Kening?!" He called out as he broke free from the Norden prince's grasp.

Indeed, the man who had rounded the corner was none other than Mingyue's physician, Kanen.

"Your Highness?" Kanen's attention was drawn to the prince in surprise, and Agnes was able to avoid his attack, grabbing hold of the physician's wrist and twisting his arm. "Aiyah! Let go of me!"

"Qian Ming, who is this?" Erik inquired as he stepped out of the shadows.

"My physician."

"Physician?" Agnes cocked her head. "Yer physician nearly struck me down! With moves like this, he could be a soldier!"

"*Tch*," Kanen yanked his arm away from her grasp. "You attacked first."

"I apologize," Agnes said. "Ye caught me off guard. I wasn't expecting we'd run into anyone else tonight. What're ya doing out at this hour? Doesn't the Empress have the palace on lockdown?"

"I should be the one asking you that question. What are foreigners doing in the Palace of Lunar Serenity?" Kanen was dumbfounded as his attention turned from her to Mingyue. "Your Highness, why are you with them? I heard that you were missing at the wedding ceremony today! Where were you?!"

"Chu Kening, there is no need to worry about them," assured the Yue prince. "Wei Hanxi and I were captured and stranded on an island in the Lake of Tranquility last night. Prince Erik and his two attendants were the ones who came to rescue us."

Kanen narrowed his eyes, seemingly unconvinced and skeptical of the story. "And how did they know where you were?"

"It's a long story," Mingyue said. "But may I ask why you're out here? Miss Agnes is correct; the palace is under lockdown."

Kanen cleared his throat. "Your Highness, Prince Jinyu often stays out in the gardens late into the night. I was on my way back to my quarters after putting him to bed when I ran into you."

He was referring to the Emperor's elder brother, Qian Jinyu. Mingyue often forgot that his granduncle had his own residence in the Palace of Lunar Serenity and that Kanen was his primary caretaker.

"Ah, I see," Mingyue nodded. "Chu Kening, Miss Agnes, I apologize for any misunderstandings between us."

They both bowed to the prince.

"Your Highness, there is no need for you to apologize," Kanen assured. "I will be on my way now. I bid you a good night's rest."

As they parted ways, Mingyue called out to Kanen once again. "Just one question, do you know of Wu Liqing's whereabouts?"

Olekina, or Wu Liqing as Mingyue referred to him, was his primary guard and tended to him nearly every day. If anyone was to notice Mingyue's absence that day, Olekina would've been the first.

Kanen shook his head. "I'm sorry. I'm afraid I haven't heard any news of him."

***

They soon returned to Mingyue's residence and hadn't come across another soul since encountering Kanen. However, as they approached

311

the door to his bed chamber, there was the sound of movement in the room, like someone was rummaging around. Agnes and Caleb both gestured for the two princes to stand back and readied their weapons to intercept whoever had intruded into the prince's quarters.

They threw open the doors.

"Who goes there?!" Agnes shouted, brandishing her blade.

Though the room was a mess, with sheets and shattered pottery strewn across the floor, it was devoid of any people. However, there was the flightless duniao that Erik had gifted Mingyue earlier, nibbling at flower petals that were scattered across the ground. The bird came waddling over in their direction.

"Dudu! I forgot she was here by herself," Mingyue examined the mess. "She must have been hungry…"

"Dudu?" Erik asked.

"Ah, yes," Mingyue nodded. "That's what I named her."

A small laugh escaped the Norden prince's lips, but he tried to refrain from showing any more amusement.

"What?" Mingyue tried his best to keep a blank face to hide his embarrassment. "I know I'm bad at naming things, you don't have to laugh at it."

"Sorry, sorry," Erik wiped away his grin. "I just think it's cute."

Agnes cleared her throat as she and Caleb waited in the doorway. "My lord, we should return to our residence and let the prince rest for the night."

"Oh, of course. Sorry for keeping you! Sleep well—"

"Wait," interrupted the Yue prince. "You should all stay here for the night. If you run into someone on the way back to the Palace of Heavenly Peace, you'll get in trouble."

"*Hm*…that is true," Agnes nodded. "But there's only one bed."

"There are extra sheets in the dressers," Mingyue began going through them and clearing out the debris on the floor to create space for a makeshift bed. "Wei Hanxi will probably be the first to arrive here in the morning. I'll have her escort you back to your residence then. Erik, you can take the bed if you want."

The Norden prince hastily denied the offer. "No, no, you take it. This is your room! And after spending the night on that island you deserve to sleep in your own bed."

"Is there enough space for the three of you?" Mingyue inquired.

Agnes threw her arms around Caleb and Erik, tackling them both to the ground. "Oh, there's more than enough space for us here. We've all had to share tents and stuff in our travels through the Keliyete Khanate. This is nothin'!"

"Don't remind me," Caleb muttered.

Mingyue took Dudu onto the bed with him while the other three settled down on the floor. It had been a long, exhausting day, and he still hadn't had the chance to fully process everything that had happened. The Emperor was dead, Zukang had been kidnapped, and there was an assassin on the loose somewhere in the palace. It was all so overwhelming that it didn't feel real to him. He didn't even bother changing out of his clothes as he slumped down into the sheets. Within his sleeve, he felt that slip of paper from the lantern. The words written on it flashed through his mind.

The raven will paint the bright moon red.

Outside the window, dark clouds rolled across the sky, covering up the light of the moon once again. He was soon fast asleep.

XIII. New Dawn

It had only been a few hours before Hansini came knocking on the door to Mingyue's chambers.

"Your Highness, the Empress is on her way here to see you. Your Highness? Are you there?"

She pushed the door open only to be greeted by three groggy-faced foreigners on the floor who'd been awakened by her incessant knocking.

"You…?! What are you all doing here?!"

"Ah, why so loud?" Agnes groaned. "Mornin' already?"

"Wei Hanxi, I asked them to stay," explained Mingyue. He hastily leaped up from the bed, hoping to quiet her down before she caused a ruckus. "There's no one else to guard my quarters tonight. It's better that they're here. Otherwise, I would be alone."

Hansini gritted her teeth but couldn't argue with that. "They can't be here. The Empress is on her way!"

Sure enough, the sound of Yinfeng's footsteps could be heard approaching, alongside several other pairs of feet. Thinking quickly, Mingyue hastily directed the three guests to the closet at the other end of the room.

"I apologize for this; it will only be for a little while."

Still half asleep, Caleb, Agnes and the Norden prince complied and were hidden away from view.

The Empress entered the room, accompanied by several of her guards.

"Qian Ming!"

Her face lightened up in relief at the sight of her grandson as she rushed over to embrace him. Mingyue was surprised by this—it wasn't common for members of the imperial family to show affection, especially in the presence of others. This was particularly true of the Empress. Mingyue wasn't sure that he'd ever seen her embrace anyone before.

He said nothing—he didn't know *what* to say. His grandmother had just witnessed the death of her husband and the kidnapping of her eldest grandson—what could he possibly say that would comfort her at a time like this? Hansini and the guards awkwardly stood by and watched in silence.

"Your brother will be brought to the gates of the palace on a boat," Yinfeng whispered. "They want Emir Abdullah in exchange for him. I am heading there now to oversee the exchange."

"Let me come—"

"No," the Empress interrupted without a second thought. "You will stay here. You were the target of their assassination attempt. It's not safe for you."

A noise came from the closet, and Mingyue was reminded of the three hidden away inside. Yinfeng's attention was drawn in that direction.

"I understand, I will stay here," Mingyue said quickly, bringing her focus back to him. He didn't want his grandmother to find the others tucked away in his room and have to explain what they were doing here.

"Yes," the Empress smiled weakly.

She ordered her two most trusted guards to remain here and guard the prince's quarters while taking the rest of them away with her. Once they had gone, Mingyue threw open the doors of the closet and the three stumbled out, Erik into the Yue prince's arms and the other two onto the floor. Caleb and Agnes quickly untangled from one another, but the two princes remained in an awkward embrace for a while longer.

"Good morning…?" Erik said, groggy and confused.

"Ah," Mingyue said. "I'm sorry for keeping you in there. Wei Hanxi, please escort them back to the Palace of Heavenly Peace so they can rest in their own beds for the remainder of the night."

Hansini nodded and they began to depart, but exiting the prince's bed chambers, Erik turned to Mingyue once more.

"Qian Ming, I pray that your brother returns safely."

"Thank you," Mingyue nodded. "I hope…you sleep well tonight."

He listened to their footsteps disappear down the pathway, leaving him alone in his room with no company other than the two guards at his door and Dudu, who remained fast asleep on his bed. Stepping foot onto the balcony, he gazed out over the frozen gardens below as a thick layer of fog hung heavy in the air. The sun would soon be rising.

***

Yinfeng arrived at the main gate of the palace a while later, accompanied by a dozen of the best and most trusted soldiers in the Imperial Guard. More soldiers were stationed at the watchtowers on either side of the gate, overlooking West Lake. The thick layer of fog that had been lingering since the previous night obscured most of the water from view. The Empress had thrown a simple, dark cloak over herself to hide her identity among the others in case they were ambushed at some point. Of course, with most of the guards towering above her in height, she was still easy to pick out amidst the crowd.

As they waited above the gate, the Empress was reminded of the threat issued by that masked figure the night before.

I demand the immediate release of Emir Abdullah in exchange for the prince. Tomorrow morning, at dawn, there will be a boat at the gates of the palace. I will bring the Crown Prince to be exchanged for the Emir. If these demands are not met, I will slit the prince's throat and cast his body into the West Lake.

She clenched her fist in frustration. How dare anyone speak in such an arrogant manner, making demands to the Empress in such a way?

"Your Majesty, do you really think the prince's kidnapper will arrive at the gates?" One of the guards whispered to Yinfeng. "How would he get outside the palace walls when we have soldiers guarding every corner?"

"They will be here," muttered the Empress.

Though the masked man who had kidnapped Zukang was certainly a cunning, formidable foe, her intuition told her that he was a

316

man of his word. Sure enough, as the sky began to lighten, they sighted a boat out in the lake drifting toward them. There were two figures on board, one rowing and the other seated. How they had managed to sneak outside the palace walls undetected was a mystery, but that was a problem to be solved later.

"It's them," she whispered, signaling to the guards below to open the gate.

A larger boat was waiting in the harbour with Emir Abdullah on board, and it began drifting out into the lake with the intent of trading the Emir for the Yue prince. The exchange took place silently as the two boats met, neither party speaking any words to the other. While the Empress's soldiers rested their hands on their swords, prepared to strike at any moment, the masked figure accompanying Zukang held a small pouch at his waist. Who knew what contents it contained? Neither side wished to be the first to strike.

The guards eyed the masked man nervously as they handed over Emir Abdullah to him. The Khorasani had been sweating profusely, his eyes full of fear and confusion, ever since they took him out from confinement and onto the ship.

"What's going on?" He had demanded. "Where are you taking me?"

None of the soldiers said anything to him.

Once Zukang was safely in the hands of the soldiers, the two boats pushed off from one another and headed their separate ways, one returning to the palace while the other retreated into the fog toward the middle of the West Lake. Before the masked man disappeared from view, Yinfeng leaned in toward the closest guard to her.

"Shoot him, but don't kill him. I will not allow the Emperor's assassin to escape. There are questions that I want answers to."

The guard nodded, notched his bow, and aimed directly at the other boat as it slipped away. The air was still as Empress Yinfeng held her breath.

Whoosh.

The whizzing of the arrow was the only sound to be heard as it sliced through the fog, leaving a trail in its wake. The boat disappeared at the precise moment that a faint *thunk* sound could be heard. Though they could no longer see the boat nor the masked man aboard, it seemed to have made its mark.

"Retrieve the Emir and that masked man," the Empress ordered as she turned her back to the lake, making her way down the stairs on the interior of the wall, "and bring him to me. I will interrogate him myself."

"Yes, your Majesty!" The soldiers shouted.

A series of deafening bangs abruptly rang out from the lake at that precise moment. It sounded as if fireworks were going off, though this was no celebration. It was only a second later that the top of the wall where Yinfeng had been standing moments before exploded into a flash of light—debris and bodies were sent flying in every direction. The force of the blast flung the Empress forward, knocking the breath out of her lungs as she was thrown down the remainder of the steps of the wall.

XIV. Trouble at the Gate

Yinfeng's ears were ringing. All she could hear were the faint calls of some of her guards as they rushed over to protect the Empress, a couple of them helping her to her feet. She raised her hand to her forehead and felt a warm, wet sensation as blood trickled down her face. She was dazed but could still recall what had just happened— there was an explosion on top of the wall. Something had been fired at them from the lake.

"Prince…Zukang…" she said, though she couldn't hear her own voice, "Where is he?"

The guards were far more concerned with her safety and didn't seem to acknowledge what she was saying as they hastily escorted her further into the palace. In frustration, she grabbed the sleeves of one of the guards and shouted out furiously.

"Find the prince! FIND HIM!"

"Y-yes, your Majesty!" A few of them obeyed her command and hurried off.

The main gate to the palace, where boats and ships passed from the West Lake into the palace's harbor, had been badly damaged by the explosion. Luckily, the guards were still able to force it open. On the other side, the boat which had rescued the prince had been utterly obliterated. Fire and debris dotted the surface of the water as blackened lumps of what must have been human flesh sank under the waves. Thankfully, the Crown Prince was in one piece, and though dazed, was brought to shore by some of the soldiers.

"Your Highness?!" They shouted. "Your Highness are you alright?!"

"*Mnn…*" he winced in pain as he rubbed the side of his head. "So loud. I want to sleep…"

The soldiers hoisted him out and hurried to take him to the Empress, while others rushed back out into the lake, scouring for other survivors. They were all confused at what had just happened. Moments after that arrow had been fired, a massive explosion had torn through both the boat and the wall. From the angle that it struck, it must have come from somewhere near the center of the lake, precisely where the boat containing the Emir and the masked assassin had been. But an explosion of such size couldn't have come from a vessel so small. Unless it wasn't the only vessel in the center of the lake…

Several looming shadows emerged from the mist, drifting toward the battered walls of the palace. Having safely made it to the inner gate, Yinfeng stared out at the sight before her with an unreadable expression on her face. While the guards around her panicked and scrambled in every direction, the Empress remained nonchalant.

"So, the war has finally come here…" she whispered to herself.

Yinfeng waited by the second gate, observing those ships as they slowly approached the walls of the palace. They were ships belonging to the imperial naval fleet, which either meant that factions of the army had joined the rebellion, or that the rebels had somehow managed to seize imperial ships without word getting out.

A single black raven appeared in the sky, making its way from the closest boat to the Empress as she stood along the wall. The bird landed alongside her, its dark eyes gazing at her as if it had a sense of awareness of the situation unfolding. It dropped a scrolled-up piece of paper from its beak before leaping into the air and returning to the ship from where it had come.

Yinfeng tentatively reached out to pick up what the bird had delivered, unfolding it to read the contents it contained.

The thousand-year reign of the Yue Dynasty has come to an end! This message is to be delivered to the imperial family—you will be given until the third sundown from now to surrender to our forces. All foreign envoys shall be safely escorted from Wuyue, including Xi Yanggui, princess of Ailao, and Prince Jingli and Princess Fengling of the Xin Empire. Empress Yinfeng will be given the choice of returning to her homeland in the Kingdom of Nanyue or remaining in Wuyue and joining the rest of the House of Qian under house arrest.

"Preposterous!"

Yinfeng raged as she read these words. She crushed the paper into a ball. Nearby, the soldiers hastily scrambled about, lining up into formation along the wall, notching their arrows and even rolling out canons that they aimed toward the approaching ships.

"Hold your fire!" The Empress shouted, analyzing the situation as best she could.

Those ships were heavily armed with artillery, and despite their defenses, the Imperial Guard would be unable to hold them off for long. After all, this was a palace, not a fortress. It wasn't built for defense in a siege, and only a few times in Wuyue's thousand-year history had it been subjected to direct assaults. The events unfolding were unprecedented, though so too had been the past few months.

"They won't attack again" Yinfeng spoke with confidence as she thought about the contents of that letter. "Technically, we were the ones who provoked this—I ordered that arrow to be fired at the Emir's ship, and their barrage was in retaliation to that. If they really wanted to fight, we would stand no chance against them."

Anxious looks appeared on the soldiers' faces. If the Empress herself was so pessimistic about their circumstances, how were they supposed to have the courage to defend the palace against such a threat?

Yinfeng breathed a sigh of relief as she spotted Zukang being brought through the second gate.

"Take him to the infirmary," she told her guards. "See to it that he has no visitors except the physician. I want to be the first to speak with him. But first, there is a more pressing matter at hand."

***

"They've found A-Kang? Where is he?"

Mingyue rose from the table with a start. Though he'd only had a few hours of sleep, satisfying his hunger after having not eaten for a day was of greater concern to him than getting enough rest. Neili had rushed over to prepare breakfast for the prince upon hearing that he had returned to his quarters, and now attended to him with platters of food.

Hansini had been the one to deliver the news to them that Zukang had been found.

"The infirmary," she said. "The Empress does not want him seeing guests."

She held him back as he tried to leave the room.

"How about Olekina?" Mingyue inquired. "Is there any news of him?"

Hansini shook her head. "He is still unaccounted for, and he is not the only one. I heard that some of the other foreign envoys were absent from the ceremony last night, though I'm not sure which ones exactly. I also heard that something happened at the main gate when your brother was rescued. But these are just rumors."

"I can confirm that those rumors are true," spoke a man's voice from the doorway.

They turned to see Narsieh Sasan lingering nearby, arms crossed as he leaned against the wall and eyed them.

"The Qinglong rebels are at the gates of the palace as we speak—the Empress has just convened an emergency meeting with the foreign envoys to discuss how they will proceed with the situation. And indeed, there *was* a foreign envoy absent from the ceremony last night—the Keliyetes, Princess Yi Seo-Yeon."

XV. The Princes' Interrogation

"Prince Narsieh, what are you doing here?" Hansini demanded. "The Palace of Lunar Serenity is not receiving guests at the moment."

"I apologize, Wei Hanxi, I simply came to pay my respects," Narsieh said, folding his hands and bowing to Mingyue. "Your Highness, I am sorry about the Emperor's passing, but I am glad that both you and the Crown Prince are in good health."

Mingyue accepted his condolences but quickly changed the subject, "You said the Yi Princess is also missing?"

"Indeed. She seems to have left the ball around the same time as your brother but hasn't been seen since. We can assume that whoever was responsible for kidnapping Zukang took her as well. That's why I'm here to ask your brother—"

"The Empress does not want visitors," Hansini repeated with frustration, as she attempted to shoo the Sassanian prince from the room.

Narsieh spoke calmly. "Wei Hanxi, my office is overseeing this case at the moment. As you know, for centuries the House of Sasan and the House of Qian have been close. As the current head of the Sasan family, it has now become my duty to act as a steward of the Imperial Family. The Keliyete delegation is distraught over the situation with Princess Seo-Yeon. As she is the betrothed to the Crown Prince, future Emperor of Wuyue, it is vital to uncover her whereabouts not only to ensure that there is no tension between Wuyue and the Khanate but also to prove our capabilities to Wuyue itself."

Hansini stood firm. "I cannot defy the Empress's orders."

Narsieh smiled. "I understand, but I was not asking for your permission. I will head over to the infirmary now. No need to worry, I will personally take responsibility for any grievances that the Empress may have."

"Let me come with you," Mingyue said quietly.

"Your Highness!" Hansini fumed.

"Ahaha…" Neili laughed nervously as he slipped out of the room, hoping to get away before things escalated.

"I will also take responsibility for the Empress's grievances," the prince nodded. "Wei Hanxi, you may retire for the day."

"*Hmph*," she huffed, following Neili out of the room.

Unfortunately, the guards standing outside the infirmary proved to be less yielding than Hansini, barring Mingyue and Narsieh from entry and suggesting that they return to their quarters.

"My soldiers are capable of protecting us," the Sassanian prince assured. "Now that the Crown Prince has returned, it is imperative that the Yi Princess and the other missing persons be found safe. That responsibility rests on me, and right now, Prince Zukang is the best person to go to for information."

"I understand," one of the guards spoke with frustration, "but I'm afraid we can't let you in. You may speak with him when the Empress allows it."

"A-Ming…?"

Zukang's strained voice came from inside the infirmary. After a few moments, he appeared in the window wearing a simple, white robe, his disheveled hair hanging down. He rubbed his eyes and groaned.

"Ah! I'm happy to see that you're okay! Come! Come inside, let's have a drink!"

"Has my brother been drinking?" Mingyue whispered in a low voice to the guards.

"The Empress said to bring him anything that he requests," one of the guards said. "He's been having a fit all morning and refused to stay in the infirmary unless we brought him something to drink."

"So, you're letting him drink but not letting us visit him," Narsieh noted. "I don't believe that's what the Empress had in mind when she asked you to take care of him."

The guards scoffed but didn't dare speak back. They knew better than to argue with someone of higher standing.

"A-Kang," Mingyue addressed his brother, "can you tell me what happened to you after the ball? Who took you?"

Zukang once again rubbed his eyes and groaned. *"Mnn...I don't...remember...any of that. I just remember Selah...dancing for me...hehe. I asked him to dance...he's a very good dancer you know..."*

"Selah..." Mingyue repeated, turning to Narsieh. "Selah is a foreigner, a Sogdian dancer gifted to my brother by the Xin envoy. Was he one of those who was unaccounted for?"

"Hm..." the Sassanian prince thought for a moment. "Not that I'm aware of. I only heard that members of the Keliyete delegation were missing. However, he is just a dancer, so had he gone missing as well, few would have noticed. But if he is the last person who was with the prince before his kidnapping, we should seek his whereabouts."

Mingyue nodded in agreement and turned back to his brother. "A-Kang, do you know where Yi Seo-Yeon might be?"

"Yi Seo-Yeon..." Zukang muttered. Then his eyes went wide in realization. "Yi Seo-Yeon! Ah! They took her! They said that if I didn't pretend to be you in the wedding ceremony, they would kill her!"

"Hold on, slow down your Highness," Narsieh tried to speak in a calm tone as Zukang's voice became louder and more frantic with each word. "Who took her?"

"I don't know! I don't know! They were wearing masks!" He suddenly froze and his voice fell quieter. "The man at the ceremony also had a mask. He...he was going to kill me...because he thought that I was you! But when he realized I wasn't you, he took me away. A-Ming, it's *you* that they're after!"

Those words from his brother sent a chill up Mingyue's spine. The first thing that came to his mind was the message he had found attached to that lantern on that island in the Lake of Tranquility.

The raven will paint the bright moon red.

"Please, I ask that you leave," the guards urged more forcefully this time. "He needs to rest."

Realizing that they wouldn't learn much from Zukang while he was in this drunken state, Narsieh and Mingyue reluctantly departed.

"I apologize for my brother's behaviour," said Mingyue, "it was a waste of time coming here."

"I disagree," Narsieh interrupted, "we uncovered a clue—that the Sogdian dancer was the last person he recalls seeing before being kidnapped. If we can find him, that will bring us one step closer to solving this mystery."

"I don't know where Selah's quarters are," Mingyue said.

"Then we shall begin where we *do* know to search," Narsieh proposed, "Prince Zukang's quarters.

***

They did search Zukang's quarters, however, they found nothing to be suspicious or out of place. The Crown Prince's servants and guards were anxious about the arrival of Mingyue and Narsieh, worried that they were suspects in his kidnapping, but the two princes simply wanted to ask them some questions.

"Why did you not report that the Crown Prince was missing before the wedding ceremony?" Narsieh wondered.

One of the servants nervously spoke up. "Your Highness, you must understand that the prince often frolics about the palace at night, going off to drink or wander about. We had assumed that he would return to prepare for the ceremony, but by the time we realized that something was amiss it was too late!"

"*Mnn*...I see..." Narsieh considered the response. "And what of the Sogdian dancer? Can any of you tell me where he might be?"

"Selah?" The servant said. "We haven't seen him since the night of the ball. His quarters are empty as well, it doesn't seem like there was an intrusion."

"I see," Narsieh muttered to himself, disappointed that their only lead was getting them nowhere.

As they began to depart, Narsieh brought up something that had been on his mind.

"One thing that bewilders me is how that masked man was able to get out of the palace with your brother. The walls and gates are heavily guarded, so how did they manage to slip through undetected? Did they have assistance from some of the soldiers, I wonder?"

"They were outside the wall?" Mingyue asked.

The Sassanian prince nodded. "In a small boat on the West Lake, is what I heard."

Mingyue thought back to the previous week when he had slipped out of the palace by boat with Erik to visit the Armenian Quarter during Jul. They had managed to bypass the guards and gates of the outer wall by exiting through a small opening hidden in the underbrush of one of the canals. Other than Erik, the others that had been with them that night included Agnes, Caleb, and Olekina. He could easily rule out the Norden delegation, as they had all been present with him at his quarters earlier that morning and wouldn't have been able to make it to the outer wall in such a short amount of time.

"There is a passage north of the main gate that leads outside the palace," Mingyue whispered.

"A passage?" Narsieh said in surprise. "Your Highness, how do you know of this?"

"I only found out recently," he replied, brushing the question aside. "Wu Liqing is aware of it as well."

"Wu Liqing?"

"My guard. He has also been missing since the ball."

"Ah, I see," Narsieh nodded, putting the pieces together. It was becoming increasingly clear that Olekina was the biggest suspect in this case. "Then shall we head to his quarters and continue to search for clues there?"

Mingyue was embarrassed that he didn't know where Olekina's quarters were, but after a bit of asking around they finally happened upon it. Most soldiers and servants in the palace shared communal living spaces, which primarily consisted of a place to sleep and eat, as most of their days were occupied elsewhere. Olekina, however, as a higher-ranking soldier who directly attended to the prince, had his own chambers. Mingyue didn't know what to expect, but he was a bit surprised to find nothing out of the ordinary upon first arriving. He suggested that they leave, but Narsieh insisted they look around a bit longer, convinced that there was more here than met the eye.

Mingyue scoured the shelves and drawers, which were tidy and mostly empty of any belongings. A few objects did stand out to him—notably the foreign, ornamental carvings and figurines depicting people and animals. These seemed to be heirlooms passed down in Olekina's family. One object in particular stood out among the others, a bamboo dragonfly, a toy that would fly up into the air when spun. Seeing the toy here, a memory came flooding back to Mingyue, one which he had all but forgotten about until now.

"Your Highness? Are you alright?" A trace of concern lingered in Narsieh's voice as the other prince noticed a shift in Mingyue's expression.

"*Mnn*," Mingyue nodded. He showed the toy to Narsieh. "I was just reminded of when I first met Wu Liqing."

Before he knew it, he was recounting the story.

Part VI

Light in the Darkness

I. Lingering Memory

13/02/11th Year of the Golden Dragon Emperor

Year of the Earthen Rat

It was nearly eight years ago, during the festival of Nowruz, the Persian New Year. Mingyue had just visited the main temple with his family, where the House of Sasan held festivities. Being one of the first times he could remember leaving the palace, Mingyue was naturally excited, and begged his mother to take him out to explore more of the city. She reluctantly agreed under the condition that he remained by her side at all times. Taking a few of her closest guards and donning simple cloaks to conceal their identities, they made their way through the bustling streets of the Persian Quarter.

Mingyue's eyes glistened at every sight— colourful lights and displays, enthusiastic street performers dancing, vendors selling dishes wafting with the scent of exotic spices, and ornately decorated painted eggs. He pulled Huamei toward one particular vendor selling all kinds of toys that would pique the interest of any child.

"Ho ho, Nowruz Mubarak my friend!"

The vendor's enthusiastic greeting startled Mingyue, who wasn't used to people behaving in such a loud and flamboyant manner. The man sported a heavy beard, spoke in a thick accent, and wore colourful robes that matched those of the lights and decorations around them. Though initially scared of his appearance, as soon as the man began showcasing the toys he was selling, Mingyue soon realized that there was nothing to be afraid of. "

Which toy would you like today? How about a set of dolls from the Roman Volga!"

He pulled out a wooden doll of a woman, opening it up to reveal another smaller doll inside. Again and again, he opened the dolls, revealing smaller and smaller ones within. The young prince was at first mesmerized by this, but soon lost interest.

"Or how about a spinning top? Or a kite? Or, if you wish for something more sophisticated, how about a set of Majiang tiles? Your mother may have to teach you how to play."

Mingyue was only half listening to the man's words, as his attention instead was drawn toward a simple-looking toy resting on the table nearby. Composed of only two thin strips of bamboo forming the shape of a T, the toy was light and nimble, and Mingyue couldn't exactly tell what it was supposed to be.

The vendor, noticing the boy's interest, smiled as he took hold of the bamboo toy.

"Ah, so you like this one? This is a bamboo dragonfly, let me show you how it works. It's very simple."

Placing the shaft of the toy between his two palms, the man quickly spun it between his hands and propelled it up. Mingyue's eyes grew wide as he watched the toy spin upwards into the sky, floating higher and higher, seeming as if it would never come down. After a while, it finally did, gently descending back toward the ground as the propellers slowed in their rotation. The vendor reached up to retrieve it before it hit the ground.

"How about it, my friend? Do you like this one?"

Mingyue, too shy to say anything, simply stared at the bamboo dragonfly with wide eyes. Behind him, Huamei smiled as she rested a gentle hand on her son's shoulder.

"He does like it. We'll buy that one."

***

As they continued through the busy streets, several guards inconspicuously trailing behind them, Mingyue held onto his mother with his left hand as he twirled the bamboo dragonfly with his right. He tried a few times to spin it as that man had so that it would fly up into the sky but was unable to with only one hand.

"You can play with it when we get back to the palace, okay?" Huamei smiled at him. "But right now, there are too many people around, and you have to hold onto my hand."

The prince pouted in disappointment but said nothing as they continued on their way. They were nearing the end of the street, about to come into view of the Fire Temple again from where they would return to the palace when Huamei steered them off to the side.

"There's a vendor here selling Sogdian delicacies," she explained to the guards behind them. "I haven't had any in a while, and I'm sure Yanlu would enjoy tasting some as well. Let me purchase some before we return to the temple."

The guards nodded in approval, and Huamei briefly let go of Mingyue's hand so she could retrieve some coins to pay the vendor with. This was his chance! With both hands free, Mingyue placed the shaft of his toy between his palms and spun it the way that man had demonstrated. It worked! But perhaps it worked too well.

The toy fluttered high above the street, soaring over the heads of festival goers and veering off to the side where it disappeared down an alleyway. The young prince instinctively chased after it.

"Your Highness! Come back!" One of the guards shouted.

They all immediately took notice of the prince disappearing into the crowd, but without seeing which way the bamboo dragonfly had gone, they had no idea which direction he was headed. The use of *'Your Highness'* stirred the attention of those nearby.

Your Highness? Is the imperial family here?

Huamei cursed silently as she drew her hood further over her head, obscuring her face as she hastily slipped away to chase after her son.

"Which way did he go?" She hissed sharply to the guards.

"I...I don't know!" One replied nervously.

They split up, frantically combing the area in search of the prince, but there were so many people around that any child would easily become lost in the crowd if they were separated from their parents. But Mingyue had not gone far at all, slipping into a narrow alleyway in pursuit of the bamboo dragonfly. The alley consisted of a steep incline, with uneven steps that led upwards toward the backstreets and away from the core of the Persian Quarter. Despite being only a few steps away from the main street, the atmosphere here was completely different—the air felt heavy, and it was dark, lifeless, and completely devoid of people. Mingyue was scared to be alone here, but he had to find that bamboo dragonfly before he turned back. A little way up the path, he spotted it on the ground. With a renewed sense of determination and courage at the discovery of his toy, he rushed up the steps to retrieve it.

Out from the shadows, a hand emerged and took hold of the toy just as Mingyue had reached it. Surprised, the young prince gazed upwards and found himself staring into a pair of deep brown eyes. He was startled by the encounter, stumbling backward, and falling down a few of the steps.

"Sorry," the boy from the shadows spoke. "I didn't mean to scare you."

Kneeling, he extended a hand to Mingyue. The prince cautiously took hold of it, getting a good look at the other boy for the first time. He must have been only a few years older than Mingyue but was far taller than the young prince. His hair was disheveled and unkempt; thin, tattered rags were the only clothes covering his frail body, despite the chilly temperature at this time of year. However, what Mingyue found to be the most striking feature of the boy was his dark skin. Mingyue could hardly see him amidst the darkness of the alleyway.

A gentle smile appeared on the stranger's face. "My name is Olekina. What is yours?"

"My name...? My name is..."

He suddenly remembered that he wasn't supposed to reveal his identity to anyone. In the world outside the palace, an imperial prince who was all alone could easily become a target. He quickly changed the conversation, pointing to the bamboo dragonfly in Olekina's other hand.

"You are holding my toy."

"'You are holding my toy'? That's a rather long name," Olekina replied with a tone of complete seriousness.

"That's not my name," the prince muttered, unsure as to whether the other boy was joking or not. "I don't have to tell you my name, but you have to give me my toy back."

"That doesn't seem quite fair," Olekina remarked.

Mingyue was growing frustrated—no one had ever treated him like this before. Was this what life was like for those who were not of nobility? He began to approach Olekina and was about to swipe the bamboo dragonfly from the other boy's hand, when Olekina suddenly backed away fearfully, his eyes going wide. Mingyue was confused, but he quickly realized that Olekina wasn't staring at him, but behind him. Before he could turn around, a bag was pulled over his head and he felt himself hoisted up onto someone's shoulder.

"Olekina!" A man's voice shouted. "You don't know how much trouble we went through tracking you down! Boss isn't gonna be happy."

Three men had emerged from the alleyway, their elegant outfits in stark contrast with the filthy grim of the side street. They spread out, cautiously trying to surround Olekina, but he swiped up a bamboo pole that was leaning against a nearby wall.

"Release him," he demanded.

"Your friend here?" The man holding Mingyue patted him on the back. "Boss will put him to good work. If you come back with us, no harm will come to him."

One of the men leaped toward Olekina, but the boy jabbed him with the pole and sent him crashing into the wall. Despite his much smaller stature and build than these men, he was a formidable fighter, subduing two of the three within seconds.

"*Tch...*" the man holding Mingyue cursed and began making his escape. The young prince was helpless throughout the entire ordeal, struggling in vain against the man's grip. "I'll take this one! You two better bring him in!"

As Mingyue was whisked away by his kidnapper, Olekina continued pummeling the other two men to the ground—they stood no chance against him.

"*Gah*!" One of the men gasped in pain. "Why fight us? No matter how many times you defeat us, Boss will keep sending men after you! Why don't you just come back to him? He'll pay you well!"

"I never wanted to work for that man," Olekina replied calmly, pointing the pole at the men's heads. "I bided my time until I was strong enough to escape and fend for myself. I'm not going back there."

"*Tch*," the man's hand slowly inched into his coat pockets, but Olekina pinned it to the ground before he could grab the crossbow hidden inside. The man screeched in agony.

These sounds drew attention from the street, including from Huamei and her guards.

"A-Ming? A-Ming are you there?" She called out for her son. It wasn't long before she was in the alleyway, followed by her guards.

"What is going on here?!" One of the guards demanded.

The sight of two grown men bruised and beaten on the ground at the hands of a child was certainly strange to behold.

Olekina looked upon the newcomers with curiosity. Though the Crown Princess wore a simple hooded cloak to conceal her identity, he could instantly tell by the quality of her makeup and hairstyle that she was no commoner.

"These thugs are kidnappers," Olekina spat. "I was just teaching them a lesson."

Concern filled Huamei's face. "My friend, can you tell if you saw another child come this way? A boy about your age."

"Ah," Olekina nodded. "'You are holding my toy'? He was taken by them." He prodded the pole deeper into the man's hand, who yelped again in pain. "Where did you take him? Say where you took him!"

"Ah! Okay okay! He's at the base! You know where that is!"

Olekina released his pole from the man's hand and turned to Huamei and her soldiers.

"Follow me, I can show you the way. And make sure these men are apprehended. Scum like them shouldn't be allowed to exist in the city."

II. Dragon of the Night

13/02/11th Year of the Golden Dragon Emperor

Year of the Earthen Rat

Olekina led Huamei and her guards through the narrow alleyways of the Persian Quarter until the group finally arrived at the crossroads with the Semu and Melayu Quarters. An extravagant building owned by some wealthy Semu merchants dominated the area. This was where Olekina was leading them.

"The Gushi Estate?" Huamei wondered with hesitancy in her voice. "This is where they took him?"

"The merchants here play a central role in black market child trafficking," Olekina explained casually. "Maybe that comes as a surprise to nobles such as you, but it's a well-known fact to most of the underclasses. If you can't afford to take care of your children, sell them to the Gushi Estate."

"I've never heard of such a thing..." Huamei said in disbelief. "Are you sure? This is the Gushi Estate that you're speaking of.

"I would know," Olekina replied dismissively. "After all, I was one of many children in their possession."

"Your Highness, what should we do?" One of Huamei's guards whispered to her. "We can't simply intrude on the Gushi Estate. They wield tremendous influence over the Semu Quarter."

Olekina didn't bother sticking around to listen to their debate. He took matters into his own hands.

"Upper-class folks are far too concerned with politics and etiquette," he sighed to himself in disgust. "This is why they can never get anything accomplished."

He hoisted himself up a wall and jumped down onto the estate's property. It wasn't long before he had caused quite a disturbance, setting small fires by taking burning lanterns and igniting paper windows along the walls of the building. Guards were called out to quench the flames, and amidst the chaos, Olekina slipped past their detection with ease.

Mingyue had been taken directly to the Boss, a burly Semu man dressed in exquisite attire.

"We found Olekina in the Persian Quarter," Mingyue's kidnapper explained, "along with this child. They'll bring in Olekina soon, don't worry Boss!"

The Boss stared at Mingyue curiously. The young prince stood frozen in place, too terrified to move or even speak. His eyes went wide in fear as the towering man suddenly approached and tore off his cloak. The look on the Boss's face shifted from curiosity to shock as the royal robes Mingyue was wearing beneath were unveiled. He turned to his henchman and slapped him across the face, sending him tumbling to the ground.

"YOU FOOL! DO YOU REALIZE WHO THIS IS?!"

The kidnapper rubbed the side of his face and spoke up in a nervous voice.

"I…I didn't see what he was wearing, Boss! But he seems to be pretty high-class! I'm sure he'll fetch a hefty price on the market!"

"IDIOT!! THESE ARE ROBES MADE WITH THE FINEST SILKS OF NANYUE! ONLY THE IMPERIAL FAMILY WEARS SUCH ROBES!"

"Ah…the Imperial family…?!" Fear spread across the kidnapper's face. "B-but Boss, if the Imperial family doesn't find out that we took him, it should be fine…"

Sudden shouts from the ensuing chaos unfolding elsewhere in the estate caught the Boss's attention.

"*UGH*! WHAT NOW?!"

It was at that moment that a figure dropped down into the room from the large windows overhead, swiftly taking out the Boss's guards before sweeping in and drawing a blade across the large man's neck. It was Olekina.

"*Tch*," spat the Boss. "He said you'd be back."

"Let him go," Olekina demanded, pressing the blade further into the Boss's skin.

Mingyue watched on in terror, unable to move.

The Boss chuckled. "The prince? He is free to leave whenever he wishes. This is Wuyue after all, isn't it? The entire country is in the possession of the Yue Dynasty! They are free to go where they wish and do as they please! But let me ask you this, Olekina—why is it that you are holding this blade against my throat and not his? Was it not *I* who clothed you and fed you and gave you a roof over your head after your parents died? I am a simple merchant who owns but a small estate in comparison to the vast wealth of the House of Qian, and yet I was generous enough to share that with you! What did this *prince* ever give to you? His family has the wealth to grant you far more than you could ever desire, yet they did not even provide you with scraps of food for you to survive. You may hate me, but I gave you everything you have! What has *he* ever done for you?!"

Olekina's hands trembled as his gaze fell upon Mingyue. "P-prince…? You're…a Yue Prince…?"

As he lowered the blade, Mingyue came to the horrible realization that perhaps the person he should fear most in this room was not the Boss, but Olekina—the scarred, orphaned boy whom he'd met in an alleyway.

The Boss slowly backed away as Olekina's attention was drawn away from him.

"Yes! Do you see the robes he's wearing? Even *I* cannot afford such expensive attire! It probably costs more money than your parents earned in their entire lives! At least your parents worked for what they had, same as me! What did he ever do to earn such a luxurious standard of living? He was born into the right family, that's all! His wealth comes from the taxes of people like us!"

Slowly, Olekina began stepping toward the young prince. He spoke in a calm voice, but to Mingyue it was not soothing, but eerie.

"My father was a Zanzibari merchant. My mother was Kunlun, descended from a prominent family that served the House of Qian during ancient times. Over the centuries, the family went into decline and soon they had lost all their status. Regardless, my father loved my mother. I was born shortly after they met, and they raised me in the Kunlun Quarter. I was barely old enough to remember when the outbreak of the Plague took place. Do you remember it? Perhaps you were too young. Though, even if you were old enough, I suppose it didn't really affect the Imperial family anyways."

Olekina rubbed the blade between his fingers.

"My parents fell ill with the Plague. My father tried to bring my mother to a doctor, but they were overwhelmed with the number of sick people coming in. There were rumors that many physicians and doctors had been brought into the Imperial Palace at the time to ensure the well-being of the House of Qian. And so as a last resort, that's where he brought my mother. However, standing before the front gates, they were chased away by the guards."

"How dare you bring the Plague to the gates of the palace!" The guards had shouted.

"There are no doctors in the city! Please, just let them see my wife!" Olekina's father had begged.

"Filthy foreigner! Leave immediately or we will open fire!"

Olekina turned over the blade in his hand, returning it to its sheath. "Just like that, my parents were turned away. They died a short while later."

"I…I'm sorry…" Mingyue didn't know what else to say. "Your parents…shouldn't have been treated that way…"

"You need not apologize, your Highness. It was not you who turned my parents away. Individuals must take responsibility for their own sins."

At that moment, the doors of the room were flung open and Huamei's soldiers came rushing in. The Boss's eyes went wide in shock.

"OLEKINA! WHAT IS THIS?!"

The boy simply raised his hand, directing an accusatory finger at the Boss.

"This is the man who kidnapped the prince."

**

The Boss was soon apprehended by the Imperial Guard, and the flames which Olekina set in the Gushi Estate were doused. Mingyue was reunited with his mother, while Olekina watched on as the two embraced.

"Thank you for leading me to him," Huamei rested her gaze on Olekina as she held her son in her arms.

Olekina was surprised by her words. He never expected that the nobility would show gratitude for anything, especially toward a commoner such as himself. He shrugged and crossed his arms nonchalantly.

"It is my duty as a citizen of Wuyue to defend the prince."

Huamei smiled and reached out to take Olekina's hand, once again catching him off guard.

"Well, it is *my* duty as the Crown Princess to care for my citizens. Tell me, child, what can I do for you?"

The young man paused for a moment before meeting the princess's gaze.

"Bringing this man to justice is the most I could ask for," Olekina replied, eyeing the Boss. "He has done far too much harm to far too many people but has gotten away with it for so long due to his status. I will be at peace knowing that he is no longer a threat to others, especially those like me."

"I will see to it immediately," nodded the princess. "Is that all?"

As Mingyue pulled away from his mother, the two boys locked eyes. Olekina stared deep into the prince's gaze—he had beautiful lashes, and his eyes had a warm, deep brown glow to them, yet they were unremarkably still the eyes of a child, no different than himself. Growing up, he had come to see those of high social standings, particularly the nobility, as being cruel and heartless. He was all too familiar with the cold, lifeless eyes of those around him—the Boss, the other merchants, the wealthy aristocrats and nobles who would spit on him in the streets if they even paid him any attention at all.

"That is all," Olekina nodded. Before turning to depart, he produced the bamboo dragonfly from his pocket and placed it into the hands of Mingyue. "Your toy, your Highness. I apologize for not giving it to you earlier."

The prince silently accepted the bamboo dragonfly and watched as the other boy began to make his way out the doors of the estate.

"Wait!" Mingyue called out.

Olekina paused in his tracks and turned to look back once again.

"Where will you go now?" Mingyue wondered.

"Back to the streets," Olekina shrugged. "Where else?"

The young prince couldn't accept that answer and ran up to take Olekina's hand. The other boy flinched with discomfort but didn't pull away.

"You can come back to live in the palace if you want," Mingyue suggested.

He blushed as he made that offer—he was worried that Olekina would be somehow offended or reject his proposal. Instead, a look of surprise crossed the young man's face.

"Your Highness…I couldn't possibly…"

Mingyue turned to his mother with pleading eyes. "Mother, he can come live in the palace with us, right? There's enough space for everyone!"

Huamei chuckled and nodded her head. "Of course, he can. But that decision is up to him."

Mingyue turned to Olekina expectantly. Olekina didn't particularly enjoy the idea of tying himself down to one particular person or place, but there was something unexplainable about this young prince that he was drawn to.

"I…I would be happy to."

Mingyue gleamed—it was one of the only times Olekina had ever seen him smile in such a genuine manner. It was at that moment that Olekina decided he would devote the rest of his life to protecting this boy, this boy who still held onto his youthful innocence and hadn't been corrupted by the darkness of the world as he had.

"For you," Mingyue said.

He stretched out his hand to Olekina, passing him the bamboo dragonfly. Olekina hesitantly accepted the gift. He hoped that one day, he would once again see the prince smile as he had on the day they first met.

III. Fated Departure

"A touching tale," smiled Narsieh, twirling the bamboo dragonfly between his fingers before returning it to the shelf.

Mingyue nodded slowly. "To be honest, I had forgotten about that memory until now…"

"Oh?" Narsieh cocked his head in curiosity. "I suppose you were young when it happened. Though, you seemed to recount your meeting with Wu Liqing quite vividly. It is strange that you would've forgotten about it."

The Yue prince agreed. He felt slightly disturbed that he had completely forgotten about how he met Olekina until now. He knew that these memories were his own but having them suddenly wash over him as soon as he set eyes upon the bamboo dragonfly was a bit overwhelming.

"It couldn't have been Wu Liqing who killed the Emperor," he muttered quietly.

Despite knowing that Olekina was currently the most suspicious person of interest involved in the incident at the wedding ceremony, Mingyue knew in his heart that it couldn't be him.

"Olekina would never do such a thing."

Narsieh wasn't as convinced. "It seemed that Wu Liqing expressed disdain toward the nobility when you first met. He even held a knife to you, isn't that correct? Pardon me for suggesting this, your Highness, but that only makes him a greater suspect than he already was. What if he decided to accept your invitation into the palace with the goal of one day carrying out the Qiantang Festival Massacre?"

"Nonsense," Mingyue clenched his fist and slammed it on the shelf, unintentionally startling the Sassanian prince, who quickly fell silent. It was rare that the Yue prince would speak in such a tone. "When Olekina first came to the palace, I expected nothing of him. It was through his own choice that he decided to enter the Imperial Guard. I did not ask him to do that."

"*Hmm*…I see…"

Something drew Narsieh's attention away from Mingyue to the floor. The Yue prince followed his gaze but didn't spot anything out of the ordinary. Leaning down to rub his finger across the ground, however, the Narsieh quickly uncovered a thin trail of white powder coating the wooden planks.

"What is that?" Mingyue inquired.

Narsieh lifted his hand to his face, hesitantly considering whether or not he should take in the scent of the powder to determine what it might be. He decided against it.

"I have no idea, but it seems that this room may not have been completely undisturbed after all. We may have yet another lead on our hands."

***

Elsewhere in the palace, Yinfeng had convened a meeting with all the foreign envoys to discuss the situation unfolding outside the palace gates. Notably absent was Princess Seo-Yeon, though others from the Keliyete delegation came in her place. Tensions were high, yet the Empress managed to relay information calmly to those present.

"The rebels have promised a safe escort out of Wuyue over the next three days," she explained. "For those who wish to depart, you may do so."

Murmurs and whispers arose as the Empress spoke those words. It seemed she had nothing else to say about the situation.

"Safe passage?!" Yanggui exclaimed in disbelief. She choked on her words as her voice filled with emotion. "Those *rebels* are responsible for the death of the Crown Princess, and the Emperor himself! Your Majesty, how can we trust them to give us safe passage?! Those monsters should be brought to justice!"

The Empress rested her head in her hand, rubbing her temple in fatigue. Having lost her husband, daughter, and nearly her grandson in such a short amount of time was overwhelming, and she hadn't had the opportunity to fully process everything yet.

"We still do not understand the complexity of the situation, and how the rebels are connected to events within the palace. For those who do not wish to accept the terms of the rebels' proposal, you may remain here. However, I cannot guarantee your safety or protection. The decision is up to you."

"I don't believe it is wise," Aysun Sultana spoke up, crossing her arms defiantly at the suggestion.

Most of the others seemed less certain. On the one hand, they were being given the option to leave the palace unharmed, returning to their home countries. Yet there was a deep sense of underlying guilt that they would be able to depart from Qiantang while at the same time leaving the Imperial Family behind, abandoning their fate into the hands of those who had already killed several members of the nobility. Would they be able to carry the burden of knowing that they left behind those who had welcomed them, as the greatest empire in the world was reduced to smoldering remains?

"We should return to Kaifeng," Jingli whispered to his sister.

Fengling's face fell dark at her brother's suggestion. "A-Li, what about Mingyue? What about Sheli and Zukang? They're our cousins! How can we just abandon them here? They could be killed!"

"And we might be too if we stay behind and don't take this opportunity to escape," Jingli said through clenched teeth.

Of course, he knew it was wrong of him to only be thinking of saving his own skin. But at the same time, he knew that it would not be helping anyone if they stayed behind.

"The rebels will not harm us if we leave under their conditions, I'm sure of it. If we return to Kaifeng, we can deliver news to Mother of what has happened. She'll be able to provide more support than we will if we stay."

"Will she?" Fengling questioned doubtfully.

Jingli also understood that the likelihood their mother offering assistance to her estranged family was low.

"We must try. We can't stay here."

The other delegates were equally torn at the decision. If they departed, what would become of their diplomatic relations with Wuyue now that they had fled, leaving the House of Qian behind? But that being said, if the House of Qian truly was on the verge of being overthrown, would any of those relations even matter anymore?

"Your Majesty, what about you?" Concern filled Prince Sundar's eyes as the Karnatan noble attempted to maintain composure.

Yinfeng waved her hand dismissively. "I have been granted safe passage to Nanyue, but I will remain here in the palace, with my family."

"Your Majesty, you can't!" Sundar exclaimed.

The Empress remained unfazed as anxiety swept through the others. Nobles and ambassadors from each of the envoys began to furiously debate one another over what actions they would take.

"Return to Kyoto," Prince Hyousuke ordered the members of his delegation.

"Your Highness, you must come with us!" One member of his delegation pleaded.

The Ansei Prince simply smiled. "I have married into the House of Qian. I must remain here in Wuyue, with Princess Sheli." His gaze then fell on Amaru Huancahuari, the Tahuantinsuyu prince who had arrived in Wuyue with him. "However, I ask that you deliver Prince Amaru safely to his homeland. We have shared many experiences during our travels, but I'm sure by now that he wishes to return home."

Amaru flashed a bittersweet smile as he nostalgically reminisced over all he'd seen and done since departing from Tahuantinsuyu.

"It was a pleasure to journey alongside you. I wish you all the best."

The delegates from the Keliyete Khanate struggled the most with their decision. With the Yi Princess absent, they were split between those who wished to leave Wuyue and those who wanted to remain and determine her whereabouts. The Volga Romans, on the other hand, were absolute in their intent to leave. Princess Irina did not hesitate in accepting the offer to return to Moskva, though her attempt to persuade Erik to depart with her were futile.

"This expedition has proved to be far more troublesome than I had anticipated," she sighed.

"I'm staying," the Norden prince said simply. Like Irina, he too was resolute in his decision.

"You can't be serious," Irina laughed bitterly. "After everything that has happened, how could you even consider that?!"

"That is why I wish to stay," he said. "The purpose of us coming here was to strengthen relations with Wuyue. If we leave now and abandon the House of Qian into the hands of the rebels, it will have all been for nothing. You can return to Moskva, but I will remain here."

Irina would hardly accept that answer. She knew that Erik's reasons for wanting to stay extended beyond simple diplomatic intentions—it was no secret that he and Mingyue had grown close over the past few months. Irina couldn't understand how exactly this had transpired. After all, the two hadn't particularly spent much time together. Yet there was some strange, underlying connection between the two. She could tell that Erik felt much closer to Mingyue than he did to her, despite having known her for much longer, and that this feeling was mutual from the Yue prince. She absolutely could not tolerate this. Allowing him to remain in Wuyue with Mingyue wasn't an option.

But before she could say anything, Erik had already turned to leave, Agnes and Caleb accompanying him on the way.

"Where do you think you're going?!" She shouted out after him. "Erik? Erik! Wait!"

The fuss she was making drew the attention of many of the other delegates, who sighed and shook their heads in annoyance and disapproval as they watched the scene unfold. Irina was oblivious to all this. She reached out, grabbing the Norden prince by the sleeve. For a brief moment, he paused and turned back to her.

"Please let go of him."

It was Caleb speaking. The young man had stepped foot between the two, taking hold of Irina's wrist and beckoning her to unhand him.

"I'm staying," Erik held a firm gaze as his jade-green eyes met her.

Irina was shocked by this development, reluctantly releasing Erik from her grasp. Knowing she would be unable to persuade him, she watched helplessly as he disappeared out into the cold winter night, leaving her behind, all on her own.

IV. Two Souls

19/11/18th Year of the Golden Dragon Emperor

Year of the Wooden Goat

Mingyue spent the coming days sealed away in his quarters, both out of the Empress's orders and of his own choosing. The past few days—not to mention months—had been utterly draining. Having to meet and interact with so many new people was tiring enough given that he was hardly used to interacting with those he didn't know. But on top of that, he had also lost so many of those who were close to him in such a sudden and traumatic manner. He didn't know how he had managed to maintain his sanity through this all and decided it would be best to take some time away from the rest of the world. However, he had also learned that the foreign envoys were soon to be departing from Wuyue. Amidst all the hardship he'd endured since they first arrived, the Norden prince had been the one person in his life who he constantly felt reassured by. He didn't quite understand why that was but felt compelled to at least pay Erik a visit one last time before bidding him off from the palace.

It was the day before the envoys were scheduled to depart, and he was just about to make his way to the Palace of Heavenly Peace when Hansini arrived to deliver him a message.

"The Norden prince is here to see you," she said, a visible expression of annoyance in her eyes.

Mingyue felt his heart flutter at her words. "Erik? Why is he here?"

Before he could even finish his question, Hansini had disappeared down the terrace, and Mingyue's attention rested upon the sight of the Norden prince lingering in the garden, gazing upwards with a smile as he observed the thin layer of snow coating the tree branches above. He turned at the sound of Mingyue's voice.

"Qian Ming!" He exclaimed.

"E-Erik...?" The Yue prince said with surprise. "What are you doing here?"

The question came off as a bit standoffish, which he hadn't intended.

"Just wanted to drop by and see how you were doing. I hope that's okay with you. I left Caleb and Agnes behind so you wouldn't be too overwhelmed."

"Ah," Mingyue nodded. "Please bid them farewell on my behalf."

"Oh?" The Norden prince cocked his head in confusion. "Oh, I'm not here to say goodbye! I've decided that the Norden envoy will remain here in the palace."

Mingyue was taken aback. "Remain here? You can't. I don't know what the rebels plan on doing with those who remain behind…"

"We'll face them together then," Erik smiled.

By this point, he had come up next to Mingyue, the two now standing only an arm's length apart. Mingyue's gaze was tilted upwards as his eyes locked with the slightly taller boy. Erik's gaze tilted down.

"You can't…" was all Mingyue managed to say.

"Well, I've already made my decision," Erik said in a gentle tone. "And I've told Irina too. I'd much rather stay here with you than spend the next several months traveling back to the West with her, haha!"

Mingyue scoffed lightly. "That's a bit harsh to say about your fiancée, no?"

"Aha…" Erik laughed nervously. "I didn't mean to sound harsh; it was an exaggeration. Is that the right word in Wuyueyu? Caleb's been trying to teach me but it's difficult to pick up. *Hm*…perhaps you don't have sarcasm in your language?"

Mingyue chuckled and shook his head. "We do have sarcasm. But are you saying you were being sarcastic about that?"

"Well…no…" Erik lowered his face. "Princess Irina is…difficult to be around. It's nothing personal. I know that to others she can be…snobbish and aggravating. But that's not the reason why I dislike her."

"Oh? Then what is it?"

Mingyue was intrigued. Irina indeed seemed to be a generally unbearable individual to be around, despite the little time he had spent with her. But if this wasn't the reason Erik disliked her, then what else could it be? Was there perhaps something even worse about the Roman princess's character that Mingyue hadn't witnessed yet?

"Well..." the Norden prince smiled nonchalantly as his attention was once again drawn to the lifeless tree in the garden, coated in a thin layer of snow. "It is because I wasn't given the choice in who I was to be engaged to. One day, I was just told that the Roman princess was to be my future wife. I'd never even met her before. I suppose I don't have to tell you what that's like though."

"It is difficult," Mingyue admitted.

Though in Mingyue's case, it wasn't being in Alaneya's presence that he found difficult. It was the pervasive feeling of emptiness, as if he were missing something, which bothered him. But that wasn't due to the Venesian noblewoman herself.

"I know it is wrong for me to dislike her for something that is out of her control as well," Erik mumbled. His cheerful demeanor had completely vanished, a somber expression now replacing it as his eyes fell downcast. "But for me, it feels like I am being forced to give my heart to her, even if I wish to give it to someone else..."

"Someone else...?" Mingyue repeated in a whisper.

"*Mnn*..." Erik nodded. "There was...someone whom I once loved. Well...I still love them. It's just...they are not in this world. Not anymore."

"Oh...I see..." Mingyue's voice was barely a whisper. "I'm sorry."

The Norden prince forced a smile. "No, no need to apologize! It was very difficult when I lost them, and I guess I just took out that anger on Irina. It was unfair of me to do that. But, ever since I came to Wuyue, I've felt like this is a new beginning for me. You know, you remind me a lot of them..."

"H-how...? In what way...?"

Mingyue felt as if his heart were going to beat out of his chest. He was flustered, but at the same time, a flood of other emotions suddenly washed over him. He reminded Erik of the person he once loved? Was that the reason Erik was deciding to stay behind? Was that the only reason Erik enjoyed being in his presence in the first place? Not because of who he was, but of who he reminded Erik of?

"*Hm*…in every way, really…" Erik gleamed.

Mingyue was overwhelmed by the conflicting emotions bubbling up inside him. Every time Erik smiled, he felt as if the entire world stood still. But was that all just fake? Did Erik only care for him because he saw him as someone he was not? But at the same time, why did Mingyue himself even enjoy being in Erik's presence in the first place? It wasn't like the two of them had known each other long or even spent much time together. Yet, whenever he was in the Norden prince's presence, he likewise always felt a strange sense of familiarity. Did Erik remind him of someone he once loved as well? But he had never loved anyone in that way before…

"*Tch*…" Mingyue rolled his eyes. Though he felt hurt, flustered, anxious, and confused all at the same time, he put forth an unfazed expression as he brushed Erik's words aside. "So just because Western men don't grow out their hair, now I look like a Western woman to you?"

"I never said that they were a woman," Erik replied simply.

The air fell still at those words. The Yue prince felt every muscle in his body suddenly tense up, rendering him completely unable to move. He didn't know why he was reacting in such a negative way to those words—he didn't want to, but he felt as if he weren't in control of himself.

"Ah…I'm sorry for making you uncomfortable," Erik took a step back hesitantly as his face flushed a bright pink. "I didn't mean to. I hope you don't think any differently of me…"

Finally regaining some control of his senses, the tense feeling in Mingyue's body instantly subsided. His legs wobbled and he feared that he would collapse to the floor. He felt as though he were going to melt away.

"So, the real reason you wanted to stay in Wuyue is because of this? Because…I remind you of the boy you once loved…?"

As that question slipped through his lips, Caleb's comments regarding Erik on the night of Jul came back to him.

It was like he was always meant to be here—I have never seen him as happy as he has been since he came to Wuyue. This place has given him a second chance.

"A second chance?" Mingyue said bitterly. "Is that all you see in me?"

In his mind, he was jumping rapidly from one thought to another, stirring up a whole host of complex emotions that only riled him up further. He didn't want to be angry at Erik, but he was losing control.

"No..." Erik muttered. His whisper was barely audible. "I...I don't see you that way at all. You are Mingyue, Second Prince of Wuyue. You aren't...the person who I loved. I know that. Perhaps I had just hoped that I wouldn't repeat the same mistakes with you as I had with him. It is selfish of me to think of you and him as the same person. But I do care about you...and not only because you remind me of him."

The Norden prince was just as overcome by emotion as Mingyue was, his eyes filled with regret and longing. The Yue prince felt guilty for turning on him so harshly, but at the same time, his own feelings wouldn't subside.

Erik hastily bowed to the other prince, averting his gaze the entire time.

"I best return to my chambers now. I bid you well this evening, your Highness."

Before Mingyue could object or even reach out to pull Erik back, the Norden prince slipped away down the snow-covered path, soon disappearing from view. Mingyue's feet remained firmly in place, refusing to move, despite desiring to chase after him.

He cursed himself silently at how he'd handled the situation, as tears welled in the corners of his eyes. He quickly wiped them away, not wanting Hansini or anyone else to see him in such a state should they return.

Why am I upset over this? He thought to himself. *Why should I care what he thinks of me? None of that matters.*

Yet inside, he felt that it *did* matter. Why? He had no idea. He didn't understand why it hurt so much to see Erik in such a state, to hear that Erik had once loved someone, and to think that the relationship between the two of them was disingenuous. Yet at the same time, there was some inexplicable attachment he felt toward Erik, a yearning for him as if he'd known him all his life, and a sense of loss that they lived in two separate worlds. None of it made any sense. How could one feel such a longing toward someone they hardly knew, yet someone who felt so familiar?

Perhaps this inexplicable feeling I have for him is the same feeling he has for me...

V. Old Departure, New Arrival

Mingyue found it difficult to sleep that night. As he tossed and turned back and forth in his bed, his mind kept bringing up his confrontation with Erik, and how much he regretted the things he'd said. He hadn't meant to say those things, but before he knew it, he'd lost control of his emotions. This wasn't typical of him, and he was both remorseful and embarrassed that it had happened in front of Erik of all people.

By morning, the last of the foreign envoys were preparing their departure. The Nipponese, Tahuantinsuyu, Volga Roman, and Keliyete delegations had each been escorted out of the palace one by one the previous day, aboard ships that were accompanied by the rebel fleets as they departed from the Imperial Palace harbour. Jingli and Fengling had sent the Xin envoy back to Kaifeng, but the twins themselves were held back by the Empress. Yinfeng arrived at Mingyue's quarters with Sheli to deliver this news to him.

"You're forcing them to stay?" Mingyue wondered in confusion.

Yinfeng nodded gravely. "There are simply too many unknowns. Zemao has already returned to Kaifeng. Meanwhile, that Sogdian dancer who they gifted to your brother is missing at the moment. All of this leads me to believe that the Xin has some role in what has been going on over the last few months. Even if your cousins are not the ones at fault, I believe it is within our diplomatic interests to keep them here. Zemao will only be motivated to provide us with assistance if she has a personal stake in the matter."

"You're keeping them hostage?" Mingyue rephrased his previous question.

"I am taking a precaution," the Empress corrected. "The rebels have promised that no harm will come to any of those who remain within the palace. Given that the Xin are our closest allies in geographic terms, and therefore in the best position to organize a counterattack against the rebels, I believe this is the best course of action to take at the moment. It may prove to be the wrong decision in the future, but I am willing to take that risk."

Mingyue was impressed with how his grandmother had taken charge of the palace since the Emperor's untimely death. She had hardly the chance to sleep over the last few days, and despite the tragic loss of her husband before her very eyes, she was somehow able to channel her energy toward ensuring the well-being of her remaining family. Mingyue hoped he could learn something from her restraint and carefully mediated judgment.

"As for the two of you, I am sending you both to Ailao with Princess Yanggui," Yinfeng continued.

"Ailao?" Sheli said in surprise. "I thought the rebels weren't allowing any of us to leave?"

Yinfeng summoned forth two of her guards, who presented a pair of simple, servant robes to them.

"You will wear these and disguise yourselves. I've already discussed the matter with Yanggui, and she's agreed to offer you refuge in Ailao."

"What about you?!" Sheli exclaimed.

"I am remaining here with those who can't leave," she said simply. "A-Kang is still in no condition to travel, not to mention Prince Jinyu. It is my duty to remain here."

"We're staying too," Sheli said.

This caught the Empress by surprise. She was about to object, but Mingyue suddenly interjected.

"Yes. If even our allies have decided to remain, then it is our duty to do so as well."

"I cannot allow this," Yinfeng sighed.

"Hyousuke is here," Sheli pointed out, "and so are you and A-Kang. I don't want to separate our family."

The Empress was highly opposed to the idea of letting them stay, but at the end of the day, she knew that she wouldn't be able to force them to leave if they were this adamant about remaining.

With a reluctant sigh, she conceded.

***

Mingyue and Sheli arrived at the gates of the palace later that day to see off Princess Yanggui in a rather unceremonious fashion. Guards stood by at every corner, and Mingyue knew that on the other side of the wall separating them from the West Lake sat the rebel fleets, prepared to open fire at a moment's notice. In such circumstances, when the threat of an outbreak of violence was so imminent, he knew he should feel more fearful than he did. Yet he felt nothing but an eerie sense of tranquility descend upon him.

"Are you sure you want to remain here?" Yanggui whispered to them.

Members of the Ailao delegation hastily scurried about the docks as they loaded the ship last minute with supplies and possessions.

"Yes," Sheli replied, answering for both her and her brother. "We appreciate your offer to grant us refuge in Ailao. But I think it is important that we remain."

The Ailao princess nodded apprehensively, taking Sheli and Mingyue's hands in hers and squeezing them tight. They didn't know when they might see each other again. Yanggui gave a simple bow to her family before embarking on the ship. They watched in silence as the battered front gates to the palace were pulled open, and the ship disappeared into the fog beyond. As the gates were hastily sealed, their last chance at a safe departure vanished.

Sheli took her brother's hand in hers. Mingyue was surprised when he noticed that she was trembling ever so slightly, though perhaps she was surprised at how calm he remained given their situation. She smiled weakly.

"We will get through this."

Mingyue remained by the gates a while after Sheli left. She said she was going to pay a visit to their brother, who remained in the infirmary, but Mingyue wasn't up to doing that. Instead, he found himself gazing up at the outer wall. He didn't know how long he'd been there—the soldiers standing guard changed their watch at least once, eyeing him with concern as he remained in place. His whole life, all he had wanted was to travel outside those gates and witness the world that lay beyond. To him, the palace had always felt like a prison of sorts. Now, it seemed that those gates were the only thing standing between him and the dangerous world on the other side.

"Ah, you're still here," Narsieh approached Mingyue from the palace interior. "I stopped by the Palace of Lunar Serenity, and Wei Hanxi said you still hadn't returned. She was worried, you know, complaining about how she should have accompanied you herself, or at least sent some guards alongside you."

"Wu Liqing would normally accompany me for such matters," Mingyue remarked softly.

The Sasannian prince nodded and presented a small vial to Mingyue. "Speaking of Wu Liqing, I have news of him. Well, not of him specifically, but regarding the substance we discovered in his quarters."

"Oh?"

This piqued Mingyue's interest. He hadn't thought much of it when that thin coating of white powder was discovered on the floor of Olekina's room, but Narsieh insisted on taking a sample, in the hopes that it might lead to some clues as to what might have happened to Olekina. Mingyue couldn't quite follow what exactly Narsieh hoped to learn from it, expecting it to be yet another dead end, so he was surprised when the other prince returned with information.

"I brought the substance to my alchemist, hoping he might be able to recognize what it was," Narsieh explained. "He said that it resembled a drug that he was unfamiliar with that was stored in the apothecary. I headed over there to learn that this drug was new to Wuyue and arrived aboard the Nipponese fleet when Prince Hyousuke arrived. The herbalist explained that it was primarily used to sedate livestock but could also be used on humans in small doses as an anesthetic."

"A sedative?" Mingyue wondered inquisitively.

"*Mhm.* I discovered that one vial was missing from the herbalist. This leaves two possibilities as to why it was discovered in Olekina's quarters. One, he stole it from the herbalist and used it to drug your brother. Second, and what I think is the more likely option, is that it was taken by someone else and used against him. I speculate this is what happened, because the amount found in Olekina's quarters was more than half a full dosage. I doubt he would've been so careless to have accidentally spilled so much on the floor. From this, I conclude that whoever stole the sedative wished to use it against Olekina but faced resistance from him. During the struggle, the attacker spilled most of the vial's contents onto the ground, but in the end, was still successful in subduing him."

"It also came to my attention that this sedative was in the possession of the Tahuantinsuyu delegation. I was able to speak to Prince Amaru before his departure yesterday to inquire him regarding this. He explained that it was used to sedate the livestock they'd brought aboard their ship, but that the Imperial Guard had confiscated it upon their arrival in the palace. He said that it was the product of the crushed leaves of a flower that was abundant in Tahuantinsuyu, colloquially known as the White Death because of how potent it is for human consumption. I asked what its effects would be on a human, and he said that for the doses typically administered to their livestock, it would almost certainly be an instant death. However, in smaller doses, the drug can render a human unconscious with minimal harm in the long term. Even smaller amounts may render a person paralyzed temporarily, but the effects will wear off after a few hours."

Mingyue clenched his jaw "If Olekina was kidnapped, they couldn't have gotten far."

Olekina was a tall, well-built man after all. Mingyue couldn't think of anyone who'd be capable of carrying him away on their own.

"My thoughts exactly," Narsieh nodded in agreement.

The thundering boom of drums from the other side of the wall interrupted their discussion. Mingyue noticed the Empress arriving from the inner court. He caught her eye, and with one stern glance, he immediately sensed her disapproval of him being there.

"We should go," Narsieh whispered under his breath, taking Mingyue's hand and pulling him back toward the palace interior.

Mingyue turned his head back as he watched the Empress approach the front gates. "What's going on? What are those drums?"

"Don't you remember?" Narsieh said. "The rebels gave three days for the foreign delegates to leave the palace. The Ailao were the final ones to depart—now the rebels will take control of the palace. The Empress has arrived to greet them."

VI. Crimson Blade

21/11/18th Year of the Golden Dragon Emperor

Year of the Wooden Goat

Mingyue didn't know what to expect now that the palace had come under rebel control. When he had heard that they were to be put under house arrest, he had envisioned being locked away in his bed chambers as soldiers scoured up and down every alleyway. He was surprised when the only action which was undertaken was that two rebel guards were assigned to his quarters to watch over him. Other than that, he was free to travel wherever he wished, and his day passed by practically the same as any other. Hansini, Kanen, and Neili were all allowed to stop by his quarters to attend to his needs, unimpeded by the two guards as they loomed silently in the background. When Mingyue first laid eyes on them, he thought they looked vaguely familiar, but he couldn't recall where he might have seen them before.

"Why have they only sent two guards here?" He whispered to Hansini as she brought a fresh pair of clothes into the room for him.

Neili stood behind the prince, combing out his hair. The rebels had permitted a funerary ceremony to be held for the Emperor in the island temple, something which Mingyue was surprised to learn. Over the past few days, everyone had been far too caught up in the chaos of the rebels' arrival to prepare a funeral.

"It's like this everywhere," Hansini said under her breath. "They don't have enough men to completely secure the palace—there are still more of the Imperial Guard present than rebels, and the rebels have to hold ground in the city as well."

"Hey, no talking!" One of the guards shouted.

"Miss, if you're finished here, please leave," the other spoke more gently. He then turned to his comrade. "Jiang Chu, refrain from speaking harshly."

"Jiang Chu?" Mingyue repeated in surprise, the mention of the man's name causing him to recognize the soldiers. "I knew you looked familiar. You two are the guards we met in the Armenian Quarter last week, aren't you?"

"Armenian Quarter?" Hansini hissed. "Your Highness, what are you talking about? I don't recall you having an outing from the palace. What were you doing there?"

"You!" Jiang Chu's face lit up in recognition as he locked his gaze on Mingyue. "You were the one sneaking around with those foreigners and...*ack*...so, I was right! That Kunlun soldier *was* the prince's bodyguard!"

"Wu Liqing?" Hansini wondered. "What does he have to do with this? Your Highness, what are they talking about?"

"It's a long story," Mingyue mused. "But what you should know is that just last week, these two were imperial soldiers. A lot has changed in such a short time."

"*Tch*," Jiang Chu scoffed.

"It's nothing personal," his comrade said meekly. "Our commanding officer decided to join forces with the rebels when they entered the city. As his subordinates, we were dragged along into this."

"*Dragged?*" Jiang Chu laughed. "He let us choose whether we wished to join the revolution!"

"I suppose you could say that," the other soldier mumbled.

Hansini glared daggers at them but said nothing. Both guards shrunk back at her expression—Mingyue knew she could have easily taken them both out if she wanted, but she departed the room without incident.

Neili was less courageous in the midst of these soldiers, and Mingyue could sense an air of nervousness about him as the young eunuch continued combing through his hair, never uttering a word.

Mingyue, on the other hand, didn't feel afraid. He was immensely curious that these rebels were treating him relatively well, at least compared to how he'd expected to be treated. He had thought that the individuals responsible for his assassination attempt during the wedding ceremony were connected to the rebels, but now he wasn't so sure. If the two groups were connected, why was one so adamant about killing him while the other was content with allowing him to go through the regular motions of his day relatively unaffected?

"Is this what you expected you'd be doing when you joined the rebellion?" He wondered casually. His back faced the two as they stood by the door and he faced the balcony. "I'm sure you're disappointed that you're watching me have my hair brushed instead of watching me being decapitated."

"Preposterous!" Jiang Chu shouted. "We would never resort to such barbaric methods of execution!"

"Huh," Mingyue huffed bitterly. "Then I suppose you don't find how my family was killed to be barbaric?"

"The revolution would never do such a thing!"

"Oh? Then who did?"

Mingyue had been hoping for answers ever since the incident which took place during the Qiantang Festival, only to be continuously disappointed when every lead seemed to be a dead end. Who had really killed his parents, and now his grandfather? And *why?* Karnatan rebels had been the initial suspect, then Emir Abdullah, and most recently the Qinglong rebels. Mingyue had had his doubts about all these suspects, but if none of these were the culprits, then who was?

"Your Highness, I believe you have a misrepresented view of the rebels," the calmer guard said. "They never sought to cause bloodshed, and whoever is responsible for those assassinations is unknown to us. Perhaps they are connected to the rebellion, but if so, they betray its core values."

"*Your Highness,*" Jiang Chu scoffed. "As if he is worthy of such a title."

"Jiang Chu," the more polite guard sighed. "It is not the rebellion's intention to dispose of the House of Qian."

"And what are your intentions, then?" Mingyue wondered.

In all honesty, he had been expecting to have his title stripped of him, losing his status as a prince once the rebels seized control of the palace. That's what usually happened when an uprising against a ruling dynasty was successful, wasn't it? He had no idea. Never in a thousand years had something like this taken place in Wuyue.

"Reform," the calm guard said simply. "The court must undergo reform to ensure peace and prosperity for all citizens of Wuyue."

This was something that Mingyue was surprised to hear. Reform? Reform what? Wasn't Wuyue already a peaceful, prosperous state?

"I don't understand…" he admitted.

"*Pfft*," Jiang Chu sighed. "Hong Xue, what use is there in talking to *him*? Nobility will never understand the struggles of the common people."

"Then it's our duty to inform them," Hong Xue said defiantly. His tone softened as he addressed Mingyue. "Your Highness, the lands around Qinglong have suffered a series of droughts over the last few years, resulting in poor harvests and famine. I haven't returned to the area for several years, but I've heard of the situation from my relatives who write to me. Despite the governor's pleas to the court for aid, his needs have been largely ignored. Rice shipments have been imported from the Xin Empire, but the burden of paying for these tariffs fell on the people of Qinglong. This is simply unfeasible—the farmers can't afford to have their taxes increased if they have no money themselves."

"I was not aware that this was happening," Mingyue admitted.

A drought in one of Wuyue's provinces that had been going on for years? How had such a thing never been brought up before?

"Of course you wouldn't be," Jiang Chu spat bitterly. "The House of Qian is merely a puppet of the bureaucracy at this point. You only hear about what they want you to know!"

"Is that so…?" Mingyue muttered.

"The bureaucrats are only interested in their own power, leaving us no choice but to rise up and depose them!"

"Can you shut up," Mingyue hissed.

"Perhaps now, after the Emperor has heard the voices of his people directly, he will finally begin to listen to us!"

"THE EMPEROR?!"

366

Mingyue pushed himself up from his seat, startling Neili, who cowered backward into the corner of the room. Mingyue turned to face the guards, his face tense with fury as his eyes met theirs.

"THE EMPEROR IS DEAD!"

He shocked even himself with the magnitude that he was able to project his voice. He had never yelled so loudly in his life.

"Your Highness, I apologize," Hong Xue said timidly as he bowed to Mingyue. "Jiang Chu didn't mean—"

Mingyue marched directly toward Jiang Chu. Blinded by his rage, he didn't bat an eye when the rebel soldier lifted his spear and aimed it at the prince.

"Step back!" Jiang Chu ordered.

Mingyue ignored him. Swiping his hand through the air, he snatched the tip of the spearhead. Everyone in the room froze in shock when instead of throwing aside the weapon or pushing it at Jiang Chu, he instead pulled it toward himself—toward his own throat.

VII. Crimson River

21/11/18th Year of the Golden Dragon Emperor

Year of the Wooden Goat

"YOUR HIGHNESS!"

In horror, a burst of adrenaline coursed through Neili's veins. The young eunuch leaped forth from the corner he'd been cowering in, grabbing hold of the blade moments before it met the skin of Mingyue's neck. He tried to pull the weapon away, but Mingyue's grip was stronger. The spearhead remained locked in place, just grazing the area under Mingyue's chin.

The two guards stood frozen in shock at what they were witnessing, and it took Jiang Chu several moments to snap back to reality.

"WHAT THE HELL ARE YOU DOING?!"

He yanked the spear away from the prince, who stumbled forward as the weapon was pulled out of his grasp.

Mingyue was in a daze, all his energy seeping out of him as if it had been pulled away from him alongside the spear. He felt nothing as a river of blood flowed from the hand that he'd gripped the spearhead with so tightly. Now, he understood why he hadn't been afraid when the rebels had seized control of the palace—it was because he wasn't afraid of death. Perhaps he even wanted to die.

"What does it matter anymore? My mother is dead, my father is dead, my grandfather is dead. Why did you pull back your spear? THIS IS WHAT YOU WANT, ISN'T IT?!"

"Your Highness…" Neili's voice quivered as he hastily tore his own sleeves to wrap the prince's hand.

Mingyue laughed maniacally as he pushed his servant's hand away. "Don't taint your sleeves with my blood."

Neili didn't know what he should do. He'd never seen the prince break down in such a manner before, but he supposed it was only a matter of time before something like this happened—there was only so much trauma one could bear before it broke them. Mingyue always put on an aloof persona and expressionless face around others, but to those who knew him well enough, there would occasionally be slight cracks in the mask he wore. Now, that mask had been completely shattered.

"What in Heaven's name is going on here?!"

The door flung open to reveal Hansini. The woman had come rushing back as soon as she heard shouts of distress coming from the prince's chambers. Taking one glance at Mingyue's bloodied hand, the look on her face transformed from confusion to fury. She lunged at Jiang Chu and pinned the man against the wall. Despite her small stature compared to the rebel soldier, she had no trouble handling him. In the blink of an eye, a dagger had been produced from her sleeve.

"YOU!"

"Wei Hanxi!" Neili shouted.

"Miss Wei, this is a misunderstanding," Hong Xue said in a comparatively calm tone given the circumstances.

The blade was pressed against Jiang Chu's throat, but Hansini halted before going any further. She knew that she would be punished if she harmed these soldiers.

"Let him go," Mingyue finally managed to say. "I was the one who did this."

Though he wasn't thinking straight, his mind was clear enough to realize that he didn't want harm to come to anyone, even if he didn't care about it coming to himself.

Hansini's attention shifted from the spear on the floor to Mingyue as she pieced together the situation. She reluctantly lowered her blade.

"Ao Neili, please take the Second Prince to the infirmary to have his hand cleaned and bandaged," Hansini ordered.

She stared sternly into the prince's eyes, and Mingyue could almost hear her scolding voice asking him *'Your Highness, what were you thinking?!'*

He shifted his gaze away from her.

***

"Ah! Where did I put it?!" Kanen's frustrated voice could be heard from within the infirmary as Neili and Mingyue approached its front doors.

369

Trailing closely behind them were Hong Xue and Jiang Chu. Both men were on their guard, unsure as to whether the prince would lash out again. Perhaps more ominous, however, was the fact that Mingyue had once again put on a stoic expression, regaining his composure as if nothing had happened at all.

As they stepped over the threshold into the infirmary, Kanen was caught by surprise. He nearly spilled the tray of tea he was holding as he turned to see who had entered the building.

"Y-your Highness…? I wasn't expecting to see you. What happened to your hand?!"

"An accident," the prince brushed him aside.

Neili, Jiang Chu, and Hong Xue shifted uncomfortably, but none of them decided to contradict his explanation.

"I'll be with you in a moment," Kanen explained as he hurried off toward the inner gardens of the infirmary's complex. "Let me bring this to Prince Jinyu first."

Mingyue nodded, taking a seat as the others lingered nearby. The atmosphere was tense as the guards and Neili both worried that the prince would attempt to harm himself again. Mingyue found this quite annoying. He recognized that he had acted rashly earlier and wasn't seriously considering harming himself again. He tried to ignore the others' presence as he examined the countless jars, bottles, and racks of hanging medicines lining the shelves and tables on the opposite wall of the infirmary. The sight of this reminded him that he was supposed to meet with Narsieh again to discuss the White Death before the funerary ceremony began. Now that he had to make a detour to the infirmary, there likely wouldn't be the time for that.

Kanen returned shortly, eyeing Mingyue and the guards nervously as he prepared medication for the prince. Though it was clear that he wanted to know about what had happened, he didn't question them any further. Knowing that the prince's hand had been cut open with a blade was enough to know how to treat it. After gently cleaning the wound with a cloth to disinfect it, he wrapped a bandage around Mingyue's hand and offered him tea alongside his medicine.

"There was a lot of bloodloss, but luckily it's not as bad as it looks," Kanen assured. "You're clear to head to the ceremony now, but you should return here afterward so I can reassess you. Understood?"

Mingyue nodded.

After a short while, Hansini returned to escort him to the funeral, and he parted ways with Neili and Kanen. Jiang Chu and Hong Xue, however, remained by their side the entire time. Though they hadn't spoken another word since departing from Mingyue's quarters, their presence felt heavy, as if they were looming immediately over his shoulders. Olekina's presence had never felt so oppressive before—in fact, much of the time he didn't even notice that he was being guarded at all. How he wished that Olekina was the one accompanying him now rather than these two men.

His stay in the infirmary hadn't ended up being as long as he'd expected, and so on their way to the Lake of Tranquility, he managed to convince Hansini to take a quick detour to Olekina's quarters. He didn't want to go back inside but simply wanted to re-examine the outside of the building to determine how Olekina's kidnapper would've been able to carry off the man undetected. Was there perhaps a hidden alleyway they could've slipped down? A secret doorway?

Hong Xue and Jiang Chu didn't know the layout of the palace, so they were unaware that Mingyue was leading them away from the Lake of Tranquility, before planning on circling back around. As they passed by the exterior of Olekina's quarters, Mingyue hastily scanned the building's exterior, hoping to come across any clue that might help them determine which way the kidnapper would've headed. There were no clear features of the area that stood out to him. Just as his heart began to sink in disappointment, they turned the corner and were greeted by the gentle rush of a stream of flowing water.

It was a canal, narrow in width, yet still wide enough to carry a small boat. It flowed through a ditch that was several feet in the ground, making it difficult to notice until one approached. Though bridges spanned one side of the canal to the other, this was the first time Mingyue realized that there was a waterway here. It was roughly the same width as the canal he had used to exit the palace during Jul, and he wondered if perhaps the two were connected. However, while that one flowed eastward, this one flowed west—directly toward the Lake of Tranquility. He began leading them along the canal's edge as they circled back toward the lake. Turning to face Olekina's quarters one last time, he noticed that the window to bed chamber was directly overlooking the canal. If someone had kidnapped Olekina from that room, dumping him into a boat and floating him down the canal would've been the easiest way to have gone about that. And if this canal emptied into the Lake of Tranquility, perhaps that meant that Olekina had found his way there as well. Just as he had been trapped on an island in the lake, that was the most likely place where they would find Olekina.

VIII. A Dark Path

Mingyue remained distracted throughout the entire funerary ceremony. As they went through the ritual motions of paying respect to the deceased Emperor, he couldn't help but feel that all eyes in the temple rested on him. This was the first time most of them had seen him since the Venesian Ball, and there was also the matter of the bandage wrapped around his hand, stained traces of red beneath from his wound. Though Yinfeng and Sheli both eyed him with concern, Mingyue sensed the most worry coming from the Norden prince.

Members of the House of Qian were positioned at the front of the temple, before the altar, as the High Priestess conducted the ceremony. All along the perimeter of the main hall stood dozens of rebel soldiers, including Hong Xue and Jiang Chu. Behind the Imperial Family stood all the delegates that had remained in Wuyue—the Oghuz Rumelis and Venesians, Prince Sundar of Karnata, and of course, Erik.

He couldn't focus as he felt Erik's eyes boring into the back of his head, the Norden prince standing only a short distance behind him. As the High Priestess offered up prayers and incense to the divine, Mingyue's thoughts were muddled. The only thing on his mind was finding who was responsible for the deaths of his parents and grandfather. He felt for some reason that this discovery was within his grasp, and that if he could uncover Olekina's whereabouts, it would explain everything to him.

Above them, the towering statue of the Son of Heaven loomed overhead, his visage hidden in haunting shadows as candlelight flickered throughout the temple. Si Lu raised a golden chalice to the altar, containing wine of the lotus flower, which was ceremonially used in funerals for Wuyue's rulers. This chalice was a sacred relic, one of the most important within the House of Qian's possession, passed down through the generations for centuries.

Mingyue's eyes fell upon the crimson orb embedded within the statue, said to contain the blood of the Son of Heaven himself, shed at his death a millennia before Wuyue's beginnings. The sight of blood sent flashbacks of Huamei's death through Mingyue's mind, as the image of her body thrown down the steps of the palace hauntingly crept up on him again.

He jolted as a hand rested on his shoulder—Sheli. She could sense her brother's unease. Instantly, his discomfort dissipated, and he was reminded that even though he had experienced much loss over the past few months, there were those whom he cared for that still lived. If anyone could understand how he felt, who else would it be other than Sheli and Zukang, his own siblings?

When the ceremony was finished, Jinlong's casket was taken to the interior gardens of the temple complex for burial. Of course, the Imperial Burial Grounds were where emperors would typically be buried, but exiting the palace was forbidden by the rebel forces. They would have to make do. Next to an imposing stone statue of Wuyue's founder, the Golden Dragon Emperor was lowered into the ground. This is where he would be put to rest, at least for now.

The delegates were ordered to return to their quarters immediately upon the funeral's completion. Mingyue didn't even have the chance to speak to his sister or grandmother before they were whisked away by the troops sent to guard them and boarded back onto their boats to depart the island. Mingyue was about to board his boat when he caught sight of Narsieh at the docks.

"Prince Niexia, may I accompany you?"

The Sassanian Prince smiled and extended a hand. "Why of course, your Highness."

Thankfully, Hong Xue and Jiang Chu didn't object to the decision, remaining silent as they followed the Yue prince aboard Narsieh's vessel. Mingyue took note that while two of Narsieh's men were present to row them back to shore, there was only one rebel soldier guarding them. With Hansini alongside them, they outnumbered the soldiers five to three.

As the boat set sail back toward the Palace of Lunar Serenity, Narsieh joined Mingyue at the rear and leaned out to gaze across the lake.

"That's quite a wound you have there," he whispered under his breath.

"I think Wu Liqing is on one of these islands," Mingyue muttered, ignoring his comment.

"A reasonable hypothesis," Narsieh's eyes darted back and forth from one island to the next, nodding slightly in agreement. "What shall we do about it?"

"I would like to circle the lake and see if any islands have signs of him."

"Very well."

"Hey! What are you whispering about?!" The soldier assigned to Narsieh barked out.

The Sassanian Prince smiled, uttering a phrase in the Persian tongue that sounded poetic to the ears. Mingyue could pick out a few words that he was familiar with, and could instantly tell that Narsieh wasn't reciting poetry, but ordering his two men to change course. They were attendant to this, and Mingyue could sense the boat shift directions slightly, though not enough for the others to notice.

"*Tch*, foreigner! Speak in our tongue!" The soldier spat.

"*Foreigner?*" Narsieh raised an eyebrow in amusement. "My family has resided in Wuyue since its founding. How long can *you* trace back your ancestry?"

Mingyue raised a hand, signaling for Narsieh to stop talking. He didn't want to cause a scene. Hong Xue was likewise able to hold back his comrade from pursuing the matter further, though it was clear that the man had much more that he wanted to say.

The fog was heavy, so the fact that they were drifting off course went unnoticed for a while. But eventually, Hansini picked up on this, shooting Mingyue a quizzical glance, but saying nothing. Most of the islands in the lake were too small to host much besides a few trees. Other than that, the only ones which appeared to have buildings

375

located on them were the island home to the Imperial Temple and the island that he and Hansini had been stranded on. He was growing increasingly disheartened and recognized that if they didn't make it to shore soon, the soldiers would start to notice.

They had arrived near the northeastern edge of the lake by the Hall of Harmony, so they hadn't even sailed past half the islands yet. But Mingyue didn't think it was likely that Olekina would've been brought to an island south of the Imperial Temple—his quarters were closer to this side of the lake, after all. But then, something caught his eye. At the edge of the water, where the wall met the lake, there was a tunnel that led into the wall. An iron gate sealed the entrance, but it seemed that it could easily be removed. The entrance was just wide enough for a boat of their size to pass through.

"There," he whispered to Narsieh.

"The grate?" Narsieh wondered with skepticism.

Mingyue couldn't be sure that this was where Olekina would've been taken, but it was indeed close to where the canal that passed by Olekina's quarters emptied into the Lake of Tranquility.

"Yes," he said with certainty.

"Shall we return later?" Narsieh whispered.

Mingyue knew that once they both returned to their residences, they would have little chance to leave again. The rebel soldiers assigned to them would be keeping a close watch at all times. It had to be now or never. Narsieh understood this as well and leaned back against the edge of the boat with a sigh. They both knew that the soldiers aboard the ship with them would prevent them from searching the tunnel. If they were to go on, they would have to first get rid of them.

"If you pretend to take me hostage, they won't attack," the Yue prince suggested.

Narsieh smirked and shook his head. "If I get injured, you owe me, your Highness. In any case…"

He suddenly leaped forth, wrapping an arm around Mingyue and pulling him into his chest. A dagger shot forth from his sleeve and pressed against the prince's throat. Even Mingyue, who had suggested this only moments before, was caught by surprise by his rapid movements. Narsieh yelled out an order to his men in Persian and they instantly responded, tossing aside their oars and ambushing two of the soldiers—the one sent to guard Narsieh, and Jiang Chu.

"Your Highness!" Hansini shouted in shock, but with one glance into his eyes, she could tell that this was part of his plot. She cursed him silently, not understanding what was going on, but trusting him enough to recognize that his life wasn't actually in danger.

While Jiang Chu and the other soldier were pinned to the floor, Hong Xue grabbed his spear and aimed it at Narsieh. Their boat was fairly small, and the weapon covered a good amount of distance between the two men. Hansini was positioned between them.

"Let the prince go!" Hong Xue demanded.

On the floor, the other soldiers struggled against Narsieh's men. The already crowded boat had become even more congested, rocking side to side in the waves as the situation unfolded.

"I didn't realize the Qinglong Rebels cared about the well-being of Yue nobility," Narsieh jested.

"*Tch*," Hong Xue eyed his comrades nervously. He turned to address Hansini. "Miss Wei, you were so quick to ensure that Jiang Chu wouldn't harm the prince. Why are you hesitating now?! Do something!"

Hansini's eyes flitted back and forth between Narsieh and Mingyue. Whatever occurred next would be determined by her. After a deep sigh, the young woman leaped forth, not at Narsieh, but at Hong Xue. The rebel went wide-eyed in shock as the prince's attendant pinned him to the ground next to his colleagues.

"Miss—?! Gah!"

"You better know what you're doing," Hansini hissed at both the Yue and Sassanian princes.

Narsieh lowered his blade and loosened his grip on Mingyue with a smile. "I appreciate your trust in me, Miss Wei."

The three soldiers soon found themselves bound together by the rope used to tether the boat to the docks, and Narsieh took charge of the vessel, steering it into the narrow waterway. It was difficult to make out anything amidst the darkness, but up ahead, a single torch cast haunting shadows dancing across the walls. It was the only direction they could head in. When they reached it, they realized that the passage divided into two smaller waterways, branching off in opposite directions. The torch was anchored to a wall above a platform that led up a dimly lit stairwell.

"What is this place…?" Mingyue whispered.

They disembarked the boat, leaving Narsieh's men behind with the rebel soldiers.

"There are hidden passageways throughout the Imperial Palace," Narsieh explained. "They were once used by servants as shortcuts, though most have been abandoned and forgotten. I wasn't aware that there were water passageways as well…"

"Huh," Hansini crossed her arms, "you know quite a bit about the inner workings of the palace, despite not being a servant."

"For centuries, it has been the duty of the House of Sasan to understand these sorts of things," Narsieh explained.

He was correct. For as long as anyone could remember, the Sassanian nobles had been second only to the House of Qian in their influence over Wuyue. The two families had always been close and had intermarried with each other numerous times over the generations— Mingyue himself had Sassanian ancestors five or six generations back.

As they climbed the damp, narrow stairwell, Mingyue's mind began to wander. Jiang Chu's words from earlier came back to him.

The House of Qian is merely a puppet of the bureaucracy at this point.

"Niexia, there is something I wish to ask you," Mingyue said.

"Go ahead, your Highness."

"Were you aware of the famine affecting Qinglong?"

Narsieh had been walking a few paces ahead of the Yue prince and paused for a brief moment before continuing.

"There is something you should know," he said. "The House of Sasan had been aware of the situation in Qinglong since it began unfolding. I had long since asked my father to relay this information to the Emperor, but he insisted that the situation was under control and could be resolved without concerning the House of Qian. After my father's death, I took on his administration and faced the decision of revealing the truth that he had kept secret and tarnishing my family name or burying that secret deeper. Of course, by then it was too late. The famine had grown out of control and sparked an all-out rebellion. The Emperor was crippled, and I could not bring myself to inform him that for years, one of his closest bureaucrats had been keeping the truth from him. The most I could do was wait for your brother to be enthroned, and then work alongside him to bring about an end to this crisis."

He turned to face Mingyue below, chuckling with a shake of his head as he reached the top of the stairwell.

"How could I have known it would come to this? Before I knew it, the rebels were at the gates of the palace. I suppose in the end, waiting for the right moment to reveal the truth was the wrong decision to make. But what else was I to do?"

"You could have told us," Mingyue muttered.

He was feeling a mix of emotions—relief that Narsieh had unveiled the truth, but also distrust that it had been kept from him for so long. Once again, he found himself questioning whether he could trust those closest to him. Even if they weren't outright lying, that didn't mean they were telling the truth.

"The Emperor would have the power to solve the famine in Qinglong," Mingyue asserted.

But as those words left his lips, a sense of doubt had begun creeping over him. Was that really the case? Was the Emperor of the Yue Dynasty really the one with ultimate authority over Wuyue?

"We already did everything we could to alleviate the situation," Narsieh explained. "My father ordered that rice shipments from elsewhere in the empire be rationed to Qinglong, but ultimately, there

379

was little that could be done. The root cause of the famine lies not in Wuyue, but in the Xin realms. You see, your Highness, the Xin have been constructing their own canal from the Chang River[32] to Kaifeng so that they can bypass Wuyue altogether when transporting goods from the south to the north. To solve the crisis in Qinglong will mean creating another crisis between the Xin and Wuyue."

Mingyue let that sink in as he reached the top of the staircase. He turned back to gaze at Hansini, expecting that she would have some further comment to make against the Sassanian Prince. He didn't know what to say, and was hoping that she might be able to come up with an adequate rebuttal to Narsieh's excuse. Instead, the young woman simply spoke up in a hushed tone.

"Why don't we save this discussion for later? Listen, there are voices coming from the other side of that door."

The two princes had been so consumed in their conversation that they hadn't noticed the faintest trace of muttering voices beyond the door at the top of the stairwell. Hansini was right, there were other people here.

---

[32]Chángjiāng (長江): Literally meaning "Long River," is the Chinese name for the Yangtze River, the most prominent river in Wuyue and one of the most important within the Tang Realms. Wuyue controls the Lower Yangtze around the Yangtze Delta, while the Xin control most of the Upper Yangtze

IX. Alcove of Glimmering Candlelight

It was Hansini who volunteered to push open the door. The voices on the other end were faint and hadn't seemed to notice the newcomers yet. As the door creaked open, they were greeted with an expansive room, ornate furniture, and decorations that were not dissimilar from those in Mingyue's own quarters. It seemed strange that there was such a large, well-kept area hidden away in such an obscure part of the palace. Despite this, it was dimly lit. A few candles and lanterns scattered about provided the only source of light—there were no windows.

As they crept into the room, it became clear that the voices they had heard came from a man and a woman on the opposite end, behind some folding screens which muffled them out. Suddenly, there was someone behind them. With a quick swipe, Hansini was knocked to the ground, and Narsieh was grabbed by the neck and pushed against the wall.

"*Gah*!" He cried out.

"Niexia!" Mingyue cried.

The ambusher was well-built and too strong for the Sassanian Prince to resist, but at the sound of Mingyue's voice, he froze and whipped his head around.

"Your Highness?!"

It was Olekina!

Mingyue blinked a few times. His eyes were still adjusting to the dark, and he couldn't quite make out the man's features just yet, but that voice was unmistakable.

"Olekina…?!"

"Wu Liqing!" Hansini shouted, pushing herself up from the ground.

"Miss Wei…?!"

Olekina was still holding Narsieh against the wall, having completely forgotten about him at the sound of Mingyue's voice.

"You mind…letting go…?" The Sassanian Prince gasped through breaths.

"Prince Niexia?!" Olekina realized in shock. He quickly released the other man and threw himself to his knees, kowtowing to the prince in repentance. "Your Highness, forgive me! I didn't know it was you! Forgive me!"

Narsieh brushed him aside but rubbed at his neck where Olekina's grip had left a mark. "No need for all this…"

From the back of the room, the man and woman whom they had heard earlier had rushed at the sounds of Olekina's confrontation— Selah and Princess Seo-Yeon. It appeared that everyone who had been missing was here.

"Your Highness!" Selah's face lit up. "What did I say, Olekina? I told you he'd be alright!"

"Second Prince Qian…" Seo-Yeon's voice had a trace of concern in it. "Is your brother…is the Crown Prince alright…?"

"He is," Mingyue replied.

Zukang was safe, but the Emperor was dead and the palace had fallen under rebel control. He didn't want to bring that up now.

"There is much to discuss," Narsieh spoke up, "and we have questions for you as well. Wu Liqing, the prince has been worried about your well-being. Can you explain to us what happened to you?"

Olekina began to relay the events which had taken place over the last few days. Following the Venesian Ball, he returned to his quarters, only to have been ambushed by a veiled figure who hurled a sachet filled with white powder at him. This corroborated Narsieh and Mingyue's discovery of the White Death in his bed chambers. When he awoke, he found himself in this room alongside Seo-Yeon and Selah. Occasionally, a panel on the ceiling would open to have food dropped down, but other than that, they'd had no contact with the outside world, nor any idea of who had brought them here. They had tried calling for help, but it seemed that no one could hear them. The opening in the ceiling was also too small for any of them to fit through, and thus the only means of escape from this place was via the canal. The only problem was that they had no boat with them, and swimming in such frigid waters at this time of year would quickly result in hypothermia. A pile of disassembled furniture in the corner was the group's attempt to create a boat out of the materials they possessed, clearly to little avail.

"We might have been stuck down here forever if you hadn't shown up," Selah chuckled, attempting to make light of their situation.

"So, you don't know who's responsible for this?" Mingyue inquired.

He was relieved that they had all been found safe, yet at the same time disappointed that they hadn't found any leads regarding their culprit.

"I was near the Crown Prince's quarters when hooded figures ambushed me," explained Seo-Yeon. "They put a blindfold over my face, and when they took it off, I was here. Selah, Olekina, and Prince Zukang were here as well. They threatened your brother with harming me if he did not go along with their plans, and so he obliged. Then they took him away, and we haven't seen any of them since."

"The prince and I were ambushed at around the same time in his quarters," Selah nodded in agreement. "I also am unaware of who exactly they were, but only one of them spoke to us. It was difficult to tell whether it was a man or a woman. Perhaps a eunuch...?"

A rush of footsteps suddenly echoed up the stairwell they'd come up from.

"Your Highness!"

The door burst open, and three figures pushed their way into the room—Jiang Chu, Hong Xue, and the third soldier. As they lunged toward him, Olekina whipped out his blade and struck forth through the air.

"Wait!" Mingyue shouted in haste. "Don't attack!"

The soldiers had their weapons drawn, pointed at Olekina. All eyes rested on the Yue prince expectantly, unsure as to whether his request was directed toward them or the opposing party.

383

"Your Highness…?" Olekina's expression was one of disbelief. "These are troops of the Qinglong Rebellion!"

"What did you do with my men?" Narsieh glared at them, though he didn't seem particularly concerned about the whereabouts of the two attendants he'd left aboard the boat.

"Tied them up and left them there!" Jiang Chu shouted. "They're lucky we didn't toss them overboard after what you did to us!"

"Your Highness…who are these people…?" Hong Xue piped up, his eyes jumping from Selah to Olekina to Seo-Yeon.

"I recognize him," Jiang Chu jabbed his weapon toward Olekina. "He's that Kunlun guard from last week."

With a deep sigh, Mingyue explained the situation to both sides in as calm of a manner as he could—the Emperor had been slain, rebel forces took control of the Imperial Palace, Olekina and the others had been kidnapped by an unknown group of people on the night of the Venesian Ball and brought to this secret room within the palace. Both sides continued eyeing one another with suspicion after the prince finished his explanation.

"So, here we have your guard, the Yi Princess, and the Crown Prince's…Sogdian dancer…?" The words rolled off Jiang Chu's tongue with distaste. "What an odd combination."

"Your Highness, how can we let them live…?"

Ever since hearing of the Emperor's death, Olekina's hand had been trembling as he gripped his blade. He was angry with the fact that these rebel soldiers were now the ones tasked with guarding the prince, a job that was *his* responsibility.

"No more fighting," the prince replied in a meek voice. "I don't want there to be any more violence or bloodshed."

He approached Olekina, slowly reaching out to take hold of the blade in his hand. Witnessing this, Hansini, Jiang Chu, and Hong Xue were momentarily alarmed as they were reminded of what had transpired in the prince's chambers earlier that day. But Mingyue was

384

not planning to harm himself. Reluctantly, Olekina sheathed his weapon, and the other soldiers quickly withdrew theirs as well.

"There won't be enough space in the boat to bring everyone back," Jiang Chu pointed out.

He was right—the boat they arrived in had barely been large enough to carry Mingyue, Hansini, Narsieh, the three rebel soldiers, and Narsieh's two attendants. Now, there were three additional people they had to bring back. There was no way the boat would be able to fit them all.

"I'll accompany Selah and the Yi Princess back to shore," Narsieh suggested. "Your Highness, if you'd like, you may leave first with your attendants and guards."

"You may go first," said the prince.

"Very well."

It was decided that Hansini and Hong Xue would leave with the first departure and would bring the boat back to pick up Mingyue after everyone else had disembarked.

Hansini and Olekina both wanted to be the one to remain behind with the prince, neither fully trusting the other's capabilities in defending him in case of an emergency. In the end, Mingyue himself had to request that Olekina be the one to remain behind. Hansini reluctantly accepted this arrangement.

This left only Olekina, Jiang Chu, and Mingyue behind as they awaited the others' return. The two soldiers stood at opposite ends of the room, eyeing the other with suspicion the entire time. Mingyue sat about halfway between them, worried that if he turned away for even a moment, they'd be at each other's throats.

"Your Highness, how can you be sure that the rebels aren't responsible for what happened?" Olekina muttered under his breath.

Jiang Chu spat. "You know, I can hear you. How do we know that *you* aren't the one to blame? Your story about being kidnapped could all just be made up."

"Enough," the prince sighed. "I trust Olekina. Jiang Chu, I also trust what you said about the rebel forces—that they weren't the ones who carried out the Qiantang Festival Incident."

Though he did think that Jiang Chu was sincere in his *belief* that the rebels wouldn't do such a thing, he had his doubts about whether that belief was correct. What did Jiang Chu know, after all? He was simply a low-ranking soldier who had only joined the rebellion in the past week. The leaders of the Qinglong Rebellion could very well have orchestrated the plot to assassinate the House of Qian without informing their subordinates.

"*Hmph*," huffed Jiang Chu. He began rummaging through cupboards, looking for something to snack on.

After a while, Hansini and Hong Xue finally returned to pick them up.

"Ready to get going?" Hong Xue asked.

"Ugh, please," Jiang Chu groaned. "I don't want be stuck in here a moment longer."

Just as they were about to depart the room, however, there was a creaking sound of a doorway opening. Confused, they glanced around the room to determine the source of that noise—there was only one door in the room, after all, so where else could it have come from?

Olekina was the first to realize what was transpiring. His gaze shot to the ceiling, and the others' attention was quickly drawn upward as well. The small window in the ceiling had been opened, and two cloaked figures peered down onto them from above. For a moment, everyone froze. As Mingyue stared at the new arrivals, he was met with nothing but the dark shadows cast over their faces by their hoods. Then, one of them tossed something down onto them.

"Your Highness, look out!"

Olekina sprung forth and tackled the prince, pushing him with the full force of his body out the door. Mingyue was nearly thrown down the stairwell, but luckily Hansini caught him and pulled him back.

They had all made it through the door, except for Jiang Chu who remained behind in the room. As Olekina slammed shut the door on him, Mingyue spotted a shattered vial on the floor, and an ominous, white powder dissipating into the air out of it. Jiang Chu was clutching at his throat as gasps of air escaped through his lips, but the door was already sealed by the time they heard his body hit the ground.

"The White Death…" Mingyue whispered.

X. Adrift on Sinking Waves

The White Death.

As the lethal powder dissipated throughout the room, Olekina hastily slammed shut the door.

"That's what they used to capture us," he said gravely. He grabbed onto the prince's arm and began pulling him down the stairs. "We need to leave."

"Wait!" Mingyue resisted. "We can't leave Jiang Chu there!"

Hong Xue began pushing open the door once again. "I'll get him—"

"*Tch*," without hesitation, Olekina handed the prince over to Hong Xue and Hansini. "I'll do it. Take the prince to the boat!"

As they rushed down the stairwell, Mingyue turned back to see his guard rushing back into the room with his shirt pulled up to cover his face from the powder. Without saying a word, they boarded the vessel and prepared to set sail back toward the Lake of Tranquility. Olekina was only a few paces behind them, with Jiang Chu's limp body hoisted over his shoulder.

Wide-eyed in fear, Hong Xue stared down at his comrade as he dared to ask, "Is he dead...?"

"He's breathing," Olekina replied. "He'll be fine, but we need to leave. Now!"

Hansini, Hong Xue, and Olekina each grabbed a paddle and began steering the ship toward the lake. With Jiang Chu lying next to him and the others paddling furiously, Mingyue couldn't help but feel like dead weight in this situation. Everyone here had been tasked with protecting his life and were even willing to sacrifice themselves to save him if necessary. He didn't want that anymore. He didn't want others to be risking their lives for him.

When they exited the tunnel and the night sky opened above them once again, Mingyue noticed they weren't the only ones out this evening. Up ahead, a silhouette emerged amidst the mist—another boat. It seemed there was only one person aboard.

"Who goes there?!" Hansini shouted out.

The newcomer didn't seem to have noticed them until they heard Hansini's voice and suspiciously began to change course. It had undoubtedly been heading directly for the tunnel they emerged from only moments before, but now for some reason decided to turn back. Whoever it was, they were aware of the secret passageway that led to where Olekina and the others were locked away. Given what had just unfolded, it was impossible that this could be a mere coincidence.

In unison, they began rowing at an increased pace. Though the figure in the fog was further ahead of them, they were unable to maintain this lead against the strength of three people rowing. They soon caught up, the sides of their boats knocking together violently. The person steering this other vessel was clothed in the same hooded garment as the individuals who had appeared in the room earlier. Olekina leaped onto the new boat confront them, but the cloaked figure reached into their sleeve and produced a small sachet from within.

"Olekina! Watch out!" Mingyue shouted as that sachet spun through the air.

The string tying together the top of the sachet was loose—once it hit the ground, it would burst open and unleash whatever contents it contained within. If Olekina was able to strike the sachet with his spear and knock it out of the way, it would still likely explode and affect him. If this sachet contained the White Death, or something even worse, they were in for trouble.

Olekina was quick-witted and calculated all of this in the fraction of a second since that sachet had been tossed at him. In a swift, graceful maneuver, he struck forth with his spear. For a moment, Mingyue feared that Olekina didn't see the sachet at all and was striking at the hooded figure. Instead, the thin tip of his weapon slashed through the air, straight through the hooped strings tying the sachet together. As it was caught in midair, the abrupt yet gentle looping of the strings around the edge of Olekina's weapon tightened them around the sachet's opening, trapping its contents safely within.

Mingyue breathed a sigh of relief as Olekina drew back the spear and took the sachet into his hands. Then, his eyes met the hooded figure with a deadly gaze.

"Now we have you."

With another slash of his spear, the hood was pulled up over the newcomer's head, their face uncovered for the first time. Their features were sharp and striking. A strong, bridged nose rested between two deep, brown eyes that shimmered in the moonlight. Their skin was soft and pale, like the glow of the moon, and their hair dark and wavy like the surface of the lake. It was difficult to tell if they were a man or a woman—on one hand, the gentleness of their lips and thick lashes struck Mingyue as belonging to a beautiful young woman, yet at the same time their sharp jawline and thick eyebrows seemed very masculine. He had seen this face somewhere before.

"Who are you?" Olekina demanded.

"Seems I've been caught," with the sly smile of someone who'd been defeated, the newcomer spoke with hardly a trace of an accent, despite being a foreigner. "I am Lusine Nazaryan, servant of Her Highness, Aysun Sultana."

"Aysun…Sultana…?" Mingyue repeated in disbelief.

"So, the Oghuz Rumeli are the ones behind this? Explain yourself!" Olekina demanded, his spear pointed at Lusine's neck.

"I acted of my own volition," Lusine replied. "The Sultana is unaware of this."

"*Tch*," Hansini glared. "Like we would believe that. I suspected the Oghuz Rumelis had something to do with this when their cups weren't poisoned during the wedding ceremony."

"We were not the ones who poisoned those cups," Lusine said, "nor the ones who killed the Emperor—"

In a swift move, Olekina swept down and grabbed the Oghuz Rumeli attendant by the throat, pushing them to the edge of the boat over the water.

"Enough with this nonsense. Stop trying to protect them."

"Wait!" Mingyue shouted.

Olekina froze as all eyes fell on the prince. Lusine, too, strained their gaze to meet his eyes. The attendant opened their mouth to speak.

"However, I do know who *is* responsible."

Mingyue ordered Olekina to release Lusine, and he reluctantly obliged. Something told him that Lusine was speaking the truth. After all, he had already been expecting that the individuals responsible for kidnapping him and replacing his role in the ceremony with his brother weren't the same people who assassinated the Emperor. The latter group had been intent on killing Mingyue, not Zukang, which is why the assassin hadn't killed his brother, but instead exchanged him as a hostage for the Emir. They had then found refuge aboard the Qinglong fleet and hadn't been seen since. Even if Mingyue was to believe that the rebels as a whole were not responsible for the Emperor's assassination, it was clear that the two groups were indeed connected in some way.

On the other hand, those who had kidnapped the princes seemed to belong to a different faction. They had forced Zukang into Mingyue's position, hoping that he would be killed during the ceremony. Therefore, while the assassin who had poisoned the Emperor had wanted Mingyue dead, those who had kidnapped them wanted Zukang to be killed instead. And if that was the case, this group must have been aware of the plot by the other faction to carry out an assassination during the wedding ceremony. Only then would their goal have been successful, and it would have been carried out unintentionally by another faction entirely.

"You knew that they were going to kill me...?" Mingyue inquired, piecing the puzzle together. "And you put my brother in my place instead...?"

"So, you've figured it out," smiled Lusine, an eerie expression crossing their face. "Then you should be thanking me, your Highness! Had it not been for our intervention, they would have killed you without hesitation!"

"You tried to get my brother killed...!" Mingyue said with growing realization. "And you knew they would kill the Emperor!"

"Don't jump to so many conclusions. While it is true that we had hoped the Crown Prince would die, we did not anticipate that the other party would try to poison the entire House of Qian as well."

Mingyue found it difficult to resist lunging at Lusine. "You...why...?!"

"Let's just say that there are forces at play that wish to eliminate you, your Highness. We wish to be rid of them just as much as you do. Your brother is closely tied to this plot. He is problematic. You won't be safe until he is gone."

"You're lying," Mingyue said defiantly. "My brother would never want to do me harm..."

"I didn't say that he was involved," Lusine assured. "But there are other, more powerful forces at play here."

"Who?"

Lusine smirked. "That's what everyone would like to know, isn't it?"

Olekina was growing impatient. "What should we do with them,[33] Your Highness? Can I toss them overboard now?"

"No tossing anyone overboard," Mingyue sighed.

"If you do that, you lose the only lead you have," Lusine pointed out.

"Then speak," Olekina demanded. "Who is behind all this?"

"The situation is complex," Lusine's gaze rested upon the prince. "I only have a small picture of the full story. But, your Highness, I'm not sure you would believe me if I told you."

"Tell me."

The attendant beckoned for the prince to come closer. Worried about Lusine's intent, Olekina pressed his spear harder against their

---

[33] In Chinese, the male pronoun is 他 while the female pronoun is 她. However, both are pronounced tā, so it is impossible to tell when which one is being used during speech. Because Olekina and Mingyue are unsure of Lusine's gender, the pronoun used is they/them.

throat. Mingyue, however, raised a hand, signaling for his guard to loosen the threat. Mingyue rose to his feet, hopping from one boat to the other. The two vessels bobbed up and down in the water as his weight was transferred.

He leaned over, turning his ear toward Lusine's face. Olekina's grip remained firm on his weapon, and Mingyue knew he would be ready to strike if Lusine made any threatening moves.

"Tell me," Mingyue repeated.

Lusine's lips curled as they whispered just loud enough for the prince to hear. "The raven will paint the bright moon red."

Mingyue's eyes went wide at those words, but he managed to restrain himself from recoiling.

"How do you know about that...?" He said in as calm of a manner as he could. His hand was instinctively drawn to his sleeve pocket, where that slip of paper bearing those very same words was tucked away.

"How do I know? I'm the one who wrote that. After I discovered who was responsible for the Qiantang Incident, and their plot to assassinate you next, I sent that message to my superior. As you are aware, your Highness, you are the 'Bright Moon.' And do you know who the 'Raven' is?"

The prince shook his head slightly, eyes meeting Lusine expectantly.

"The raven is..."

Mingyue held his breath as Lusine uttered the name of the one responsible for killing his parents. His whole body froze up in shock. Impossible! He refused to accept that this person could be the one to have carried out such an act.

"I knew you wouldn't believe me," Lusine smiled.

"What is it, your Highness?" Hansini pressed. "What did they say?"

"No..." Mingyue shook his head, brushing the others aside. "Nothing." He pushed himself back to his feet and returned to the first boat. "Let's go back now."

"What about them?" Olekina wondered.

"We'll bring them back to the Palace of Lunar Serenity," Mingyue turned to address the rebel guard. "Hong Xue, you will watch over them."

Hong Xue objected. "Your Highness, we should report this and turn them over to my superiors—"

"No," Mingyue interrupted. "I apologize, but I do not yet trust the rebels. I still think that they're connected to the death of my parents and the Emperor." He exchanged a brief glance with Lusine, who simply smiled with a glimmer in their eyes. "I do, however, trust you and Jiang Chu to watch over them. Can you do that?"

Hong Xue was taken aback by the prince's request. "I...okay. I will do my best, your Highness."

"What about the rest of them?" Olekina wondered. "Those hooded figures who tried to ambush us back in the secret room. They're still a threat, your Highness."

Mingyue nodded in understanding. Lusine refused to disclose the identity of their comrades, so it was up to him to figure out who they might be and apprehend them.

"They must be connected to the Oghuz Rumeli envoy in some way. Tomorrow, I will meet with Lady Alaneya and Aysun Sultana to discuss this matter. If, as you say, they are innocent in this affair, then they will not be punished. However, I expect them to fully cooperate in bringing those responsible to justice."

For once, Lusine did not express a smile on their face. "My Sultana will not approve of the measures we've undertaken. But I hope she can at least recognize that it was in her best interest. As it was yours, your Highness."

XI. Hidden Refuge

When they returned to the Palace of Lunar Serenity, Mingyue had Lusine locked away in a room down a hallway that few passed through, stationing Hong Xue at the door. They decided it would be best for Mingyue to stay somewhere other than his own quarters for the time being—if there really were people looking to kill him, it would be best not to stay somewhere he'd easily be found.

"Where should we go then?" Hansini wondered. "There's nowhere else in the Palace of Lunar Serenity where you could stay."

"I don't want to stay in the Palace of Lunar Serenity," the prince muttered.

Just being here now made him feel nervous. He found himself constantly checking over his shoulder, sensing that someone was watching them. Lusine's haunting message continued to occupy his mind.

The raven will paint the bright moon red.

"How about the Palace of Heavenly Peace?" He suggested.

"The Palace of Heavenly Peace?" Hansini repeated. "Only the foreign envoys take up residence there…"

"Exactly," nodded the prince. "No one would expect that I'd be there. How about we go to the complex where Prince Amaru stayed? Since the Tahuantinsuyu envoy has departed, it should be empty now."

"Do you want to take this soldier to the infirmary first?" Hansini nudged the still unconscious Jiang Chu who lay next to them in the boat.

"No," he said quickly. "Let's take him with us."

They stopped by Mingyue's bed chambers only for a brief moment to take some clothes with them, and of course Dudu as well. The duniao squawked in delight at the sight of them. Mingyue didn't want to leave her alone there by herself, not knowing when he might return. Arriving at the Palace of Heavenly Peace a short while later, they made their way to the residence where the Tahuantinsuyu envoy had been lodged. It was just to the east of the complex where the

Norden envoy was staying. As Mingyue gazed out beyond the wall that separated the gardens and courtyards between them, he felt a sudden urge to pay a visit to Erik.

"Your Highness? Your Highness?" Hansini called out.

"*Hm?*"

"This way," she gestured to the entrance of the building. Stepping foot inside, they found a room vaguely resembling Mingyue's own bed chambers. He would have no issues settling in here for a while.

Olekina entered behind them, laying Jiang Chu's body onto the floor.

"Olekina, put him on the bed," Mingyue requested.

"Your Highness, the bed is for you," Olekina said.

"We can bring in more beds later," the prince suggested. "There must be more in the nearby rooms."

Olekina lifted Jiang Chu up once again, plopping him down on the sheets.

"I'll go fetch Neili and tell him we're here," Hansini said as she turned to leave.

"Wait!" Mingyue said abruptly.

Hansini froze and turned back toward him in surprise. "Yes, your Highness?"

"Ah…nothing. Is Neili the only person you're going to tell?"

"Is there someone else you'd like me to bring over?"

"No."

Hansini nodded. "Then he'll be the only one. Don't worry, I'll sure we're not followed. I'll be back shortly."

With her gone, Mingyue found himself alone with Olekina once again. Well, alone with him and the still unconscious Jiang Chu. The soldier let out a loud snore that startled them as he rolled over in bed. It seemed he would be awake soon.

"You used to make sounds like that in your sleep, your Highness," Olekina noted with a chuckle.

Mingyue felt his face turning red. "W-what do you mean? My mother always told me I was a quiet sleeper."

"Your mother wasn't the one standing outside your chambers for half the night," Olekina pointed out. He nodded at Jiang Chu as the man began tossing and turning. "You used to do that too."

The prince was at a loss for words. Olekina never talked to him about these sorts of things—he was typically silent, never uttering a word as he carried out his duties guarding the prince. It seemed something had changed over the last few days that they'd been apart.

"Olekina…" Mingyue said in a soft voice. "Why did you decide to join the Imperial Guard? When I invited you into the palace, it wasn't because I expected any favours from you."

"I did not want you to pity me, your Highness," he said. "Becoming a guard was one way of showing my gratitude to you. But…it was also more than that. Before I met you, my only goal was to bring down the Gushi Estate. But after that day, I had a new reason to live. You gave me a new purpose in life, your Highness."

"A new purpose? What purpose?"

Mingyue didn't quite understand what Olekina was saying. Olekina remained silent for a while, and Mingyue began to wonder whether he had heard the question at all. Finally, he opened his mouth to speak, but before the words came out, the doors to the bed chamber suddenly swung wide open.

"We will have a feast tonight!" A voice exclaimed, filled with excitement.

Both Mingyue and Olekina's attention were instantly drawn toward the front of the room, where several figures had suddenly barged in. At the front of the group was a handsome, young man with tan skin and thick, dark hair. His eyes glowed in a vibrant, green hue, even more striking than those of the Norden prince. Dressed in thick robes of crimson and golden-coloured wool to bear the winter cold, it took Mingyue a moment to recognize who this man was.

"Prince Amaru…?!"

The Tahuantinsuyu prince paused at the sound of his name and soon realized that there were already others present in the room.

"Prince Mingyue?! What are you doing here?!" His face lit up in enthusiasm as he rushed over to greet them. "Did Prince Erik invite you over too?"

Olekina instinctively stepped between the two, halting Amaru's advance. Behind him, Mingyue noticed that the others who arrived with Amaru were none other than Erik, Agnes, and Caleb. The Norden prince flashed Mingyue a slight smile, which quickly fell short as he was reminded of their last encounter. He wasn't sure Mingyue would be happy to see him. Mingyue sensed this and felt guilt over how he had treated Erik. He greeted them with a nod of acknowledgement.

"What are *we* doing here?" Mingyue inquired. "How about *you?* You were supposed to have left with the Nipponese envoy. Why are you still here?"

"Aha, yes," Amaru laughed nervously. "I *was* supposed to leave with them, but at the last moment I decided to stay, so I snuck off the ship just before it set sail. They've certainly noticed my absence by now, but with the rebel forces surrounding the palace, there's no way they'll be able to come back and get me. Looks like I'll be staying with you a while longer, hehe!"

"Why did you choose to stay...?" Mingyue wondered in confusion. He couldn't understand why anyone would willingly remain here given the unfolding circumstances.

Amaru, who was usually in an upbeat, positive mood, grew somber. "Well, I don't want to return to Tahuantinsuyu."

He didn't say anything more, and so none of them pressed for details.

"But in any case," the prince shifted the conversation, "since you're here, why don't you join us for a feast, your Highness? Prince Hyousuke and your sister will be over with some dishes later! They're the only ones who know that I stayed behind in the palace. Well,

Prince Erik found me wandering around the courtyard, so now he and his people know…and so do you…wait, who's that on my bed?"

"Ah…one of the rebel guards assigned to protect me," Mingyue replied. "He's…"

"He's drunk," Olekina replied hastily. He didn't want to explain their encounter with Lusine and the White Death powder. For now, it was best to keep that between them.

"Drunk?!" Amaru burst into laughter. "Well, of course he is. These soldiers they assigned are really slacking off, aren't they? The ones sent to guard your sister and Prince Hyousuke do nothing but sit around and gamble all day! They won't even notice when the two of them stop by here later."

Olekina was hesitant to stick around and whispered to Mingyue whether they should leave and look for somewhere else to stay.

"No," Mingyue said in a soft voice. "My sister will be coming, and I trust everyone else who will be here as well. Let's stay."

There were many other rooms within this complex, so they decided to move Jiang Chu to one of those instead, rather than keeping him here while everyone else was present. A short while later, Hansini returned with Neili, and they had to explain to them the situation regarding Prince Amaru. Like Olekina, Hansini was skeptical about remaining, but Mingyue insisted that they do so. Not long after, Ansei Hyousuke and Sheli arrived together, carrying with them a large platter filled with various Nipponese delicacies. Amaru's eyes lit up at the sight of this.

"Wow! Did you make these yourselves? It looks delicious! Ah, I miss the taste of Nipponese cuisine!"

"I taught Sheli how to roll sushi and make dango," smiled Hyousuke.

"It's my first time, so I apologize if it isn't up to your tastes," Sheli added sheepishly. "I've never cooked before…"

Amaru whipped forth a pair of chopsticks, plucking a roll of sushi off the platter and plopping it into his mouth. After a couple of seconds of chewing, he let out a satisfied *ahh* and clapped his hands together.

"Tastes wonderful!"

"*Tch*, how undignified for the princess to be doing servants' work," Hansini muttered with a sigh.

Mingyue eyed the platter put together by his sister and her husband. Each roll was compact, intricate, and delicately crafted in a careful fashion. He imagined Sheli and Hyousuke, and how they must have spent countless hours alongside each other as they cooked up this meal. It brought a smile to his face.

"It sounds like it could be fun," he said. "Neili, perhaps you could teach me to cook sometime?"

"Ah...I..."

A shocked expression appeared on the young eunuch's face as he nervously glanced from the prince to Hansini and Olekina. The latter two unsurprisingly disapproved of the idea, but if the prince wanted him to do something, how could he refuse?

"Of course, your Highness!"

"I would like to learn sometime as well," Erik commented.

Mingyue hadn't noticed until now, but the Norden prince had slipped in between them, leaning over to scoop up a strange salad Amaru had provided, containing fruit, vegetables, and peculiar grain-like seeds.

"Prince Amaru, this is amazing! What is it?"

"Ah, that's kinwa!" Amaru replied. "It's nothing really, we eat it all the time in Tahuantinsuyu. That was the last of our stock though, but I'm glad you enjoy it!"

Erik sighed longingly. "I wish we had such tasty things to eat in Norden. The only thing we brought is this fried fish," his voice then fell into a whisper, "and I don't think Caleb cooked it properly."

"Hey!" Caleb protested. Despite the prince's best attempts, his attendant still overheard him. "It's not my fault. I don't know how to cook the local fish. There's no cod in Wuyue."

Erik giggled. "Relax! I was only teasing. You cooked it well."

"*Tch*, whatever," Caleb muttered, reaching over to scoop some of the kinwa salad onto his own plate.

"Haha," Erik leaned back, next to where Mingyue was seated. "Mind if I sit here?"

"Yes," Mingyue replied. There were no chairs present in the room, and no designated seating, so everyone simply sat on floor cushions wherever they liked.

"Oh…" Erik said in a quiet voice. "Alright…I'm sorry…"

"I mean no…" Mingyue corrected.

"Oh…" Erik paused. "No…?"

"I mean…you can sit here. Yes."

"Ah," Erik smiled. "Then I suppose I'll sit here after all."

XII. Gazing Upon the Open Window

Erik eyed Mingyue as he reached to scoop a spoonful of kinwa onto his plate.

"Hold on, I'll get it for you," Erik offered.

Mingyue's bandaged hand had drawn his attention, but Erik decided against commenting on it. Of course, if Mingyue wanted someone else to help him out, he could've requested Neili, Hansini, or even Olekina to do so. It was their duty to serve him, after all.

"It's fine," he brushed Erik off. "I can handle it."

As he scooped up some of the salad into his spoon, however, he quickly realized it would be more difficult than he anticipated. The wound from earlier was still fresh, and he found it difficult to grip onto anything, even something as simple as a spoon. His hand cramped up as he tried to lift the spoon out of the bowl, and soon, he spilled the whole spoonful onto the floor.

"*Tch*," he sighed, both out of embarrassment of having made a mess, and out of the discomfort and pain in his hand.

"I'll clean it up, your Highness!" Neili exclaimed as he came rushing over.

"No need," Erik said. "Enjoy your meal, I'll handle it."

He had already pulled out a cloth to wipe up the salad. Mingyue sat by in silence, awkwardly observing the other prince as he dealt with the mess of his own making. When Erik was finished, he reached back into the bowl to scoop up a fresh spoonful of salad.

"Is this enough for you?"

Mingyue nodded, and Erik poured it out onto his plate.

"Guess I don't need my attendants as long as you're around," Mingyue joked.

He meant for it to sound lighthearted, but it ended up coming off as somewhat condescending. He cringed and cursed himself silently for saying such a thing. It sounded better in his head.

Luckily, Erik was easygoing and chuckled at the attempt to make light of this situation. He gestured to Agnes and Caleb, as the former teased the latter over the fish he had cooked.

"What can I say? When these two are the ones attending to me, I've gotta learn to do things by myself."

"Hey!" Agnes protested. "We're doin' our best!"

"I also did my best with the fish," muttered Caleb.

"Sorry, but there are *no* excuses for that fish," Agnes faked a gag.

"Oh, Miss Agnes, don't be so harsh on him," Sheli said in a gentle voice. "I think you did a splendid job, Mister Caleb. I quite enjoy the fish you made."

Caleb blushed at the princess's response. "Ah...your Highness...you are too kind..."

Agnes scooted over to Erik and nudged him at the side as she whispered, "If anythin' ye should thank us for how we raised ya. You'd make a great housewife y'know! Haha!"

"Oh, shut up," Erik couldn't resist holding back a smile as he turned back to the Yue prince, glancing at his bandaged hand. "As good of a '*housewife*' that I might be, I don't think I'll be able to help you with that. Perhaps you should head over to the infirmary?"

It was at that moment that Mingyue was reminded that he promised Kanen he would return there after the funeral. "Maybe later..."

Coo!

They were interrupted by a flurry of feathers as Dudu leaped up from behind Mingyue and scuttled over to Erik.

Coo coo!

"Dudu! I missed you too!"

The duniao bounced up and down with excitement, bumping against Erik's leg as she anticipated head rubs from him. He caved in.

"What...what on Earth is going on here?!" Jiang Chu's groggy voice interrupted them as the young soldier wobbled his way into the room. It was clear he hadn't yet fully recovered from the effects of the

White Death from earlier. "Your Highness...who are they...? Why are we here...? What happened...?"

"Ah, the sleepy soldier has finally awoken!" Hyousuke laughed, raising his cup into the air.

He and Sheli had brought with them a jug of Nipponese alcohol to the feast. While Sheli and Mingyue hadn't drunk any, as they were still in the period of mourning for their grandfather, Hyousuke and Amaru both had, and were having a good time joking and messing around with one another.

"I am the Ansei Prince!" Hyousuke exclaimed with enthusiasm. "Come! Have a drink! This is the best sake in Nippon!"

"Uh...I'll pass..." Jiang Chu muttered. "Your Highness, where's Hong Xue? We should—"

"Let him enjoy this evening," Hansini said under her breath.

She had risen from her seat and snuck up behind Jiang Chu without him noticing, catching the man off guard. As she pulled him out of the room to explain the situation to him, she turned back to address Mingyue.

"I'll prepare your bed chambers for the night, your Highness. And I've also sent word to Lady Alaneya's residence that you will be over tomorrow afternoon for tea."

Mingyue nodded and watched as Hansini disappeared out of the room, dragging Jiang Chu along with her.

"Oh, you're seeing Lady Alaneya tomorrow?" Erik asked casually.

"*Mhm*," Mingyue said. "I haven't seen her since the Venesian Ball. There are some things we need to discuss..."

"I see," Erik said in a quiet voice. "I suppose you will need to reschedule your wedding ceremony..."

"Oh...yes..."

Mingyue was too embarrassed to admit that he'd completely forgotten about that. His planned meeting with Alaneya tomorrow was meant to question her on the affairs of the Oghuz Rumeli envoy and gauge whether Lusine was indeed telling the truth when they insisted that Aysun Sultana and the others were not connected with the events that had unfolded.

"I think I will call off the wedding," Mingyue said.

"Oh?" Erik said in surprise. "I wonder how she'll take that news…"

"It is for the best, for both of us," Mingyue said resolutely.

As he thought of the Venesian noblewoman, he was reminded of all the times he had seen her alongside Shenzhong, and how the two of them always looked so happy in each other's presence.

"I'm sure it will come as a relief to her," he added. "After all, there is someone else who she loves…"

Mingyue made eye contact with his sister, who sat across the table from him. She flashed a gentle smile and nudged Hyousuke's side as he and Amaru continued poking fun at one another.

"Perhaps it's time we return to the Palace of the Golden Dragon," Sheli said. "We don't want those guards to notice that we've been missing."

"Ah, yes! You're right!" Hyousuke exclaimed. "See you later Amaru, Erik, Mingyue. It was fun! We should do this again sometime!"

"Alright, let's get going," Sheli laughed, helping her husband keep his balance as they exited the estate. She turned back and gave a bow to the other nobles before departing. "Have a good rest and stay safe. I pray we will be able to return soon."

After they departed, Amaru stumbled over to his bed and soon fell asleep on top of the sheets—perhaps he had drunk too much of that alcohol. The Ansei Prince had even offered the drink to Erik and Mingyue's attendants. Of course, Hansini and Olekina, both regarding it as improper to dine, let alone drink, in the company of nobles, politely declined. On the other hand, Agnes and Caleb wouldn't pass up the opportunity to taste Nipponese alcohol. Agnes's laughs and jeers filled the room, mostly as she poked fun at Caleb. And Caleb, for once, was actually smiling and giggling as this took place, his rosy face glowing in drunken bliss.

Even Neili had decided to have a taste, though Mingyue figured it must have been his first time consuming alcohol. After a few sips, the boy passed out. At first, his head slumped into Olekina's shoulder, who was seated next to him. Olekina, being as he was, simply ignored this at first, and continued observing the others as if Neili wasn't even there. After a while, Neili slipped forward and his head came to a rest in the other man's lap, yet Olekina remained unfazed. As time went on, however, it became increasingly difficult for him to ignore Neili. Erik kept stealing glances at Olekina and forced himself to stifle his laughter at the sight of the man's stoic expression as Neili was curled up at his feet.

"Olekina, why don't you take Neili to one of the rooms and lay him down to sleep?" Mingyue finally suggested.

Olekina seemed relieved by this suggestion, as though he'd been waiting for the prince to give the order so he wouldn't feel as if he were acting out of place. With a nod, he gently scooped up the boy in his arms and carried him off to one of the other rooms. Mingyue couldn't help but feel a light, fluttering feeling in his chest as he watched the two of them go. Back at the table, Agnes and Caleb were now both passed out as well, Caleb's head against Agnes's shoulder, and Agnes's head tilted back against the wall as she snored with her mouth hanging wide open in a rather unflattering manner. The two princes remained the only ones who were awake.

"You didn't drink any sake," Mingyue noted.

"Neither did you," Erik pointed out.

"It's still the mourning period for my grandfather."

"Ah, I see. How long does that last?"

Mingyue paused for a moment. Prior to this year, there hadn't been any deaths in his family, not even among extended relatives. He never had to go through the mourning period before, so he didn't exactly know how long it was supposed to last.

"I'm...not sure..." he admitted.

Erik's wistful eyes fell away from the Yue prince and gazed off into the distance. "I'm also in a mourning period, I suppose you could say."

"For whom...?" Mingyue wondered.

"A friend."

"I see..." Mingyue's voice softened. "The one...that you loved...?"

"*Mnn*," Erik managed a slight nod. "It's been a long time, but he abstained from drinking alcohol. I thought by doing the same, I might be honouring him in some way. I know it's silly—"

"No," Mingyue interrupted. "I don't think it's silly. It's very thoughtful of you to do that."

He found himself blushing as he said those words.

A slight smile appeared on Erik's face. "I'm sorry for comparing you to him. He and you are two different people, and I didn't mean to imply that I only liked you because you reminded me of him. I'm sorry if that's how it made you feel."

"No, I should be the one to apologize." Mingyue admitted. "I know you didn't mean it. I shouldn't have gotten upset about that."

Erik's face glowed a rosy pink, but Mingyue couldn't tell if it was from embarrassment or the cold. Some of the windows remained open, and as a storm began to blow through, the cold wind wafted into the room and sent shivers across their skin.

"We should probably close those," Erik said, hopping to his feet and heading for the nearest window. "Caleb's a bit sensitive, he might catch a cold."

As the Norden prince turned his back to pull down the shutters, a sudden urge overcame Mingyue. He didn't know what it was within him that compelled him, but he found himself leaping to his feet. Before he knew it, he had wrapped Erik in an embrace from behind, their bodies pressed up together as he pulled his arms around the other boy's waist.

"Ah…" Erik gasped in surprise, but not discomfort, as they stumbled slightly forward against the windowsill. "Qian Ming…? What are you doing?"

Mingyue didn't know what he was doing. He had acted on a sudden instinct but now realized that perhaps he had gone too far. He had never hugged someone else before other than his parents and siblings when he was young. He almost forgot what it felt like. In his head, he told himself he should pull away before he made the situation too awkward, but his body resisted, refusing to let go of the other prince.

"It's cold…" he whispered.

Up against the window, the frozen winter air outside sent chills up his spine. But in his heart, there was a warm, fuzzy feeling that seemed to only grow stronger, radiating out to the rest of him.

Erik was tense as Mingyue held him in his arms, a natural response when one has been abruptly grabbed by someone else from behind. But as they remained in that position for a few moments longer, he began to relax, leaning back to accept the other prince's embrace.

"Yes. It is."

The warmth of Mingyue's body up against his was calming, and the slightly shorter prince rested his head on Erik's shoulder. Erik gently reached up to pat him on the head.

"We should get some sleep," he said in a gentle voice.

As Mingyue loosened his grip on him, Erik suddenly turned his head around and pulled him back in toward him once again. Mingyue's eyes went wide as he felt the gentle peck of Erik's lips against his own. After Erik pulled away, Mingyue remained frozen in place, unblinking and unmoving as he tried to process what had just happened.

"Haha," Erik giggled, "you're cute when you make that face."

Mingyue tried his best to hide how flustered he was, to little success.

"Why did you do that?! What if someone saw?!"

He anxiously eyed the others in the room, but Caleb and Agnes remained asleep against the wall, while from the bed came the snores of the Tahuantinsuyu prince.

"What?" Erik teased. "You're the one who initiated it."

"A hug…not…a kiss…!"

It was as if the Yue prince forgot how to speak.

"*Hmm,* true," nodded Erik. "Should I ask you first? Or perhaps, you should be the one to initiate it next time. Don't worry, you don't need to ask for my permission."

As a wide grin lit up the face of the jade-eyed prince, Mingyue felt his face burning bright red. He could only hope that in the candlelight, it wouldn't be too obvious to Erik.

Bump.

Mingyue felt something brush up against his robes. The two princes both gazed down to see that Dudu had come up behind them and started nuzzling her head against the Yue prince's legs. Mingyue scooped up the bird into his arms.

"Ah…Dudu. I forgot you were here…"

"Are you worried I'll steal Qian Ming from you?" Erik chuckled. He gave the bird a gentle pat on the head, and she ruffled her feathers in delight. "Don't worry, he's all yours!"

"Your Highness, your room is ready."

Momentary dread filled Mingyue as he heard Hansini's voice from the corridor. He breathed a heavy sigh of relief when he turned to see that she had just entered the room. Thankfully, she hadn't seen anything, though she eyed the two princes with curiosity as they remained standing by the window.

"Yes. I'm coming."

As he rushed out of the room without turning back to look at Erik, he heard the Norden prince call out from behind.

"Good luck in your meeting with Lady Alaneya tomorrow."

Mingyue paused and turned back to face the other prince. "Thank you. Have a good evening, your Highness."

409

"You too. Oh, your Highness, if you would like, perhaps we can meet again tomorrow? How about at the place we first met?"

Mingyue thought for a moment and was reminded of his first encounter with the Norden prince all those months ago when they had run into each other in that alleyway on the outskirts of the Palace of Heavenly Peace. How the world was simpler then. He longed to go back to that time.

With a hint of a smile, Mingyue nodded.

"See you then."

Part VII

By the Flickering Firelight

I. A Bond of Glass and Jade

"Do you want me to wait out here, your Highness?" Olekina asked the prince.

He and Mingyue had arrived with Jiang Chu at Alaneya's quarters in the Palace of Earthly Tranquility. The sun was already low in the sky on this chilly winter day.

"No," Mingyue replied. "You can come inside with me."

Olekina was surprised but pleased with his response. It wasn't often that he was allowed to be present when Mingyue met with others for private affairs.

"What about me, your Highness?" Jiang Chu inquired.

"You stay here."

"Very well," the rebel soldier sighed. "But don't take too long in there. I'd like to get back before sunset."

"Lady Alaneya is ready."

The face of a young man popped out from the room they were waiting in front of. Mingyue recognized him as the eunuch named Azaria—he was struck at how closely this boy's features resembled Lusine. Were the two perhaps related? He hadn't considered this before coming here, but it was possible that there might be collaborators within Alaneya's quarters as well. Suddenly, he felt very grateful that Olekina was here with him.

"Welcome, your Highness," Alaneya smiled.

Mingyue took a seat opposite the table from her, and as Olekina took his place behind him, the Venesian noblewoman's eyes lit up.

"Oh, this is your guard, isn't he? I heard he was missing."

"Did you?" Mingyue inquired. "Who told you that?"

"Ah…Aysun Sultana. Sorry, was I mistaken?"

"No," Mingyue shook his head. "It was him. He was kidnapped by the same individuals who took me, but I managed to find him yesterday."

"Oh!" Alaneya's eyes lit up. "You rescued him yourself? That sounds dangerous...but exciting! I'm glad you're both okay. Do you know who the ones that kidnapped you are?"

Mingyue's eyes flicked up toward Azaria, wondering if the boy would exhibit any response to Alaneya's question. His eyes wandered about the room, not seeming to pay any attention to the topic of conversation. Alaneya, however, noticed Mingyue's attention on the eunuch. She quickly turned to him.

"Azaria, why don't you go fetch the tea?"

"Y-yes, my lady," the boy stammered, hurrying out of the room.

Rather than address her question, Mingyue instead diverted the topic of conversation. "I apologize for my absence at the wedding ceremony."

"No, no, you need not apologize!" Alaneya said with haste. "It wasn't your fault. Actually, I should be the one apologizing. I...I don't know if you know this, but I was the one who poured the tea for everyone that day—the tea that was poisoned. It...it's the reason that the Emperor died..."

"Yes," Mingyue said quietly. "I know. The bride pours tea for the groom's family, and the groom for the bride's."

"Oh...yes. I'm sorry. I keep thinking that if I had noticed that there was something suspicious about that man who gave me the teapot, maybe—"

"You don't have to apologize. It wasn't your fault; it was the man who poisoned the tea. Him and his accomplices."

"Was he the one who kidnapped you too? Have you found him yet?"

"No. He took the Emir out of the palace to meet up with the rebels..."

Mingyue paused before he continued. Lusine's words to him on the boat suddenly came back to him.

The raven is...

If what they had said was true, then the person who had exchanged Zukang for the Emir wasn't the same one who had assassinated the Emperor. And the one who had assassinated the Emperor was still within the palace...

"Your Highness?" Alaneya's voice drew the prince back to reality. "You were saying?"

Once again, Mingyue shifted the conversation. "My lady, do you know why that hooded man decided to poison the teapot you served, but not the one my brother served?"

Alaneya paused for a moment as she considered his question but shook her head. "I'm afraid I don't, your Highness."

"Do you think that maybe it was because whoever was behind this incident only wished to harm the House of Qian, but not the Oghuz Rumeli delegation?"

Alaneya again hesitated before replying. "I suppose that would make sense..."

"Do you think it is possible someone in the Oghuz Rumeli delegation was aware of what was happening and interfered with the situation to ensure that only one pot of tea was poisoned, and not the other?"

He knew he was pressing too directly with these questions—if Alaneya was aware of conspirators within her delegation, then it would be obvious by now that Mingyue had caught on as well.

"Interfered...?"

That was all she managed to say. It didn't seem she was following what he was getting at.

"Tea time!"

They were interrupted as Azaria rushed back into the room, carrying a pot that he began pouring for the two nobles. Coming out of their previous conversation, both Mingyue and Alaneya suddenly felt turned off at the thought of drinking tea. Azaria noticed this and paused as he was serving the prince.

"Is everything alright?"

Mingyue wrapped his fingers around the teacup. "Yes."

"Wait," Olekina snatched the cup from the prince's hand. Before Mingyue could even react, he threw back his head and downed the tea himself.

"Olekina—?!" The prince exclaimed.

The young guard paused for a moment as he gazed at the contents of the cup before turning to Mingyue. "It's safe to drink, your Highness."

Mingyue felt slightly embarrassed as he accepted the cup back from Olekina. "Sorry, Wu Liqing was just taking a precaution."

"Not to worry, your Highness," assured Alaneya. "After what happened at the wedding ceremony, this is completely understandable."

"*Mnn,*" the prince tapped his fingers along the rim of the cup but didn't drink from it. "Speaking of the wedding, I expect that the Empress will want to hold another ceremony, probably sometime after the new year…"

Alaneya's head lowered. "Oh…yes. With the rebels here, I assume it will be a smaller ceremony than before. I should tell my father and Aysun Sultana—"

"I want to call off the marriage," the prince said suddenly.

Alaneya blinked in confusion, unsure if she had heard him right. "Pardon? You want to…call it off…?"

"Yes."

The noblewoman slumped back in her seat, and though relieved at his suggestion, she tried her best not to show it.

"What will the Empress say? What about Aysun Sultana? Oh, I'm not sure she'll like to hear that. What will become of Wuyue's alliance with Oghuz Rumelia…?"

"It doesn't matter," Mingyue said simply. "The palace is under rebel control now. There is no more alliance."

"B-but surely it won't be this way forever," Alaneya spoke nervously. "Are the rebels going to…depose you?"

He thought back to what Jiang Chu and Hong Xue had told him, how it wasn't the rebels' intent to overthrow the House of Qian, but merely to reform the system.

"I don't know."

"Then an alliance could still be beneficial!" Alaneya proclaimed. "The Oghuz Rumelis have many fleets stationed across the Southern Ocean. They could arrive in Wuyue within a month if a formal alliance was made—"

"I thought you also wanted this marriage to be called off," Mingyue interrupted abruptly.

"I...well...you're right. I do. But at the same time, I also want what is best for Wuyue. For the last year, this has been my home. I am heartbroken to see what has become of it. If an alliance with the Oghuz Rumelis can save Wuyue—"

"There can still be an alliance can't there?" Mingyue wondered. "Even if we don't marry?"

"H-how...?"

"You are in love with A-Shen, are you not?"

The noblewoman's face turned a bright red at his words. "Ah...I..."

Mingyue felt for the necklace hanging on his chest—the crystalline dove that Alaneya had gifted him for Jul. He pulled it over his head and beckoned Azaria over to bring it back to Alaneya.

"If you marry A-Shen, there can still be an alliance between our two countries."

As Alaneya accepted the dove from Azaria, she was suddenly reminded of the gift Mingyue had given to her. Tucked within the collar of her shirt, she pulled out the ornately carved Fenghuang necklace.

"You don't need to return that to me," Mingyue rose from his seat as he turned toward the door. "After all, it was Shenzhong who picked it out. That is a gift from him, not from me."

"A-Shen picked this one...?" Alaneya turned the jade Fenghuang over in her hand as if she was seeing it in a new light. With just those words, it had suddenly become a lot more precious and valuable to her. "W-wait. You're leaving so soon?"

"I should be back before sunset," Mingyue said. "And I was hoping to speak with Aysun Sultana before I returned."

"Aysun Sultana? She might be busy at this time of day," Alaneya warned. "Azaria, take them to Aysun Sultana's quarter."

"Y-yes, my lady."

"Oh, and your Highness," Alaneya called out to the prince one last time. "T-thank you. You were right...I do love A-Shen. I hope...that he and I can be together. And...I hope that you can be with the one you love as well..."

An image of the Norden prince, smiling with his hand outstretched, suddenly materialized in Mingyue's mind.

Perhaps we can meet again tomorrow? How about at the place we first met?

His heart fluttered at those words, but he quickly brushed that feeling aside and shook his head.

The one I love...? Is he really the one...?

"*Mhm*," Mingyue nodded, and pushed open the door, letting in a chilly breeze from outside. "Thank you."

Stepping foot outside, the sight of an anxious Jiang Chu was waiting there to meet them.

"There you are. Your Highness, I think we should return to your residence—"

Boom...boom...boom...

A low, rumbling rang out in the distance. It could be heard a few times in a row before ceasing, only to start up again a few moments later. As it echoed across the walls and between the mountains, it was impossible to tell which direction it was coming from. It did, however, seem to come from outside the palace.

"What is that?" Mingyue asked.

Jiang Chu shook his head nervously. "I don't know, your Highness. It's been going off for the past few minutes. I think we should head back..."

"Not yet."

That noise unsettled the prince, and he could sense that something wasn't right. But he felt that if he didn't take this chance to see Aysun Sultana, he wouldn't get the chance to later.

"Let's find the Sultana."

Boom...boom...boom...

Whatever that sound was, it was getting closer.

II. Thunderous Echoing

The deep booming sounds continued to resonate louder as the group made their way through the Palace of Earthly Tranquility. None of them knew what it might be, but it was clear that something was going on outside the palace. Mingyue felt uneasy.

"It sounds like cannon fire," Jiang Chu commented. He was a soldier; he would be the first to recognize a sound like that.

"*Tch*," Olekina huffed. "Are the rebels having a celebration? Why do they keep firing them?"

"I don't think it's the rebels," Jiang Chu stated. "At least, it's not *only* them. It sounds like they're engaged in combat outside the palace walls."

"Combat…?" Mingyue asked nervously.

Jiang Chu nodded. "Perhaps imperial reinforcements have arrived to attempt and expel us from the palace."

At those words, they anxiously eyed the rebel soldier. If imperial and rebel troops were engaged in battle, would he turn on them? He seemed to sense their anxiousness.

"You need not worry, your Highness," he assured. "I was tasked with watching over you, and I will continue to do that, regardless of whether or not our sides are at war."

That might be true now, but what if you receive new orders from your superiors? The prince wondered to himself. Olekina seemed to have the same thoughts and eyed Jiang Chu with increased suspicion.

They arrived at a building that Azaria said was where Aysun Sultana was staying. The young eunuch approached one of the Oghuz Rumeli guards standing outside the residence and asked in the Oghuzi tongue if she was present. The guard shook his head, giving a short reply.

Azaria relayed the message to them. "He says she's not here—she went to the gardens. Also, he's wondering what that sound is…"

"I don't know," the prince replied with frustration. "Does he know when she'll be back? Or maybe we should go to the gardens and find her…"

"I advise against that, your Highness," Jiang Chu said defiantly.

"For once, I have to agree with him," Olekina muttered. "Whatever that sound is, it seems to be coming from the east. The gardens are in that direction. I think we should head back to your residence."

Mingyue didn't have the energy or motivation to argue. Plus, he couldn't deny that he was also worried about whatever that noise was.

"I can send her a message if you like, your Highness," Azaria suggested. "Would you like to meet with her tomorrow?"

"*Mnn,* okay. I'll come back at the same time."

"Okay! I'll be sure to tell her that!"

As he turned to leave, Mingyue called out to him, "Thank you. By the way, what was your name again?"

"Azaria," the young eunuch responded.

"Azaria," Mingyue nodded approvingly. "There was another servant in the Oghuz Rumeli delegation who spoke Wuyueyu without a trace of an accent. Do you know who they are, by chance?"

A glimmer of recognition flickered in the boy's eyes. "Oh, you mean Lusine? Yes, we're cousins."

"Cousins…" this intrigued Mingyue. He knew the two of them looked related. "Then can you tell me where they learned to speak the Wuyue tongue so fluently?"

Olekina and Jiang Chu both shot the prince a sharp glance, warning him that he was making it too obvious that he wanted to know about Lusine. Azaria, however, didn't seem to think this was odd.

"Actually, the Nazaryan family has had connections with Wuyue for centuries," he explained. "We were merchants, so we traveled back and forth between Qiantang and Constantinople. My aunt is originally from the Armenian Quarter, so Lusine learned the language from her. I tried to learn as well, but I wasn't as good at picking it up."

"So, your family maintains connections in the Armenian Quarter?"

"Moreso in Suzhou," Azaria corrected, "since it is the base from which the Venesian merchants operate."

"Your Highness, we should head back now," Olekina urged.

"Right...yes..." Mingyue said. "Thank you for your time, Azaria."

"No worries, your Highness."

"Your Highness! Your Highness, here you are! And...Wu Liqing?!"

Several of the Imperial Guards passing by suddenly caught sight of the prince and rushed over. They were just as surprised to see Olekina as they were to see him.

"Wu Liqing, take the prince back to his residence and seek shelter immediately!"

Mingyue gave him a quizzical look. "Shelter? What's going on?"

Just as he said that the booms echoed through the palace, much louder and more rapidly than they had earlier.

"Imperial reinforcements have arrived in Qiantang! At first, the rebels were keeping them at bay outside the city, but they've broken through their ranks. The palace will be liberated soon!"

"*Tch*," Jiang Chu clutched his spear tightly as he heard the news.

The guards seemed to notice his presence for the first time. Glancing up and down at his uniform, their eyes lit up with rage.

"Y-you! You're one of the rebels! Seize him!"

"Wait!" Mingyue shouted. As both Jiang Chu and the Imperial Guards drew their weapons, the prince threw himself between them. "He was assigned to protect me!"

"Step aside your Highness!" The guards ordered. "Victory is upon us! We must assist our brethren in disposing of the rebels within the palace!"

"I won't allow it," the prince stood his ground.

"But your Highness—"

"You heard His Highness," Olekina drew his spear and directed it at his fellow soldiers.

He wasn't doing this because he cared about defending Jiang Chu, but because he was worried for Mingyue's safety. He didn't want blood to be spilled here.

"Now put down your weapons!" Olekina demanded. "That is an order from the Second Prince!"

The guards saw no choice but to obey, though they continued to protest his decision.

"You can't protect him, your Highness. Once the rebels are expelled from here, he will be punished!"

"That is not your decision to make," the prince said in a stern tone. "Now return to your duties. And do not even *think* of harming anyone you come across, rebel or otherwise. DO YOU UNDERSTAND?!"

Everyone present was taken aback by his outburst. There were only a few times in his life that Mingyue had spoken in such a tone. None of them had expected that he could be capable of projecting his voice to such an extent. Even Olekina flinched.

"Y-yes, your Highness…!"

When the guards had all departed, Jiang Chu finally mustered up the courage to ask, "Your Highness, why did you do that…?"

He stood motionless, confused, and utterly shocked that the prince would stand up in his defense to protect him from his own guards.

"Don't make me question my decision," Mingyue muttered before softening his tone. "Now, escort me back to the Palace of Heavenly Peace."

***

As they made their way to Amaru's residence, the sound of cannon fire only grew louder. Plumes of black smoke appeared in the skies east of the palace, rising from the West Lake. It was clear by now to everyone that a battle was waging just beyond the front gate. On their way back, they passed by dozens of soldiers, both Imperial Guards and rebel troops. Some were rushing toward the front of that palace, others in the opposite direction. Overall, the palace was in a state of confusion, with no one seeming to know exactly what they should be doing. Then, a huge explosion rang out from the east, and tongues of fire were spotted raging from the rooftops of a building near the front gate. That building was within the walls of the palace.

"Those must be the storehouses," Olekina noted. "*Tch*, why are imperial troops firing into the palace? Come on! We need to get back now!"

After a strenuous trek, they managed to find their way back to the Palace of Heavenly Peace, but this did little to put them at ease. They were located around the middle of the palace, a little too close to the front gate for comfort.

"Your Highness, maybe we should head back to the Palace of Lunar Serenity? Or even the Palace of the Golden Dragon?"

Mingyue didn't think that was such a bad idea, but he remembered his promise to meet up with Erik in the place where they'd first met. Was Erik waiting there for him now?

Jiang Chu threw open the doors of the bed chambers they'd stayed in the previous night, only to be greeted by a long pole that came crashing down on his head.

"*Ack*!" He staggered backward, clenching his head in pain before stumbling to the ground.

"Oops, I'm sorry! I didn't know it was you!"

The one standing on the other end of the door was none other than Amaru, with the pole in his hands being one of the many bamboo lamps decorating the room. He quickly tossed the makeshift weapon aside and hurried to Jiang Chu's side to check on the soldier's condition.

"*Tch*, who else would it be?! Ugh, my head. Why are you brandishing a lamp around like a weapon?!"

"I heard all those explosions outside. I thought someone was coming to get me! I don't wanna go back to Tahuantinsuyu! I don't wanna!"

"*Tch*, not everything is about you," Jiang Chu rubbed his head and reluctantly took Amaru's hand as he pushed himself back up on his feet.

Amaru cocked his head. "What is it then?"

There was no time to explain. Hansini and Neili soon came out from the back rooms to join them, the latter holding Dudu in his arms as she scrambled to break free of him. Mingyue told them to head over with the Tahuantinsuyu prince to the Palace of the Golden Dragon.

"My sister's residence is there," he explained. "She'll take you in. It will be much safer than it is here—the cannon fire won't be able to reach that far west."

"What about you, your Highness?" Hansini pressed.

"Olekina and Jiang Chu will accompany me. We need to find the Norden prince first. Then we'll have to head to the Palace of Lunar Serenity and fetch my brother."

"Your Highness, go with the others," insisted Olekina. "I'll find the Norden prince.

Mingyue shook his head. "I...I don't think he'll be in his residence right now. Only I know where to find him."

A deep *boom* rattled the building, throwing them off balance. It was clear that the cannon fire wouldn't cease any time soon and was only getting closer and closer to them with each passing minute.

"Hansini, Neili, take Prince Amaru and Dudu to my sister's residence," Mingyue raised his hand and gestured at the door for everyone to leave.

"Let's go!"

III. Down the Bloodstained Corridor

22/11/18th Year of the Golden Dragon Emperor

Year of the Wooden Goat

"Your Highness, where are we going?"

Olekina was growing increasingly nervous the further they walked. They were nearing the outer wall of the palace—beyond that lay the steep mountainside. Even if it was impossible for anyone to scale those cliffs and infiltrate the palace from the north, he didn't like the fact that they were so close to the outside world.

"We're almost there," Mingyue assured.

Sure enough, as they came around the corner of the alleyway into the next courtyard, he caught sight of the Norden prince lingering under the snow-covered branches of a tree.

"Your Highness, you came!"

Erik's face lit up at the sight of the Yue prince. Another loud *boom* echoed across the courtyard, but he didn't seem to notice. Nearby, Agnes and Caleb were clearly more unsettled than their prince was about the sound, and sighed in relief at the sight of Mingyue and the others.

"He refused to leave until ya showed up," Agnes shook her head. "What's goin' on out there?"

"We'll explain on the way, but we need to leave," Olekina pressed.

"Where are we going?" Erik wondered.

"The Palace of the Golden Dragon," Olekina replied.

"Not yet," Mingyue interrupted. "My brother is still in the Palace of Lunar Serenity."

"So is Hong Xue," added Jiang Chu. "And…well…"

Lusine. They still hadn't decided what should be done with the Oghuz Rumeli servant.

"Yes," Mingyue nodded. "We need to find them."

***

They realized something was wrong soon after stepping foot into the Palace of Lunar Serenity—it was eerily quiet, as if everyone had already deserted the place. Zukang should've been in either the infirmary or back in his own quarters, but they couldn't find him in either place. Prince Jinyu and Kanen were also missing. Mingyue was growing increasingly unsettled.

"They're not here," Olekina noted, stating the obvious. "We need to keep going. Maybe they're already at the Palace of the Golden Dragon."

Mingyue was reluctant to depart but saw no other option. "Okay. Then let's get Hong Xue and Lusine."

Entering the corridor that led to the room where Lusine was being kept, however, things went from bad to worse. The smell hit them first—a foul, metallic scent lingering in the air. Mingyue went wide-eyed as they turned the corner. A thick pool of dark blood around a body drenched the floor and a trail of bloodied handprints was stained across the walls, leading away from the door that swung wide open at the end—the door to the room where Lusine was being kept. The body was not Lusine, however, but Hong Xue.

"Hong Xue!" Jiang Chu rushed over in shock at the sight of his comrade motionless on the floor. "Hong Xue! Hong Xue what happened?! Are you alright?! Speak to me!"

He pulled at his hair, freezing in horror as he took in the blood-filled scene. Olekina drew his spear and became alert as he pulled Mingyue into a protective position behind him. Those bloody handprints were still wet as they dripped down the walls—this attack had only taken place shortly before they arrived. The attacker could still be nearby.

Mingyue tried to push past to see Hong Xue's body, but Olekina held him back. Erik, on the other hand, hurried over to kneel at the soldier's side. Hong Xue was face down, dark streams of blood still pouring out from his abdomen as he lay pressed against the ground. The Norden prince gently felt the man's neck for a pulse, and his face lit up.

"He's still alive! We have to stop the bleeding!"

Jiang Chu remained frozen in terror, utterly shocked that his friend could still be alive after so much blood loss. He stood motionless, unable to do anything at all except tremble in fear. Caleb and Agnes sprung into action. While Caleb applied pressure on the wound, Erik and Agnes carefully turned over his body to get a better handle on the injury.

"I need a cloth!" Caleb yelled.

The young man's hands were covered in blood as they remained pressed up against Hong Xue's abdomen, yet he was unfazed. Jiang Chu, on the other hand, stumbled back against the wall and collapsed to the floor in shock.

A cloth? Mingyue's eyes scanned the corridor. There was nothing in sight that could be used as a cloth to stop the bleeding except the clothes on their backs.

"Olekina, cut off my sleeves," he ordered.

"Y-your Highness, I beg your pardon?"

Mingyue held out his arms to his guard. The sleeves of his outfit were wide and made of thick cloth. The clothing everyone else wore was either too thin or didn't have enough material to properly wrap around Hong Xue's body, but his own sleeves were the perfect material for the job.

"Do it. Quick, there's no time."

Olekina knew that Mingyue wouldn't back down, and if they didn't act soon, Hong Xue would be dead. With a reluctant swipe of his weapon, he cut through the prince's sleeves at the shoulders in a clean fashion, and the two large sheets of fabric flopped to the floor. Mingyue scooped them up and hurried over to Caleb with haste, who quickly began wrapping the sheets around Hong Xue's body to seal up the wound.

"This won't last very long," Caleb warned. "He needs proper medical attention."

"I'll carry him," Olekina mumbled. He knew it was only a matter of time before someone asked this of him anyways—after all, he was the only one strong enough to carry a full-grown man.

They carefully hoisted Hong Xue up and into Olekina's arms. Blood continued to leak through the cloth, tainting Olekina's clothes. He grit his teeth but didn't object.

"We should bring him to the infirmary," Olekina suggested. "Kanen should be able to help him."

"No," Mingyue said quickly. "Kanen…isn't here…"

"Then I'll find him," Olekina huffed. "I don't think I'll be able to bring him all the way to the Palace of the Golden Dragon."

Mingyue shifted uncomfortably. They had already been here longer than he wanted to be. Kanen was nowhere to be found, and neither was his brother or Prince Jinyu, or anyone else for that matter.

"Fine."

Olekina nodded and rushed off in the direction of the infirmary. He turned back and glared at Jiang Chu, who remained huddled against the wall.

"*Tch*, how can you be a soldier if you cower so easily at the sight of blood? Make sure you bring him too."

Caleb held his hand out to help Jiang Chu up from the ground, but the man simply stared back in a daze and did nothing.

"C'mon," Caleb sighed, leaning over to hoist the man up. The two began fumbling their way after Olekina.

"You okay?" Erik wondered, coming up from behind Mingyue. He had taken off the outer layer of his coat, draping it across the Yue prince's shoulders.

"Oh, you don't have to…" Mingyue said softly, though truthfully, he very much appreciated the gesture. The coat was warm against his skin, Erik's body heat still lingering on it. He pulled it tighter around himself.

"No, it's no problem at all," Erik leaned in and buttoned the top of the coat together at the base of Mingyue's neck. He chuckled. "You really are a 'cut-sleeve' now, huh?"

"*Tch*," the Yue prince shook his head. His eyes scanned the corridor as he carefully tiptoed around the stains of blood on the floor.

"Where are you going?" Erik wondered.

Mingyue was walking in the opposite direction that Olekina and the others had headed.

"The room," he gestured to the door at the end of the hall, swinging wide open. "This is where Lusine was being detained."

"Lusine?"

Mingyue nodded. "One of Aysun Sultana's attendants. They were the ones who kidnapped Olekina."

"Damn, didn't see that comin,'" Agnes raised an eyebrow. She hopped down to the room and peeked in before turning back to them with a shaking head. "No one's inside. Seems they escaped."

Mingyue sighed as he gazed into the room and realized she was correct. "They were our only lead. Maybe they wouldn't have escaped if I turned them over to the Imperial Guard…"

"I don't think they escaped," Erik objected. He leaned down to reach for a large key laying in the doorway. It was coated in a thin layer of white powder.

"Don't touch it!" Mingyue shouted abruptly.

Erik froze in place and withdrew his hand.

"It's the White Death," Mingyue explained. "This is what they used to knock Jiang Chu unconscious yesterday."

"I see…"

"So, the person who opened this door used the key, which Hong Xue had, but also used this powder, which Hong Xue didn't have," Agnes concluded.

She looked back down the corridor. The stains and pools of blood were about halfway down the hallway, while there was not a drop of blood near the doorway.

"Hong Xue was attacked down there, while the key and the powder are over here. Whoever stabbed him must've been coming down the hall toward this door. They took his key once they stabbed him and unlocked the door to free that attendant. Then they tried to use this powder on the attendant but failed."

Mingyue nodded. Agnes's conclusion seemed to be perfectly reasonable.

"You could figure that all out just by a few clues?" Mingyue said in awe.

"*Mhm*, I do a lot of huntin'," Agnes explained. "Ya have to pick up on the little details and piece together the puzzle if yer gonna track down yer prey."

"Why would someone want to let Lusine out only to try and kill them?" Erik wondered. "Wouldn't they be trying to rescue them?"

"Not if they wanted to silence them," Mingyue said in a barely audible voice. "Lusine knew who was behind the killing of the Emperor. They told me..."

"You don't have to tell us," Erik said. "Only if you want to."

Mingyue breathed a sigh of relief and nodded. "I still have to confirm if what they said was true. But...first we need to find them..."

"Aye," Agnes concurred. "We should head to the infirmary first, make sure that guard is alright. Do ya think ya can find yer physician?"

Mingyue remained silent, responding with nothing but a slight nod.

IV. Piercing the Heart

Once they had gotten Hong Xue to the infirmary, they were able to properly bandage his wounds and obtain medicine for him. However, none of them were doctors. If he was going to receive proper care, they would need to find someone to treat him.

"Can we take him to the Palace of the Golden Dragon?" Mingyue inquired.

He shifted uncomfortably in his seat by Hong Xue's bedside. As his eyes flitted from the injured man to the others shuffling back and forth throughout the room, to the gardens through the window, he was growing increasingly unnerved at the absence of anyone else in this wing of the palace. There were never many people in the Palace of Lunar Serenity to begin with, but for the place to be completely devoid of anyone other than themselves was unsettling.

"We can't," Olekina huffed. "If we move him around too much, the wound will reopen. He must stay here for at least a few days."

"We need a doctor," Jiang Chu persisted. He turned to Mingyue with a frantic look in his eyes. "Ah! Where's your physician? We need to find him!"

"There will be other physicians in the Palace of the Golden Dragon," Olekina pointed out. "Your Highness, I can take you and the Norden prince there. I'll return here once we find someone to care for Hong Xue."

Mingyue considered the suggestion for a moment before reluctantly agreeing.

"I will stay to watch over Hong Xue," Caleb said.

"I'm staying too!" Jiang Chu quickly added. His nervous gaze met Mingyue. "I know it is my duty to guard you, but Hong Xue is my friend. I don't give a damn about my responsibilities right now."

Mingyue chuckled and shook his head. "I won't repeat those words to your superiors."

It was decided that Erik and Mingyue would set off for the Palace of the Golden Dragon accompanied by Agnes and Olekina. A storm had picked up by the time they departed, dumping large amounts of snow onto them. They could only see a few steps ahead. Everything beyond was nothing but a blurry blanket of white.

"This is just like the winter storms in Norden," Erik remarked, his voice muffled by the roaring wind. He tucked his chin into the collar of his shirt to shield his face.

Mingyue shuddered as he rubbed his hands together for warmth. In their rush to leave, they hadn't had the chance to find gloves or more adequate attire for the freezing weather. He still wore his torn-sleeved robes beneath the coat that Erik had offered him.

"There are pockets on the side," the Norden prince explained.

He took hold of Mingyue's hands and directed them to the hem of the coat to show him where they were. A momentary calm washed over the Yue prince as the warmth of Erik's hands grasped onto him. Of course, Erik's hands were also cold, but they were still less freezing than his own.

"Your Highness," Olekina popped an umbrella out and waved it in front of them.

"Oh, thank you for this," Erik took hold of it and lifted it up to block out the snow and wind.

The umbrella was only large enough to cover one person, but Mingyue's hands were far too cold to hold onto it. He shoved them deep into the coat pockets, digging for as much warmth as he could find. Suddenly, Erik's arm looped through his, pulling them together under the umbrella.

"Erik...what are you doing...?"

Mingyue nervously glanced toward Agnes and Olekina's direction. While Agnes paid them no attention, Olekina stared back momentarily before quickly averting his gaze.

"What? Do you wanna get covered in snow? Besides, I'm cold. I need to steal some of your body heat."

"You're warmer than I am," Mingyue muttered.

Erik laughed. "That's not how it works though."

"Will Agnes approve of us...being so close together?"

433

Erik flashed Mingyue a quizzical glance. "What do you mean? Does Olekina disapprove? I can let you take the umbrella if you prefer—"

"No," Mingyue said quickly. He tightened his grasp on Erik's arm, pulling the two even closer together. "This is fine."

Erik flashed a smile. Their journey toward the Palace of the Golden Dragon was slow, as they tread through the thick layer of snow that only continued to pile up higher and higher with each passing moment. The wind howled in their ears, pushing furiously against them as if it didn't want them to make it any further. A few times, Mingyue was afraid that it would blow him over and that he would drag Erik down with him. They hadn't made it very far, and it was difficult for anyone to make out the direction they were headed in. On the right, they came up against the side of a building, and it took Mingyue a few moments to realize it was his own residence.

"The Palace of the Golden Dragon is up ahead," Mingyue shouted through the wind. He pointed into the bleak emptiness of the winter night. His residence was just east of where the walls of the Palace of Lunar Serenity and the Palace of the Golden Dragon met.

A warm glow in the distance caught their attention, off to the south in the direction of the Lake of Tranquility. At first, they thought it was just an illusion, but after a short while it began to grow brighter—an orange hue that danced into the sky amidst the onslaught of snow.

"What is *that?*" Agnes wondered. They had all been asking that question in their heads, but no one had dared to bring it up.

"It looks like a fire," Olekina said gravely. "Let's keep going."

"Wait!" Agnes's voice caused them to halt in their tracks. She held up a hand, signaling for them to be quiet. Ironic, considering she was the one speaking the loudest. "Do you hear that up ahead?"

At first, none of them knew what she was talking about. All they could hear was the sound of swirling snow and the wind tearing through their ears. Soon, however, they detected the faint sound of voices. The next thing they knew, the shadows of half a dozen figures emerged from the blinding white. They were slightly up ahead and headed in the same direction as the Palace of the Golden Dragon. They didn't seem to have detected Mingyue and the others yet, but the paths of the two groups would soon converge.

"I have a bad feeling about this," Olekina held his arm in front of Mingyue to prevent them from going any further. "We should take a different path."

This route was the most direct way for them to get to the Palace of the Golden Dragon, but they unanimously came to the agreement that it would be safer if they didn't trail behind a group of unknown individuals. Instead, they detoured toward the north, traveling within the Palace of Lunar Serenity a while longer. The plan was to return heading west once they had put some distance between themselves and that other group, but their plans were upended yet again. This time, they were spotted first.

"Hey, someone's coming!"

The gruff voice of a man startled them from up ahead, coming somewhere from the north. By this point, it was dark out, and they could only make out the faint outline of buildings up ahead amidst the snowstorm. The voice must have come from the alleyways between one of those buildings, or perhaps from inside.

"Who are you?!" Olekina demanded, he drew his weapon at the ready but was unsure of where exactly he should direct his attention. "State your identity!"

"It's one of the soldiers in the Imperial Guard!"

Another voice shouted.

Whizz.

Something zipped through the air past them.

Thump.

Less than a moment later, it had made impact with the wall behind them. An arrow! Whoever was ahead of them had fired at them without a second thought.

"Your Highness, run!" Olekina yelled.

435

The man threw himself in front of the prince to shield him with his own body as a volley of arrows rained down on them.

Mingyue froze in shock, and it was only thanks to Erik grabbing hold of his hand and pulling him along that their bodies didn't become peppered by arrowheads. Everything that followed was a blur to him. All he knew was that Agnes led the way as Erik maintained a tight grip on Mingyue's hand so they wouldn't get separated. At some point, the umbrella he'd been carrying fell to the ground, disappearing behind them into the darkness. Agnes threw open the doors to a large building complex and they hurried inside. Mingyue didn't know how long they'd been running, but he was exhausted, collapsing to the ground as he huffed to catch his breath.

It was only then that he realized that someone was missing from their group.

"Where's Olekina?"

"You don't remember?" Agnes gave the prince a confused glance. "He said he'd stay to buy us time to escape! I doubt he'll be far behind."

As Mingyue pushed himself back to his feet and scanned the room they had entered, he came to the quick realization that they were back in his own bed chamber! It took him a moment to recognize the place—there were almost always at least a few candles or lanterns present in the room to light up the space, but tonight it was completely dark. Despite this being his own room, he felt like they were stepping foot into a foreign land.

As Mingyue attempted to take a step toward the bed, a sharp pain shot up his leg. He became faint. The next thing he knew, he was stumbling forward onto the ground.

"Qian Ming!" Erik shouted. "What's wrong—?"

It was then that he and Agnes noticed a long rod protruding from the back of the Yue prince's thigh. He had been behind the two of them as they made their way over, and at some point, one of the arrows must have struck his leg without them noticing.

"It's cold..." Mingyue whispered. "I want to...lie down..."

His voice grew fainter with each passing word.

"Qian Ming? Your Highness?! Hey, don't close your eyes!"

"*Mnn,*" Mingyue groaned. "Too loud. I'm...tired..."

"It ain't a deep wound," Agnes noted calmly. "I can remove the arrowhead easily, but you'll need it to be treated."

At this point, she was speaking more to Erik than to Mingyue. The Yue prince was dozing in and out of consciousness.

Erik gave her a nervous nod. "What do you need me to do?"

"Just hold his leg still while I take it out," Agnes replied. "He might scream, but he'll be fine. Can ya get some cloth to bandage him up once it's out?"

Erik obliged, digging up some rags from the dressers in the room. The hard part came when they had to remove Mingyue's robes to access the wound. It was too difficult for them to take everything off while he was laying on the floor, so instead, they cut part of the cloth off to expose his leg.

"I'm sorry," Erik whispered. "I promise I'll get you a replacement for this outfit."

"*Mnn,*" Mingyue groaned. He was no longer fully aware of what was going on.

Luckily, the arrow hadn't pierced his flesh too deeply, and he wasn't bleeding extensively. Once Agnes yanked out the arrow, Erik hurried to wrap the prince's leg in cloth to prevent further blood loss.

"How do you feel?" Erik asked.

"*Mnn...*"

There was no other reply from the Yue prince.

"We should let him rest," Agnes said. "Don't worry, he'll be fine."

Erik leaned over to scoop up Mingyue into his arms. The prince had still been on the floor up to this point, but he decided it would be better to let him rest in his own bed. He gently set him down, tucking him under the covers.

"Olekina still isn't here," Erik whispered in concern. "Do you think he's…"

"He'll be here," Agnes said with confidence.

"Qian Ming needs medicine," Erik said. "And we should disinfect the wound. We need to get him back to the infirmary."

"He's in no condition to walk," Agnes sighed.

"Then can you go get some and bring it back for him?" Erik pressed.

Agnes paused at his request. "Milord, it's my duty to protect ya—"

"And I'm asking you to do this," Erik said. "Please. The infirmary isn't far, so it shouldn't take too long."

Agnes sighed and gave him a nod. "Alright, alright, fine. I'll be back as soon as I can. In the meantime, you better protect the prince. Don't draw any attention to this place. Hopefully Olekina will be here soon…"

Erik watched as Agnes disappeared into the blackness of the winter night. The storm was still raging, with snow piling up halfway to her knees. After a few moments, she disappeared completely into the darkness, leaving him alone with Mingyue.

"*Mnn…*"

The sound of the prince's groans drew his attention back to the bed.

"I'm here," Erik said softly as he came back to Mingyue's side. "Don't worry, I'm not going anywhere."

"Cold…" Mingyue said, his voice barely louder than a whisper.

Erik sat next to him as he scanned the room for any extra blankets or clothes that he could bring over for the prince. Just as he was about to get up, however, the frozen grasp of Mingyue's hand wrapped around his wrist. He shuddered at the cool touch.

"Qian Ming, your hand is freezing," he said. "Let me get you some—ahh!"

438

He gasped in surprise as he was pulled down into the bed next to Mingyue. "Your Highness! What are you doing?!"

He was caught off guard by the force Mingyue was able to exert. Though the prince appeared weak and fragile in his current state, Erik found himself unable to break free of his grasp. He quickly gave up on his struggle and collapsed into the sheets next to him, Mingyue still holding onto his wrist with a death grip.

"Stay with me…" Mingyue muttered. His eyes weren't even open at this point.

"I…okay…alright," Erik sighed and chuckled in defeat. "I will."

Mingyue managed a slight nod of approval and rolled onto his side in Erik's direction. Erik froze as the Yue prince's body pressed up against his. He didn't want to push him away, but at the same time, he was already at the edge of the bed and couldn't put any more distance between them.

"Cold…" Mingyue whispered again.

Though he said that, his breath was warm as it brushed across the skin on Erik's neck. Hesitantly, Erik put his arms around Mingyue, pulling him closer into an embrace. He hoped his body heat would be enough to satisfy the other prince.

"It's okay. I'm here. I'll keep you warm."

"*Mnn*," a slight smile of satisfaction appeared on Mingyue's face as he dozed off to sleep. "Warm…"

Erik's heart raced as he gently brushed aside the hair in Mingyue's face. Part of him secretly wished that they could stay like this forever, but he knew that Agnes would be back soon. He'd have some explaining to do once she returned, but he knew she wouldn't pass too much judgement on him. For now, though, he didn't care about any of that. All that mattered was the prince in his arms, and that he could be here for him when he needed it most.

V. A Hearth in the Blizzard

Erik was awoken by the unpleasant feeling of being shoved off the bed. He landed with a thud on the ground and sprung back up with the blanket still wrapped around his head.

"What's happening?! What's going on?!"

As he tore the sheets off him, he was greeted by the sight of Mingyue huddled up in a ball on the other side of the bed. His face was flushed red in embarrassment.

"I-I'm sorry. I didn't mean to push you so hard. You just startled me. But…w-why were you in bed with me?"

Erik quickly hopped back onto the bed and reached for the bandage on Mingyue's leg. "Qian Ming, calm down. You'll open the wound."

It was only at that moment that Mingyue realized that he wasn't wearing anything on the lower half of his body, other than a short cloth covering his groin. He squirmed away from Erik and yanked the bedsheets over his legs. "W-what are you doing…why am I naked?!"

"Relax," Erik assured in a soothing tone. "You were injured, remember? We had to cut your robes to bandage the wound. Don't worry, you'll be fine."

"And why were you in bed with me…?" He wondered, returning to his first question.

Erik blushed at this. "Well…I didn't really have a choice. You pulled me down into the bed and said you were cold. I tried to get up, but you wouldn't let me go, so I had no choice but to stay with you. You don't remember?"

Mingyue looked like he would die from embarrassment. He buried his face into the sheets and refused to look back up again until Erik repeatedly assured him that they had done nothing more than huddle together for warmth.

"It was you who initiated it," Erik chuckled.

Mingyue remained in denial. "You better not mention this to anyone."

"Of course not," Erik replied. "It would be just as embarrassing for me. You're lucky you woke up before Agnes returned though."

It was only then that he remembered that Agnes was supposed to be back soon. How long had they been asleep? He hadn't planned on falling asleep before she returned, but it felt like they had already slept for quite some time. Peeking out the window, they saw that it was still dark outside, the snowstorm still raging on. There was no sign of Agnes, or Olekina, or those men who had chased them for that matter.

"She should be here…" Erik muttered to himself.

"What's wrong?" Mingyue asked.

"Nothing. Now, let me see your leg."

"W-why do you need to see it?"

The prince buried his face into the sheets once again.

"Because we should change the bandages," Erik explained. "Come on. I promise I'll do my best so that it doesn't hurt."

"I'm not worried about it hurting," Mingyue muttered.

"Then?" Erik asked. When he received no response, he decided to press on. "Are you embarrassed about me seeing your legs? Qian Ming, I've already seen everything. There's nothing to be embarrassed about."

"E-everything?!"

This clearly didn't calm the prince's nerves.

"I didn't mean…never mind!" Erik rested his face in his palm. "Now come on, let me switch the bandage."

Reluctantly, Mingyue lifted the blanket and exposed his legs to the Norden prince. His face, however, remained buried in the sheets. Erik inched in. The bandages indeed needed changing—they were stained dark red with the prince's blood, which had gotten into the bed sheets as well. Mingyue flinched as Erik gently rested his hand on his thigh but didn't resist any further as he began undoing the wrappings. Luckily, the wound was shallow and didn't bleed much when the bandages were removed. He swiftly rewrapped Mingyue's leg in a fresh layer.

"I hope that's not too tight," Erik said.

441

His eyes involuntarily scanned up and down the smooth, pale skin of the other prince's leg.

"Stop staring," Mingyue hastily pulled the sheets back over him.

"I-I wasn't staring!" Erik objected. "Goodness, do you get this flustered every time your attendants see you naked?"

"That's different," Mingyue's muffled voice came from under the blanket.

Erik chuckled and shook his head. "Well, there's nothing to be ashamed of! You have very nice legs…"

"Just get me some clothes," Mingyue muttered.

"Y-yes, your Highness!"

Once he had dressed, Mingyue attempted to step out of bed but ended up stumbling forward instead into Erik's arms.

"Steady now," Erik said.

Mingyue's leg had fallen stiff, and he only managed to stay upright thanks to Erik supporting the complete weight of his body. Mingyue's arm was over Erik's shoulder, and he attempted as best he could to hobble along, but they only managed a few steps before they both collapsed to the floor. Erik bore the brunt of the fall, cushioning Mingyue with his own body as they landed on the ground.

"Doesn't look like we're going to make it very far," Erik chuckled. "It'll probably be at least a few days before you can walk normally again."

"I can't get up either," Mingyue grumbled. "You'll have to help me with that."

Erik tilted his head back against the floor with a sigh. "Why don't we stay like this for a while? I'm quite comfortable."

"Well, I'm not," Mingyue objected.

He shuffled around, trying to get up on his own, but was only able to use the strength of his upper body and one leg in the process. This only led to him accidentally jabbing the Norden prince with his elbows and knees in some less-than-ideal places, finally convincing Erik that perhaps this wasn't so comfortable after all. He rolled out from under Mingyue's body and hopped to his feet, extending a hand to the other prince to help him up. Mingyue took hold but winced as he grasped Erik's hand. The wound on his palm from the other day still hadn't recovered.

"Oops, sorry," Erik said. "I forgot your hand was injured too."

In the end, he had to scoop Mingyue up using a bridal carry to minimize causing further damage to his leg or hand. He might have had a slightly larger build than the other prince, but it was still a difficult feat to carry someone nearly the same weight as oneself in such a manner. Luckily, it was only for a few moments. He plopped Mingyue back onto the bed and collapsed next to him, legs dangling off the edge.

"Ah, my back! That was harder than I thought it would be."

"Are you saying I'm heavy?" Mingyue muttered.

"No, but do you want to try carrying someone? I doubt you'd be able to."

Mingyue shook his head with a sigh. "How long are we going to be here for?"

"I promised Agnes I'd wait here with you for her to return," Erik answered. "We'd best wait for Olekina too."

Neither of them said it, but there was a chance that neither Olekina nor Agnes was coming back. Several hours had already passed since their encounter with that mysterious group of men. Did the imperial troops manage to retake the palace from the rebels? If that was the case, then why had they opened fire when they realized Olekina was a member of the Imperial Guard? None of it made any sense.

"That wound on your hand," Erik said, hoping to change the conversation. "How did you get it?"

"A cut," Mingyue mumbled.

"Well, obviously it's from a cut. But how? Were you attacked?"

"It was from Jiang Chu's spear."

"Jiang Chu?!" Erik exclaimed. "That rebel soldier who was stationed to guard you?! He attacked you?!"

443

"No," Mingyue said. His voice was barely audible. "I...wanted him to kill me. I asked him to."

"You...what...?"

Mingyue said nothing, simply turning over on his side to face away from Erik. Erik remained still as he faced the ceiling, and for a while, no one spoke.

"Life is hard to live," Erik's whispers finally broke the silence. "But we only get this chance once. As hard as it may be, I still think it's worth it."

"Why did I not die?" Mingyue wondered out loud. "Why did my parents have to be the ones to die? My grandfather? Why couldn't I die instead of them? The people who deserve to live are the ones who die, and the people who deserve to die are the ones who live."

"You don't deserve to die," Erik said firmly.

"But I want to."

Erik turned over to face Mingyue, who was still facing the other direction. His body was shaking ever so slightly. At first, Erik thought it was from the cold, but he soon realized it was because the other prince was crying. He didn't make a sound—it was clear that he didn't want Erik to notice he was shedding tears—but nevertheless, the Norden prince noticed. Erik shifted himself over toward Mingyue. He knew he might face resistance, or even outright rejection for what he was about to do, but he decided to go ahead with it anyways. Wrapping his arms around the Yue prince, he pulled him close and sheltered his body with his own. Surprisingly, Mingyue didn't resist. Perhaps he no longer had the energy to.

"It's okay," Erik whispered. His face was right up against the back of Mingyue's hair, his breath blowing through it and tickling the other prince's ear as he spoke. "I know how you feel. When my parents and sister died, I felt the same."

As he continued holding Mingyue in his arms, he noticed that the other prince had started to shake more, and the sound of his ragged breathing as he cried became more apparent. He was no longer trying to hide his tears from Erik.

"It's okay," Erik said in a soothing tone. "I'm here. You can cry all you need to."

"I don't want to be alone," Mingyue managed to say through his tears. "Everyone always leaves. I don't want them to leave me behind…"

"I'm not going anywhere," Erik assured. "I'll be here. Whenever you need me, I'll be here. Forever. I promise."

Mingyue shook his head. "You can't promise that. Nothing lasts forever."

"That's not true," Erik said. "Faith lasts forever…so does hope…and love. But the greatest of these is love. I promise that I will always be here. And if we are ever apart, I promise I will always be searching for you, no matter where you are."

This all felt so surreal to Mingyue. He didn't know what he had done to deserve someone like Erik. To be honest, he didn't even know if he entirely believed what he was hearing.

"I don't deserve that."

"It's not about deserving," Erik replied. "Someone once showed me that kind of love, even though I didn't deserve it. And now in return, I want to show that same kind of love."

"Why?" That was all Mingyue managed to say.

Erik said nothing for a while, but then he finally spoke. "Because I made that promise once before. I couldn't keep it then, but I intend to keep it now."

With the boy you once loved? Mingyue wanted to ask. But he didn't. He simply exhaled, allowing himself to surrender as he wrapped himself in the warmth of the other prince's arms. He couldn't help but notice how Erik talked about that *someone* he had once loved, the one he had made a promise with, as if he were the same person as Mingyue. But even if this was a second chance for Erik, a chance for him to redeem his broken promises of the past, that was good enough for Mingyue.

The storm continued to howl outside, and Erik soon found that the Yue prince had dozed off once again in his arms.

VI. Shadows Over the Bright Moon

23/11/18th Year of the Golden Dragon Emperor

Year of the Wooden Goat

Erik awoke once again a short while later. This time, it wasn't from Mingyue, but rather a crackling sound that seemed to be growing louder with each passing minute. At first, he ignored it, passing it off as the howling wind, or even a figment of his imagination. As time passed, however, he became increasingly annoyed and rolled off the side of the bed in search of the origin of that sound. It came from outside the window facing the east. He inched over to it, and throwing them open, a gust of chilly air wafted into the room. He squinted as snow blew into his eyes, but that wasn't the only thing that caught him off guard as he looked outside.

The atmosphere was brighter than it had been earlier yet remained dim with the heavy torrents of snow still coming down. And in the distance, glowing tongues of flames licked up into the sky from one of the buildings. It was only then that he remembered how they had seen flames coming from near the Lake of Tranquility earlier. He wondered if perhaps it had spread from there, or if the two fires had been ignited separately.

"Qian Ming, get up," he said in a frantic, yet gentle voice.

"*Mnn,*" the Yue prince groaned groggily as he strained to open his eyes. "Tired…"

"There's a fire," Erik warned. "It's getting close. We should get out of here in case it spreads."

"A fire?" Mingyue repeated in confusion.

He rubbed his eyes, glancing out the window toward the east. It took him a few moments to process what he was seeing, but once he was fully awake, he quickly sat up and tore the covers off himself.

"That's the infirmary."

"The infirmary…?" Erik said.

It took him a moment to realize that indeed, that building *was* the infirmary. They had backtracked toward the infirmary on their way to the Palace of the Golden Dragon, and Mingyue's residence was just slightly to the west of there. If the infirmary was on fire, and that was where Agnes had gone, and where the others had been staying…

"We have to make our way over there," Mingyue said.

He attempted to push himself out of the bed, but Erik quickly stopped him.

"Your leg is still injured," Erik reminded the other prince. "And we don't know if they're still…if they'll still be there…"

"We have to find them," Mingyue said firmly. "Olekina too."

"I'm not sure that's a good idea right now," Erik objected. "Maybe we should get you to the Palace of the Golden Dragon first. Then we can get the Imperial Guards to send out a rescue operation."

"Are you planning on carrying me there?" Mingyue wondered half-jokingly. Erik was holding him back from getting out of bed, still worried that he would be unable to stand due to his injured leg.

"I can," Erik replied unironically.

Mingyue stared back blankly, but the Norden prince was being serious. He hopped down and leaned in to wrap his arms around the Yue prince, but Mingyue brushed him aside.

"We won't get very far. I think it's better we stay here for now, at least until the storm blows over. We can move to other quarters in case the flames blow over here."

They came to a compromise, deciding that they would take this option, slowly making their way toward the Palace of the Golden Dragon. They did this by sneaking through the corridors and alleyways connecting the various buildings of the Palace of Lunar Serenity, avoiding the main pathways so that they would not come across anyone—friend or foe. Erik supported Mingyue's weight as he assisted him in a slow hobble down the hallways. As they made their way through one corridor in particular, the sound of voices just outside caught their attention.

"Did you find the prince?" One called out.

"NO!" Another shouted with rage. "Maybe if you didn't burn down that building we would've found him by now!"

Their bickering continued as the group of strangers approached. Erik and Mingyue quickly ducked as they passed by. They remained on the ground for a while, long after the voices of those strangers disappeared.

"They're setting fires," Mingyue said weakly.

"Yeah. We need to get out of here as quickly as possible."

"Your Highness, what are you doing here?!"

A sudden voice from down the hall led to both princes nearly jumping out of their skin. They whipped around and spotted a figure lurking in the shadows of a doorframe down the corridor. Erik shifted himself in front of Mingyue and hastily attempted to get the other prince up, but Mingyue's leg was in no condition to allow him to escape. As he tried to push himself back up onto two feet, he gave out and collapsed onto the ground once again.

"Qian Ming!" Erik called out with concern.

"What happened?" The voice of the man in the shadows grew more audible as he approached.

Erik desperately reached for something to defend themselves with in case this newcomer had violent intentions, but he had nothing on him. Just as he was about to stand up and confront this mysterious figure himself, however, he caught sight of the man's face as he stepped forward and the dim light from behind the window illuminated him. His features were handsome, his long, dark hair tied neatly back, and though his eyes were fixed on them, they seemed to be gazing into the distance.

"Y-you...!" Erik's face lit up in a pleasant surprise. "You're Qian Ming's physician, aren't you?"

Kanen's expression soured as he heard the Norden prince refer to Mingyue as simply 'Qian Ming,' but he didn't comment on this. He simply knelt next to the Yue prince and examined his leg.

"Chu Kening...?" Mingyue went wide-eyed, his whole body falling stiff.

"Help me bring him into the room," Kanen addressed Erik. "I need to treat his wound."

"Ah, of course!" Erik said.

He came to the other side of Mingyue, and together they began to hoist him up. Erik made eye contact with the other prince and was surprised by the look of shock and bewilderment on his face. It seemed that Mingyue had something he wanted to say to him, but he remained silent.

They hoisted him up and hurried into the room where Kanen had come out of. After settling Mingyue into a chair, the young physician peeked up and down the hall, ensuring that they hadn't been followed, before sealing the door behind them.

"We were attacked," Erik explained quickly. "There was a man injured in the infirmary and we went looking for help, but there was no one around. The infirmary caught on fire, and we were separated from the others…"

"What is that…?" Mingyue muttered.

A glimmer of light from something on the ground caught his attention. As his eyes adjusted, he could see that it was a blade—the blade of a sword tainted red with stains of blood.

"Some of those intruders attacked me and Prince Jinyu," Kanen explained. "I dealt with them and took one of their swords in case more came back."

"Wow, you fought them all on your own?!" Erik asked. "You have quite some skills for a physician."

"Where is Prince Jinyu now?" Mingyue inquired of his grand-uncle's whereabouts.

"In a safe place," responded Kanen. "I will take you to him later."

Mingyue's hands trembled. Kanen noticed this instantly. He headed off to a dresser along the side wall, where a pile of towels alongside other linens and clothes were stacked.

"You must be cold, your Highness. Let me find something to warm your hands."

As the physician rummaged, Mingyue glanced nervously between Kanen and the bloody sword on the ground.

"I never knew you were a skilled combatant," muttered the prince. "Why did you decide to become a physician rather than a guard?"

"Because my abilities are better suited for this field," Kanen replied.

"I see…"

Erik was attentive to Mingyue's discomfort. He leaned in and asked in a low voice. "Is something wrong?"

Mingyue hesitated before responding, his voice barely louder than a whisper.

"The reason we had detained that Oghuz Rumeli servant was because they claimed to know the identity of the one who killed the Emperor."

Erik held his breath.

"The poison used on that day was the White Death, the same one used to kidnap Olekina," Mingyue continued. "It was being kept in the apothecary, a place only someone like a physician would go to."

His gaze fell to Kanen's side, where several sachets hung at the man's waist. Alongside them was a tassel of black feathers—black feathers from a bird. A raven.

The Raven will paint the Bright Moon red.

VII. The Raven

Mingyue rose from his seat as inconspicuously as he could, taking hold of Erik's hand as the Norden prince led the two of them toward the door. Kanen bid his time at the other end of the room, seemingly oblivious to their attempts to leave. However, this wasn't the case.

"You shouldn't exert yourself while your leg is injured," he spoke without even turning back to look at them.

The two princes froze. Mingyue's heartbeat rapidly increased in pace, and he could swear that he could hear Erik's as well. He didn't want to be here. Ever since Lusine had told him that his own physician was the one responsible for the death of his parents and the Emperor, a feeling of dread had settled in his chest. He hadn't believed Lusine when he first heard this news, but out of precaution decided to stay elsewhere in the palace, somewhere Kanen wouldn't know where to look. Even now, with Kanen standing just across the room from them, he found it hard to believe that this seemingly innocent young physician, only a few years his senior, could be the one responsible for ruthlessly slaughtering his family. How could that be? Had Kanen not been the one who had served as his physician for years, bandaging every wound and concocting a cure for every illness that had befallen him? Not only did it contradict his principles as a doctor to commit such unspeakable crimes, but it completely went against his character as a gentle, kind-hearted young man. Mingyue couldn't bring himself to look at Kanen.

"Your hand was also injured, was it not?"

As the physician spoke, he began to turn back around toward them. In his hands, he clenched not the bandages and medication which he had gone over to retrieve, but a long, thin blade.

"Your Highness, didn't I tell you to return to the infirmary the other day? You never came back."

Mingyue found himself unable to move. If it wasn't for Erik pulling him out of the way, Kanen's blade would have sunk into his chest. The knife made a *thunk* as it cut into the wall just behind where he'd been standing only a moment before. The physician had whipped it at them from across the room. He had another blade in hand.

Kanen's expression was calm—eerily calm. Mingyue couldn't help but think that the man standing before them appeared unrecognizable compared to the innocent physician he thought he knew. This time, Kanen didn't fling his weapon at them. He lunged.

Mingyue was thrown backward onto the ground. The back of his head smacked hard against the table. A wave of nausea washed over him. He tried to push himself up into a seated position, but a heavy weight on his stomach was pinning him to the ground.

"Qian Ming!" Erik cried out.

Mingyue caught sight of Erik stepping out from the darkness. Amidst the shadows, the dim glow of lanternlight illuminated the room. Mingyue could just make out the young man's features—the lighting distorted his visage. His handsome face appeared haunting with his downcast expression; his jade-coloured eyes now flickered with a bloody, crimson tint.

"Do not move," Erik said. His gentle, rose-petal lips spoke the words firmly.

Mingyue's vision began to clear. Erik stood several steps away, the bloodied sword that had been cast on the ground now clenched tightly in his hand. It wasn't pointing at Mingyue, but at Kanen. Kanen had pushed Mingyue to the ground and was enveloped by the darkness of the room. He had Mingyue pinned to the ground with his legs on either side of the prince's body. The edge of Erik's sword flashed through the blackness against Kanen's throat. Mingyue could sense Kanen holding a knife that hovered just above his face. His heart was racing, but he managed to speak up with three simple words.

"Was it you?" His voice trembled as he asked the question.

Kanen breathed heavily as he pinned down Mingyue, simultaneously focusing on the one prince beneath him and the other behind him, wondering who could strike faster. He didn't respond to Mingyue's question. To Mingyue's surprise, he felt a warm, wet drop drizzle down onto his forehead. Kanen was crying.

453

"It was you who killed them, wasn't it!" Mingyue reasserted. This time, it was an accusation, not a question. Mingyue channeled all the anger and disgust that had been pent up over the last three months into those words.

"I...I didn't have a choice..." the physician managed to whisper. He sounded as though he were the one in pain, as if he'd been the one knocked against the floor with a knife pressed up against his throat.

"Step away from Qian Ming," Erik warned again.

"You wouldn't understand," Kanen's shadowy figure spat. "None of you would understand!"

At this point, he was starting to laugh hysterically. The jade-eyed prince gripped his sword nervously, prepared to strike at any moment.

The laughing ceased. Several long moments of silence passed. Other than the lanternlight casting eerie shadows dancing across the walls, it seemed as if time had frozen.

"I'm sorry..." Kanen muttered. His voice was so soft that even amidst the silence, Mingyue struggled to understand what he was saying. "Please...forgive me..."

Before Mingyue could respond, Kanen lurched forward. Mingyue could sense the knife coming toward his face. Erik didn't hesitate—his sword swung down in an instant. Mingyue's eyes flicked toward him.

"Erik! Don't!"

It was too late. The sound of steel ripping through flesh slashed through the deafening silence of the room, splattering blood across the floor. The lanternlight went out, casting the world into darkness.

***

Erik's fears had materialized—the flames to their east had begun spreading in their direction and were soon dancing across the rooftops of the buildings in their vicinity.

"Damn," the Norden prince cussed with a ragged breath as he carried Mingyue through the gardens and alleyways.

The Yue prince lay unconscious in his arms, his robes stained red by Kanen's splattered blood after Erik impaled the physician. Erik, too, was drenched in blood, though he didn't know if it was his own or not. Their encounter with Kanen was a blur to him. He was surprised they even managed to make it out of there at all. He remembered glimpsing the blade in Kanen's hand, yanking Mingyue toward him as he heard that blade slicing through the air, and the *thump* which followed when it sunk into the wall.

Erik moved quickly, but Kanen was quicker. Erik had only managed to take Mingyue a few steps forward before Kanen had reached them. The Norden prince made a futile attempt to put himself between them, but the physician was stronger than he looked, knocking Erik aside and tackling the Yue prince to the ground. With his fight or flight responses kicking in, there was only one thing Erik could do. He couldn't leave Mingyue behind—he had to defend him. He reached for the closest object he could grasp, which by chance turned out to be the bloodied sword.

"Step away from Qian Ming," he had warned, the weapon aimed at the back of Kanen's neck.

Kanen didn't heed those words. As soon as Erik detected the slightest movement from Kanen, he brought down his weapon. But Mingyue wasn't Kanen's target. The young physician whipped himself around, catching Erik off guard as he lunged at the Norden prince instead.

"Erik! Don't!"

It was too late. The sickening sound of a blade slicing through flesh echoed throughout the room as Erik jabbed the sword through Kanen's side. Blood spluttered forth from his mouth as the physician stumbled backward. Erik pushed him to the side so that he'd collapse onto the ground and not on top of Mingyue, who still lay against the floorboards.

"Qian Ming!" He called out frantically. "Qian Ming! Are you alright!"

The Yue prince's eyes were open, but his gaze was empty as he stared up into Erik's face. Erik couldn't tell whether he could even see him. Next to Mingyue lay Kanen. The physician was still alive, a dark pool of blood coagulating around his body. He clenched his side in pain, where the sword remained protruding from his side. He was struggling, making a failed attempt to push himself up, only to collapse back into the pool of blood. His strained gasps for air made Erik sick to his stomach.

"I've got you," the Norden prince muttered.

He turned his back to Kanen and tucked Mingyue into his arms. He didn't know if he'd be able to lift the other prince, but with adrenaline coursing through his veins, he somehow was able to. Behind him, the dying physician reached out to him in a pathetic attempt to counterstrike. He had dropped his blade once he was stabbed, but even if he still held it in hand, he would've been too weak to have done any harm to the Norden prince.

Without turning back, Erik pushed himself to his feet, carrying the semi-conscious Mingyue in his arms.

"I'm sorry," he muttered to Kanen. "May God rest your soul."

With that, he stepped out into the corridor, and back into the blinding snowstorm that continued to rage beyond. Flames danced across the rooftops, painting the sky as red as that blood-stained sword.

VIII. Liminal Space

They didn't make it far before Erik collapsed from exhaustion. He had felt his body growing weaker, dizziness creeping in, as he carried Mingyue through the snowstorm. As his body gave out, he tried to steer them into one of the buildings, but there was nowhere to go. Flames jumped from rooftop to rooftop, seemingly engulfing the entire Palace of Lunar Serenity.

"So…hot…"

Mingyue coughed for breath. The air was quickly filling with smoke. It was a strange scene, for everything to be set aflame while snow still blanketed the ground, continuing to fall from the sky. The fire must be burning with unbelievable intensity to not be put out by the snow.

The two princes collapsed into a snowbank next to one of the buildings. It was a soothing sensation to have the coolness of snow around them, but even this was rapidly melting away.

"I'm sorry…" Erik muttered. "I don't think I can…go any further…"

Mingyue turned toward him as they lay on the ground. The snowflakes in his hair had already started to melt, turning into droplets of water that trickled down his face. Erik reached out to wipe them away.

"Maybe we should…stay a while…"

Erik's voice was growing faint. Mingyue quickly realized the Norden prince was losing consciousness. He pushed himself up from the snowbank. His leg was still in pain from the night before, not to mention his head after smacking it against the ground, but he knew they couldn't stay here. If they didn't die from smoke inhalation or get burned up by the flames, they would catch hypothermia and freeze to death. After all, it was still the middle of winter.

"We can't," Mingyue whispered.

Glancing up ahead, he glimpsed the walls of the Palace of the Golden Dragon. They were so close; they couldn't give up now. He nudged Erik, and when this didn't elicit a response, he grabbed him by the arm and shook his body gently.

"Get up. We have to keep going."

Holding on to Erik's arm, a strange feeling of warmth emanated from the Norden prince. At first, Mingyue found it to be soothing, but soon he realized that it wasn't just warmth, but also a wet sensation, coming out of Erik's arm. He hastily withdrew his hands and saw that they were covered in blood.

"You're bleeding!" Mingyue said in surprise.

"Ah," Erik winced. "Is that why I feel so cold...?"

There was also the fact that they were laying in a pile of snow, but Mingyue didn't bring this up. Erik turned over his arm to get a better look at the wound. He vaguely recalled Kanen jabbing Erik with the knife before the Norden prince drove the sword through the physician's side.

"Don't move," Mingyue ordered.

He shed his outer coat, the one which Erik had given to him, making a clumsy attempt to bind Erik's arm. This was difficult—his hand was still injured from the other day.

"Keep the coat," coughed Erik.

Mingyue still wore the same sleeveless outfit as the previous night. He shivered as the cool winter breeze brushed over his skin.

"No," Mingyue responded stubbornly. "You've done everything for me tonight. It's my turn."

Erik smirked. "Are you gonna carry me too?"

Mingyue unironically began scooping up Erik's legs into his arms. "I can try."

"Whoa, whoa wait!" Erik resisted. "I wasn't being serious! I'm bigger than you in both height and weight, there's no way you'd be able to carry me."

"I can," Mingyue insisted, but as he struggled to lift the Norden prince into his arms, it was clear that this wasn't the case.

"Your leg is still injured," reminded Erik. "Not to mention your hand. You can't exert yourself."

"Well, we can't stay here," Mingyue was growing increasingly frustrated, not with Erik, but with their situation in general.

"Why not?" Erik remained calm, much too calm given their circumstances. He knocked his head back and sunk into the snow. "This wouldn't be such a bad way to die, would it? Snuggled up here with you…what more could I ask for?"

"No dying," Mingyue protested. "How are you supposed to replace my robes that you tore if you're dead?"

"I suppose you're right," Erik sighed. "Ah, you're really guilt-tripping me here, aren't you?"

Mingyue rolled his eyes. "You *should* feel guilty if you die on me now and leave me all alone out here in the cold."

"Ouch," Erik chuckled. "Was that sarcasm? It felt a bit too honest to be sarcastic…"

"It wasn't," the Yue prince said bluntly. "Now let's go."

They once again attempted to head for the Palace of the Golden Dragon, but had to stop after only a dozen or so steps—Mingyue's leg was too weak to support him, and Erik was in no condition to carry him. This time, they came to a rest in a door frame that led into one of the buildings. At least it was a bit warmer here than in that snowbank, shielded from the chill of the wind.

"Looks like the flames are dying down," Erik noted.

Mingyue followed his gaze. Indeed, it seemed that the fire wasn't burning as brightly as it had been only minutes before. Perhaps the snow was finally dampening its intensity.

"That physician of yours really packed a punch, huh?" Erik winced. He prodded his arm, where blood was already soaking through the cloth wrapped around his wound.

"Kanen…" Mingyue muttered softly. "Is he…?"

"Don't worry," Erik assured. "He won't be coming after us."

He expected this news to relieve Mingyue, but instead, the prince's expression became grim.

459

"So, he's…dead…"

"If he didn't die from the wound, then…" Erik gestured to the building they had come from, its roof now engulfed in flames.

"I see," Mingyue said,

"I'm sorry…" Erik's tone became gentle. "Were you close to him?"

"I've known him for a while…" Mingyue recounted.

Before he knew it, he was reminiscing over how the two of them had met. It was only a few months after Olekina had begun training to become an Imperial Guard. It was autumn, and Mingyue was in the Imperial Gardens alongside his mother and Hansini as they observed the leaves changing colour.

"Mingyue! Look at this one!" Hansini waved a large, bright red leaf in the prince's face. "Isn't it pretty?"

"'Mingyue?'" Mingyue repeated in confusion. "You're supposed to call me 'Your Highness' or 'Prince Mingyue,' not just 'Mingyue.'"

Hansini froze in surprise and went wide-eyed in fear. "Ah…I…"

"A-Ming!" Huamei scolded her son as she overheard him.

Mingyue tensed up at the sound of her voice, wondering what he had done to deserve that tone.

"I told her she could call you by that name," Huamei explained. "Don't get mad at her."

Mingyue was flabbergasted. Hansini had been serving his mother for quite some time now, but they were by no means familiar. There was not a significant difference in age between them, and he couldn't understand why his mother deemed it permissible for her to refer to him without his titles.

"I-it's fine," Hansini forced a smile. "If he prefers it, I will call him your Highness!"

Huamei sighed and shook her head, and a twang of guilt tugged at Mingyue's heart, though he wouldn't admit it.

Not too far off was Olekina, awkwardly on standby under the shade of a tree as falling leaves fluttered down on him. He paid them no attention. The young man had grown quite a bit taller since he'd first met the prince, and was partaking in his regular duties, practicing serving Mingyue as his personal guard.

"Wu Liqing, why don't you come on over and enjoy the gardens with us," Huamei suggested with a smile. "See if you can find a leaf bigger than the one Hansini found!"

"I must attend to my duties, your Highness," Olekina insisted.

Huamei chuckled. "Very well."

"Your Highness!" Voices of Huamei's attendants could be heard as they frantically came rushing into the gardens. "Your Highness, there is urgent news!"

"What is it?" Huamei wondered inquisitively.

Based on their tone, she wasn't sure if it was good or bad news that they were bringing her.

"A ship has docked in Qiantang," one attendant said. "One that returned from a recent voyage to Tsimshian."

Tsimshian was a trade outpost of the Wuyue Empire far on the opposite side of the Taiping Ocean. Despite officially being under Wuyue's rule, there was little interaction between the two lands. Traders and merchants from Wuyue would often travel there to import exotic lumber and gold, but other than that, Wuyue did not have a heavy presence in the Land of the Heavenly Mountains.

"And?" Huamei wondered. "What of it?"

"There is a man aboard that ship," the attendant continued. "A man who claims to be Prince Jinyu. Qian Jinyu, the Emperor's eldest brother! The original heir to the throne!"

IX. The Raven and the Moon

"Mother," Mingyue tugged at Huamei's sleeve. "Who is Prince Jinyu?"

Huamei had the guards escort them to the palace harbor as quickly as possible to greet the returning prince.

"The Emperor's brother," she responded quickly. "He's...my uncle."

Mingyue cocked his head in confusion. "Like Prince Jinxin?"

He had never heard that his grandfather had another brother before.

"Yes," the princess nodded.

The comparison wasn't exactly accurate—Jinyu was the Emperor's elder brother, after all. He had been the heir to Wuyue's throne before his disappearance on a voyage to the Land of the Heavenly Mountains. That was more than half a century ago—Huamei had never even met her uncle. Ever since she was born, it had been her father who was the Crown Prince. He had been next in line for the throne after Jinyu. No one had expected that the original Crown Prince would one day return home. It had simply been assumed that he had been lost at sea, never to be heard from again.

"*Hmph,* how will they know it's him and not some imposter?" Yinfeng huffed in annoyance as Huamei and Mingyue entered through the gates that led to the port.

"I'm sure Father will be able to recognize his own brother," Huamei said.

On the balcony overhead stood Jinlong, overlooking the harbor as an incoming ship sailed in from the lake. The other nobles and officials hastily assembled on the docks, unsure of what they should expect from the returning prince. Few were old enough to have remembered him, and even for those who *did* know him, fifty years was a long time. The man who emerged from the ship might be a very different one than the man who departed more than half a century ago.

The ship made a landing, and disembarking was an assortment of merchants, sailors, and soldiers. Some were of Wuyue stock, but most were dressed in strange attire and spoke in an unintelligible tongue— foreigners from Tsimshian and other regions of the Land of the Heavenly Mountains who had come to Wuyue.

Amongst the crowd, they didn't spot anyone who matched their expectations of what the Yue prince would look like. Certainly, none of these people were old enough to be him. But finally, the last of the voyagers stepped foot off the ship, a group of four men carrying a fifth, frail, elderly man, seated on an elaborate wooden chair.

"That must be him," whispered Huamei. "Prince Jinyu."

Mingyue peaked through the crowd to get a glimpse at him. He was dressed in simple robes, his hair unkempt, with a distant gaze in his eyes. This man was a prince? A noble of the House of Qian? Mingyue certainly didn't see it.

On the balcony above, the Emperor stared down at his elder brother. Jinyu was no more than a frail, old man, no longer the lively youth he once knew.

"Come," Yinfeng said. "We must greet him."

They went through the motions of forming a procession, lining up to greet the elderly prince in order of their familial relations to him. Mingyue found this process tedious and boring. He didn't see what the big deal was in the arrival of some old man who was supposedly a distant relative. Once they had paid their greetings to Jinyu, Mingyue slipped away from his mother's side and found himself wandering along the docks. Huamei was just about to call her son back when she caught sight of Hansini and Olekina rushing over to the prince's side. Olekina addressed Huamei with a simple nod, signaling that they would take over watching over him. She needn't worry whilst they were on guard. Huamei responded with a smile. She understood that her son was far more interested in examining the strange foreign visitors and the goods they brought back with them than lining up to greet a strange old man.

"Your Highness, don't go too close to the water," Hansini warned. "I'm not scooping you up if you fall in there."

"What's that?" Mingyue wondered. He pointed at a large wooden pole, almost the size of a small tree, which had colourful faces of humans and animals carved into it.

"Looks like some form of art," said Hansini.

Mingyue cautiously approached. The faces carved into that pole certainly resembled animals, but none that he had ever seen before. At the very top of the pole were two wooden wings, protruding out from the side of a face that had large, brightly painted blue eyes, and a striking red mouth beneath what appeared to be a beak. Was this some sort of bird? He hesitantly extended his hand to touch the pole. He found those faces staring back at him to be unnerving, yet at the same time fascinating.

"A raven."

"Ah!"

Mingyue tore his hand away from the pole in surprise as a voice spoke out from it. As he did so, his hand scraped against the wood, causing a splinter to become embedded in his finger. He gripped his hand in pain.

"Your Highness!" Olekina rushed over in a hurry, quickly assessing the situation with one glance at the prince's hand.

Stepping out from behind the pole was a young man around their age, dressed in the colourful attire of the foreigners, a cloak hanging over his body. The boy's features were handsome, his long, dark hair flowing openly as it was adorned with black feathers.

"I apologize," the boy said, "I startled you."

Without warning, he took hold of Mingyue's hand and began examining it.

"Hey!" Olekina and Hansini both shouted in unison.

"What do you think you're doing?" Hansini fumed. "This is the Third Prince of Wuyue! You can't lay a finger on him!"

"He has a splinter," the boy said simply, seemingly unfazed upon hearing of Mingyue's status. "Are you going to help him remove it, or should I?"

"Can you?" Mingyue winced.

It was only a splinter, but even that small amount of pain was exceedingly uncomfortable for him.

"No problem at all," the boy replied simply. He produced a simple instrument from a sachet hanging at his waist, and within a few moments, the splinter was out of Mingyue's finger. The Yue prince blinked in surprise.

"How did you do that?"

"What kind of doctor would I be if I couldn't do something so simple," the boy said.

From another sachet, he produced an ointment that he rubbed on Mingyue's hand to soothe any lingering discomfort.

"You're young for a doctor," Hansini noted as she crossed her arms. "And you speak the Wuyueyu almost fluently, but this must be your first time in Wuyue. I don't think any natives of Tsimshian have ever come to Wuyue before."

"Many of my people who live near the coast learn your tongue to communicate with your merchants," the boy replied. "But in my case, it was Prince Jinyu who taught me."

He gazed into the distance, eyes resting on Jinyu as the elderly man remained surrounded by the crowd.

"I served as his physician," the boy continued. "I had no family in Tsimshian, so he became a sort of father to me. But his health has deteriorated in the last few months. When Wuyue merchants discovered he was once the Crown Prince, they insisted he returned home. I had no one else, so I came with him."

"What is your name?" Mingyue inquired.

"Prince Jinyu gave me the name Chu Kening," replied the boy. "But by birth, my name is Kanen."

"Kanen," Mingyue did his best to repeat the boy's name with the proper pronunciation. "Welcome to Wuyue, Kanen."

***

"Kanen began his apprenticeship with the court physician shortly after his arrival," Mingyue concluded his story to Erik. "Then, a few years ago, he was assigned as the chief physician of the Palace of Lunar Serenity. He wanted to be close to Prince Jinyu."

"I see…" Erik mused. "I wonder if that was the *only* reason he was assigned there…"

"What do you mean?"

"Well, he tried to kill you," the Norden prince pointed out. "And if he really was the one who killed the Emperor and your parents, he must've been planning this for a long time. But how did one man do this all by himself? Do you remember the day we found you on that island, we came across Kanen on the way back? I thought it was suspicious for him to be out at night."

Mingyue thought back to that encounter—the palace was under curfew, yet Kanen was still wandering about.

Prince Jinyu often stays out in the gardens late into the night. I was on my way back to my quarters after putting him to bed when I ran into you.

That had been Kanen's excuse.

"But," Erik continued, "a few hours later, the same masked man who assassinated the Emperor exchanged Emir Abdullah for your brother and left the palace with the rebel fleets."

"Yes," Mingyue nodded in agreement. "That's what I heard."

"It seems like an awful lot for one person to coordinate all that without getting caught," Erik said. "In which case, I suspect that the man who exchanged your brother for the Emir must have been different than the one who killed the Emperor."

"And?"

"And that means that Kanen has accomplices! He has connections within the palace which allows him to work behind the scenes. And I don't just mean other servants. There must be powerful officials, guards, perhaps even nobles, who are pulling the strings behind him. But Kanen is young, and he came to Wuyue only recently.

466

He had no connections to anyone when he arrived, so how would he have found such a strong backing in only a few years?"

Mingyue shook his head in confusion. "I don't know. Outside of the princes he serves and the other servants in the Palace of Lunar Serenity, I don't know who he has connections with."

"Are any of the princes a possibility?" Erik prodded. "We can rule out your brother, but how about Prince Shenzhong, or Prince Jingli?"

"It can't be Shenzhong," Mingyue said definitively. "He would never do something like that. As for Jingli...the Empress put Jingli and his sister under house arrest. She is suspicious of them, or rather their mother. But I don't think it could be them either—they have only visited Wuyue a few times in their lives, and I don't recall them ever meeting Kanen."

"And what about Prince Jinyu?" Erik asked.

"No. Prince Jinyu has lost his mental capabilities. He has been that way since he returned to Wuyue. It couldn't be him either."

"*Hm.* Then it looks like we still have no leads. *Ack!*" Erik slumped against the wall, letting out a groan as his arm pressed up against it. He smiled sheepishly. "I keep forgetting about this injury."

"We need to keep going," Mingyue said. "The Palace of the Golden Dragon is just up ahead."

"There you are!"

A voice drew their attention to a narrow alleyway across from them. Emerging into view was a head of flaming-red hair and a tall, well-built man carrying a spear.

"Olekina?!" Mingyue gasped in relief.

"Agnes!" Erik called out. "Took you long enough!"

"Where in the bloody pits of hell have ya been?!" Agnes fumed. Her face flushed red with rage, but behind her scowl, she was delighted to see the two of them in good condition. Well, mostly in good condition.

"Your Highness!" Olekina rushed over to examine Mingyue's leg. Worry set into him as he glimpsed Erik's injury. "What happened?"

"We'll explain on the way to the Palace of the Golden Dragon," Erik said. "Let's get going, it's freezing out here."

X. Clashing of Blades

They weren't the only ones that had evacuated to the Palace of the Golden Dragon. Upon reuniting with Hansini, Neili, Prince Amaru, and Dudu, they discovered that Shenzhong, Narsieh, Sundar, and many of the others had found their way here as well.

"What happened…?" Hansini fell silent as Olekina strode into the room with Mingyue in his arms.

"He needs a physician," Olekina said bluntly.

"Where is Chu Kening?"

"Dead."

"DEAD?!"

"He needs a physician," Olekina repeated.

"Wu Liqing, I'll take you to the infirmary," Sheli said upon noticing their arrival. She gestured for him to follow, and he hurried after with Mingyue.

Hansini sighed. "I knew I shouldn't have left you behind."

"Not like it would've done ya any better to be with us," Agnes noted. "We were attacked by some men on the way here and they shot the prince. Now would someone care to explain who those people shootin' canons and lightin' fires all over the place are?"

"They are Xin soldiers," Zhen Yinfeng's voice resounded as the Empress marched into the room.

"Xin soldiers?!" Shenzhong remarked with confusion. "What are they doing here? Why are they attacking the palace?!"

"I received word earlier today that Xin fleets were spotted from the west heading down the Qiantang River," the Empress explained. "They claim to be sent to liberate Qiantang of the rebels, but no doubt this is simply a pretext for them to seize control of Wuyue themselves. That Zemao! This must be her doing!"

"They attacked us…" Erik said. "They hunted us down and shot Mingyue, despite knowing that we were not rebels…"

"They've probably been ordered to assassinate us," Yinfeng said gravely. "Dispose of the House of Qian, blame the attack on the rebels, and then portray themselves as liberators when they drive the rebels out of the palace. If they've wiped out the House of Qian, they'll be free to place a puppet on the throne. Where is the Crown Prince?"

"Prince Zukang…?" Erik wondered. "He's not here…?"

"He was supposed to be in the infirmary in the Palace of Lunar Serenity," Yinfeng said. "Isn't that where you came from?"

"It was empty…" Erik said. "When we arrived, there was no one there. The physician, Chu Kening, he tried to kill Mingyue. He…he told us he was the one who killed Princess Huamei and the Emperor!"

The room erupted into gasps and murmurs. The prince's physician? How could that be?

"Erik…are you sure…?" Agnes rested a gentle hand on the Norden prince's shoulder. Even she was doubtful that what he was saying could be the truth.

"That's what he told us! You can ask Qian Ming yourselves! He'll say the same thing!"

"Chu Kening was supposed to be watching over the Crown Prince…" Yinfeng's voice wavered. "Then…where is Zukang…?"

The room fell silent. None of them could say where he might be, and after all the trouble they had gone through to get him back, they all dreaded the thought of going through that again.

"Stand back!"

Sudden shouts from outside disturbed the momentary silence in the room. The sound of scuffling and clanging weapons was quickly followed by yells and shrieks. One of the Empress's guards hastily burst into the room.

"Your Highness, we're under attack!"

He collapsed to the ground a moment later as an arrow protruded from his back. The scene erupted into chaos as panic ensued. The Empress's guards grabbed her and whisked her away as Xin soldiers overwhelmed their defenses and swarmed into the room.

"Get down!" Jiang Chu shouted.

He dove in front of Erik, throwing the prince behind himself as he blocked an attacker. Caleb took hold of the Norden prince, pulling him out of the room, while Agnes leaped to Jiang Chu's side.

"Get the prince to safety!" Jiang Chu ordered, deflecting another attack. He slashed his sword through the air and sliced down the Xin soldier before him. "There's too many! We must leave!"

Agnes whipped forth a dagger, slashing a couple of soldiers, but quickly realized that Jiang Chu was right. They wouldn't be able to hold them off. Half of the Imperial Guard had already been cut down, while those that remained tried their best to hold off the assault and allow everyone to escape. However, some of the nobles had already been captured. As Erik slipped out of the room, he spotted Narsieh being taken captive by the Xin troops. Hyousuke also attempted to put up a resistance but was soon struck down by a blade. Erik was unsure as to whether he was still alive as his body slumped to the floor.

"This way! Quick!" A voice shouted from up ahead.

"Prince Shenzhong…?!"

"The infirmary is this way!" He shouted as he ran toward them. "Protect A-Ming!"

Erik turned back in surprise as Shenzhong flew past them, dodging the blades being swung by Xin soldiers and knocking them to the ground.

"What about you?!" Erik shouted in concern. "Where are you going?!"

"Lady Alaneya still isn't here," Shenzhong said, taking down another soldier. "Neither is my father. I must find them! Now go!"

Before Erik could object, Shenzhong disappeared into the frenzy, while Caleb, Agnes, and Hansini continued dragging the Norden prince down the corridor.

They followed the hall in the direction Shenzhong had pointed them in, arriving at the infirmary a few moments later. Mingyue and Hong Xue lay in separate beds, while Sheli, Neili, Amaru, and a physician watched over them. Olekina was on his guard as soon as the others arrived.

471

"What's all that noise?!"

"They're coming!" Jiang Chu shouted, racing into the room just after them. "We have to leave!"

"We can't leave the prince behind!" The physician said.

"Well, we can't stay here either!" Jiang Chu fumed.

The physician rushed to the door, slamming it shut and sealing it with a lock.

"What are you doing?!" Jiang Chu raged. "We can't stay here!"

"Shush!" The physician hissed. "There's a way out of here. But you must remain silent and follow my lead. Do you understand?"

They nodded hastily.

"Good," the physician nodded. He gestured to Caleb and Jiang Chu and pointed to a set of stretchers along the back wall of the room. "You two, carry the injured man on that. Wu Liqing and I will handle the prince."

They did as they were told, and once Hong Xue and Mingyue were boarded onto their stretchers, the physician led them to one of the cabinets. Opening the cabinet door revealed that behind it was not shelves containing herbs and medicines, but a secret passageway.

"This way!" The physician ordered.

They obeyed, filing into the passage one by one. First went Caleb and Jiang Chu carrying Hong Xue, then Olekina and the physician carrying Mingyue. Sheli and Amaru were close behind, followed by Neili carrying Dudu, and Hansini.

"Open up!" The Xin soldiers had arrived at the infirmary, furiously pounding at the door.

As Erik ducked into the passageway, he glimpsed it slowly coming off its hinges. Thinking quickly, Agnes quickly grabbed a chair and tossed it through the thin paper window along the wall, opening a hole to the gardens outside. She and Caleb then slipped into the cabinet and shut it behind them just as the Xin soldiers burst into the infirmary. With one glance at the broken window, they assumed that everyone had already escaped outside.

"Clear!" The soldiers shouted. "No one's in this room!"

Erik and the others breathed a collective sigh of relief as the Xin soldiers moved on.

"That was close," the physician sighed. "Come. Let's get moving."

"Where does this tunnel go?" Olekina asked.

"It leads toward the western gate of the palace. The Empress is planning an evacuation from there."

XI. Saffron Dusk

The passageway ended in a warehouse at the westernmost edge of the Palace of the Golden Dragon. This was the highest point of the Imperial Palace, looking out from the top of the mountain down to the West Lake and the city of Qiantang. With one glance to the east, Erik could see that much of the palace was ablaze or had already been burnt down. A thick layer of ash blanketed the sky, casting a dark atmosphere overhead, despite it already being late into the morning.

"Your Highness!" Several of the Empress's guards rushed over as they spotted the group. "Your Highness! There's a ship docked at a village to the west that is prepared for an evacuation."

"Where's the Empress?" Sheli inquired.

The guards gestured to the gate. There, Zhen Yinfeng was being ushered out of the palace by her most trusted guards. Despite her protests, and demands to remain, they refused to heed her request.

Sheli nodded and turned quickly to Erik and the others. "Go with them. Take care of my brother for me."

"Your Highness, what about you?!" Hansini exclaimed.

Sheli smiled wistfully. "Hyousuke is still in the palace, and so is Zukang. I must find them."

"Your Highness…" Erik wavered. "Prince Hyousuke…he…"

Erik was unable to finish his words as he recalled the sight of Hyousuke being struck down by a Xin soldier. Dread filled Sheli's face, yet she remained persistent.

"I must find them."

Erik nodded in understanding. "We'll take care of your brother. I promise."

Sheli knelt next to Mingyue's stretcher, taking hold of his hand. The prince's eyes were only half open, and he seemed to be fading in and out of consciousness.

"We'll see each other again soon," Sheli whispered. "I promise."

"*Mnn*," Mingyue responded with little more than a simple nod.

With that, Sheli rose and disappeared back into the palace.

It took half a day's journey for them to arrive at the fishing village. They traveled discreetly, in commoner carriages along back roads to avoid detection by citizens and soldiers alike. They kept their distance from the shores of the Qiantang River, which remained in the distance to their south as they journeyed west. Dozens of Xin ships could be spotted from this point sailing down the river toward the city.

The ship waiting for them in the village turned out not to be one ship, but several smaller boats that would take them out to the larger merchant vessel waiting for them in the river. They set sail from a tributary of the river so they wouldn't draw attention to themselves from the Xin fleets stationed further to the east.

"Welcome aboard!"

A voice exclaimed upon their arrival aboard the ship. Erik was surprised to see that it was the Merinan noblewoman, Lady Ramanantsoa.

"I've managed to get my ship out of the city before the soldiers arrived," Arivesto explained. "I'll secure our safe passage to Ailao."

Jiang Chu scoffed. "Isn't it a bit paradoxical to be avoiding the Xin when we have to sail through their territory to reach Ailao?"

"We have no other choice," Hansini explained. "The rebels control the east and aren't letting any ships pass."

The Empress was unhappy with their situation but had refrained from further voicing her frustration. She knew they couldn't remain in the palace any longer. Not now. It was clear that the Xin wanted their heads. Glancing over those who had made it aboard the ship, Yinfeng was disheartened that Mingyue was the only member of the House of Qian among them. Other than some of her guards and servants, as well as Arivesto and the ship's crew, the only others who had made it aboard were Prince Amaru, Prince Sundar, Jiang Chu, Hong Xue, Erik, Agnes, Caleb, Neili, Olekina, Hansini, and of course Mingyue.

"Rebel troops?!" One of Yinfeng's guards spat when he spotted Jiang Chu and Hong Xue. "What are they doing here?! We should dump them overboard!"

"They helped Mingyue and me escape," Erik said defensively.

"*Tch,*" the guards shoved Jiang Chu, who put up no resistance.

To everyone's surprise, it was Olekina who stepped between them.

"Enough," he growled.

The guards froze, unsure of how to respond until Zhen Yinfeng finally spoke up in a stern voice.

"Stand down. We don't have space on this ship for fighting. If the Norden prince says these two rebel soldiers protected my grandson, I will take his word for it."

As tensions subsided, the physician took Hong Xue and Mingyue into the cabin to rest. Hong Xue's condition had deteriorated over the course of the day, his face now deathly pale and his breathing ragged. No doubt having been jostled around as they made their rapid escape from the palace had only worsened his situation. Jiang Chu remained by his friend's side the entire time, refusing to leave until he eventually passed out with his head resting on the bed next to Hong Xue. Erik sat nearby, next to Mingyue. It wasn't until dusk that Mingyue finally began to stir.

"A-Ming," Erik whispered, leaning closer to the prince. "Are you awake? The sun is about to set. You always wanted to see it, didn't you?"

"*Mnn,*" Mingyue groaned. He attempted to push himself up into a seating position but was far too weak.

"Hey, hey don't exert yourself. Your bed is just across from the window. I'll put an extra pillow under your head, and you should be able to see it from here."

As Erik said, the window was facing directly to the west, the same direction in which they were sailing down the Qiantang. The bottom of the sun had just touched the horizon, sending a brilliant display of shimmering light dancing across the surface of the waters as long shadows were cast upon the river by the mountains bordering it to the north and south.

"Can you see?" Erik wondered.

"*Mnn*," Mingyue managed a slight nod.

It was only a few minutes before the sun had completely sunk below the horizon, but Mingyue savoured every moment of it. The sky and water glowed various shades of colour, from crimson to deep orange, to golden, warm magenta, and royal violet. He had never imagined that such colours even existed.

"It's beautiful…"

"Yeah…" Erik whispered. "I've seen many sunsets before, but this one's definitely prettier than any of the others…" He turned to Mingyue, the glow of the sun glimmering in his jade-green eyes. "This is the first time you've seen it, right?"

Mingyue nodded.

"Well, it won't be the last!" Erik promised. "We should take every chance we get from now on to come out and watch the sunset. This is just the first of a hundred more to come!"

Mingyue shook his head. "Not enough."

"*Hm?*"

"A hundred is too few."

Erik blinked in surprise and chuckled. "Alright then, how about a thousand more to come?"

"Too few."

"Then let's say ten thousand," Erik laughed. "Is that enough?"

Mingyue thought for a moment before responding with a slight nod, satisfied with that number. He reached out and took hold of Erik's hand.

"Ten thousand more sunsets. Promise?"

Erik wrapped both his hands around Mingyue's.

"Yes, I promise."

End of Book One

Character Profiles

House of Yue

An Yanlu

An Yanlu was the father of Mingyue, Sheli, and Zukang, and the husband of Princess Huamei. He was a member of the House of An, a mercantile branch of the former Sogdian royal family that has resided in Wuyue for several generations. He was notable for his light-coloured hair and eyes, a common feature among Sogdians. Despite not being an heir to the throne, he was nevertheless granted the title of First Prince, which he held until his passing.

Qian Huamei

Qian Huamei was the mother of Mingyue, Sheli, and Zukang, and the wife of Prince Yanlu. She was the daughter of Emperor Jinlong and Empress Yinfeng, and elder sister of Empress Dowager Zemao of Xin. She bore the title First Princess and was the Crown Princess of Wuyue until her passing.

Qian Jinling

Qian Jinling was the mother of Xi Chengxin and Xi Yanggui, and grandmother of Xi Shenzhong. She was also the elder sister of Emperor Jinlong, Prince Jinyu, and Prince Jinxin.

Qian Jinlong

Qian Jinlong was the Emperor of Wuyue, husband of Empress Yinfeng, father of Huamei and Zemao, and grandfather of Mingyue, Sheli, Zukang, Jingli, and Fengling. The era of his reign was known as the Era of the Golden Dragon Emperor and lasted for eighteen years.

Qian Jinxin

Qian Jinxin is the youngest brother of Princess Jinling, Prince Jinyu, and Emperor Jinlong. He renounced his royal titles in his youth to become a monk at the Jingjiao Monastery.

Qian Jinyu

Qian Jinyu is the eldest brother of Emperor Jinlong, and the original heir to the throne prior to his disappearance in Tsimshian more than half a century ago. In the eleventh year of the Golden Dragon Emperor, he returned to Wuyue aboard a merchant vessel and now resides in the Palace of Lunar Serenity with the other princes. With his memory and health deteriorating, he has little interaction with anyone other than Kanen, who accompanied him on the journey from Tsimshian and now cares for him as his physician.

Qian Mingyue

Qian Mingyue is the youngest child of Princess Huamei and Prince Yanlu, and the younger brother of Sheli and Zukang. He has spent almost his entire life within the walls of the Imperial Palace, not even witnessing a sunset for himself. He was engaged to marry Lady Alaneya of Venesia. Originally bearing the title of Third Prince, he now bears the title of Second Prince following the death of his father.

Qian Sheli

Qian Sheli is the eldest child of Princess Huamei and Prince Yanlu, and the elder sister of Mingyue and Zukang. She is married to Prince Hyousuke of Nippon. Originally bearing the title of Second Princess, she now bears the title of First Princess following the death of her mother.

Qian Zukang

Qian Zukang is the middle child of Princess Huamei and Prince Yanlu, and the older brother of Mingyue. He is engaged to marry Princess Seo-Yeon of the Keleyite Khanate. Originally bearing the title of Second Prince, he now bears the title of First Prince and was declared Crown Prince of Wuyue following the deaths of his parents.

Zhen Yinfeng

Zhen Yinfeng is the Empress of Wuyue, wife of Emperor Jinlong, father of Huamei and Zemao, and grandmother of Mingyue, Sheli, Zukang, Jingli, and Fengling. She originally hails from the Kingdom of Nanyue to Wuyue's south, and is the younger sister of the King of Nanyue.

<u>Wuyue (Other)</u>

Ao Neili

Ao Neili is a young eunuch in the service of Prince Mingyue, originally hailing from the Ailao Empire.

Arivesto Ramanantsoa

Arivesto Ramanantsoa is a noblewoman from the island of Merina, a tributary state of Wuyue located in the Southern Ocean. She commands a merchant fleet that travels throughout the world and makes frequent visits to Wuyue.

Hansini Villarvattom

Hansini Villarvattom, also known as Wei Hanxi, is an attendant in the service of Prince Mingyue and is responsible for managing his daily affairs. She originally hails from Malabar, a protectorate of Wuyue bordering the Karnatan Empire.

Hong Xue

Hong Xue is a former soldier of the Imperial Guard who recently joined the Qinglong resistance and was assigned to watch over Prince Mingyue alongside Jiang Chu. He was badly injured following Lusine's escape from captivity.

Jiang Chu

Jiang Chu is a former soldier of the Imperial Guard who recently joined the Qinglong resistance and was assigned to watch over Prince Mingyue alongside Hong Xue.

Kanen Kukhhittan

Kanen Kukhhittan, also known as Chu Kening, is the chief physician of the Palace of Lunar Serenity. He originally hails from Tsimshian, a distant trade outpost on the far side of the Taiping Ocean.

Keiy Dimasalang

Keiy Dimasalang is a young Melayu woman and a member of Arivesto's crew.

Mister Zhang

Mister Zhang is a tutor who serves in the Palace of Lunar Serenity, teaching Mingyue, Zukang, and Narsieh history and politics.

Narsieh Sasan

Narsieh Sasan, also known as Li Niexia, is the head of the House of Sasan, one of the most prominent families in Wuyue. He is a descendent of the old Sassanian Dynasty that once ruled over Persia, which fled to the Tang Dynasty for shelter before rising to prominence in Wuyue's Court.

Olekina Lenku

Olekina Lenku, also known as Wu Liqing, is the primary guard who serves Prince Mingyue. He is of Kunlun and Zanzibari descent, and lost both his parents in an outbreak of the Plague when he was young.

Selah Melekh

Selah Melekh is a Sogdian dancer who was given to Prince Zukang by the Xin envoy as an engagement gift. He is known to be one of the most skilled dancers in the world.

Si Lu

Si Lu is the High Priestess of Qiantang and presides over many of the important festivals and ritual celebrations in Wuyue.

Xi Chengxin

Xi Chengxin is the son of Princess Jinling, brother of Yanggui, and father of Shenzhong. He is the governor of Suzhou, and helped form the alliance between Wuyue and Oghuz Rumelia due to his role in arranging the marriage between Mingyue and Alaneya.

Xi Shenzhong

Xi Shenzhong is the son of Chengxin and second-cousin of Mingyue, Sheli, Zukang, Jingli, and Fengling. He developed a close relationship with Lady Alaneya after she arrived in Suzhou, and helped teach her Wuyueyu.

Ailao

Xi Yanggui

Xi Yanggui is the daughter of Princess Jingling, sister of Chengxin, and cousin of Huamei and Zemao. She is married to the Crown Prince of Ailao.

485

Karnata

Ahi

Ahi was a Karnatan princess and daughter of Rajah Devaiah. She was the wife of Prince Sundar.

Devaiah

Devaiah was a Karnatan Rajah and heir to the Karnatan throne. He was the father of Princess Ahi.

Sundar Singh

Sundar Singh is a Karnatan prince and husband of Princess Ahi.

Keleyite Khanate

Yi Seo-Yeon

Yi Seo-Yeon is a princess descended from the former Hanguk Kingdom, now a part of the Keleyite Khanate. She is engaged to be married to Prince Zukang.

Khorasan

Abdullah ibn Amin

Abdullah ibn Amin is a Khorasani emir and the nephew of the Khorasanshah. He was initially one of the prime suspects behind the Qiantang Festival Incident.

Nippon

Ansei Hyousuke

Ansei Hyousuke is the son of the Emperor of Nippon and the husband of Princess Sheli.

Norden

Agnes Laec

Agnes Laec is an attendant in the service of Prince Erik. She is notable for the fiery-red colour of her hair.

Anna Nylund

Anna Nylund was the younger sister of Prince Erik and Prince Erlend. She died in an outbreak of the Plague several years ago, along with her parents, spurring Erik to leave Norden and travel abroad.

Caleb Selkirk

Caleb Selkirk is an attendant in the service of Prince Erik. He hails from the mysterious land of Vinland, a territory under Norden's rule.

Erik Nylund

Erik Nylund is the Crown Prince of Norden, and the younger brother of King Erlend II. After the deaths of his parents and sister, he left Norden behind and traveled widely throughout the world, eventually leading him to Wuyue with the intention of forming official relations between the two nations.

Erlend Nylund II

Erlend Nylund II is the elder brother of Prince Erik and is the king of Norden.

Sven Nylund IV

Sven Nylund IV is the former king of Norden, and the father of Erlend, Erik, and Anna. He and his wife, together with Anna, died in an outbreak of the Plague several years ago.

Oghuz Rumelia

Alaneya Fatima Maria

Alaneya Fatima Maria is a Venesian noblewoman, the niece of the Doge of Venesia, and daughter of a merchant who oversees most of the trade between Wuyue and Oghuz Rumelia. On her mother's side, she is cousins with Aysun Sultana. She developed a close relationship with Prince Shenzhong during the time she spent in Suzhou, but was later engaged to marry Prince Mingyue.

Aysun Younanoglu

Aysun Younanoglu is the daughter of Sultan Osman VI of Oghuz Rumelia, and cousin of Lady Alaneya on her mother's side.

Azaria Nazaryan

Azaria Nazaryan is a eunuch in service of Aysun Sultana.

Lorenzo Belini

Lorenzo Belini is the son of Patriarch Sergio II of Rome, and cousin of Lady Alaneya. He is a priest serving as the head of the Constantinian Missions in Wuyue.

Lusine Nazaryan

Lusine Nazaryan is an attendant in the service of Aysun Sultana, whose mother traces her origins back to the Armenian Quarter of Qiantang.

Tahuantinsuyu

Amaru Huancahuari

Amaru Huancahuari is the grandson of the Emperor of Tahuantinsuyu. He accompanied Prince Hyousuke on a voyage across the Taiping Ocean to visit Nippon and Wuyue.

Volga Roman Tsardom

Irina Aleksandrova

Irina Aleksandrova is the younger sister of Tsarina Sofia Aleksandrova III of the Volga Roman Tsardom. She is notable for her pale skin and crimson eyes. She is engaged to marry Prince Erik.

Xin

Jiao Fengling

Jiao Fengling is the daughter of Empress Dowager Zemao, granddaughter of Emperor Jinlong and Empress Yinfeng, and twin sister of Jingli. She is the cousin of Mingyue, Sheli, and Zukang. She is also half-siblings with Emperor Hongli of Xin. She and her brother remained behind in Wuyue after their mother returned to Kaifeng.

Jiao Hongli

Jiao Hongli is the Emperor of Xin, and half-brother of Jingli and Fengling.

Jiao Jingli

Jiao Jingli is the son of Empress Dowager Zemao, grandson of Emperor Jinlong and Empress Yinfeng, and twin brother of Fengling. He is the cousin of Mingyue, Sheli, and Zukang. He is also half-siblings with Emperor Hongli of Xin. He and his sister remained behind in Wuyue after their mother returned to Kaifeng.

Qian Zemao

Qian Zemao is the daughter of Emperor Jinlong and Empress Yinfeng, younger sister of Princess Huamei, and mother of Jingli and Fengling. She was married to the previous Xin Emperor, and became Empress Dowager after his death.

Kingdoms and Empires

Ailao

Formal Name: Empire of Ailao

Capital: Dali

Ruler: The Ailao Emperor

Languages: Ailaoyu, Ao, others

Description: A landlocked, mountainous empire between Karnata and the Tang Realms, comprising most of the territories south of the Himalayas and north of Burma. It is made up of many tribes, with no one group dominating over the region. Thus, over the years they have derived Ailaoyu as a common tongue based on the languages of the Tang Realms in order to communicate. Xi Yanggui is married to the Crown Prince of Ailao.

Isbaniya

Formal Name: Sultanate of Isbaniya

Capital: Qurtuba

Ruler: Emir Yuhana

Languages: Isbaniyan Arabic, others

Description: A large nation at the westernmost point of the Old World, stretching along the shores of the Atlantic Ocean. Historically, Isbaniya was one of Oghuz Rumelia's greatest rivals over maritime control of the Mediterranean Sea, but in recent years they have begun to cooperate. Aysun Sultana is engaged to marry Crown Prince Asada ibn Yuhana ibn Nabil of Isbaniya.

Karnata

Formal Name: Empire of Karnata

Capital: Vijayapura

Ruler: Maharaja of Karnata

Languages: Karnatan, Punjabi, Gujarati, Sindhi, others

Description: One of the largest empires in the world both in terms of geography and population, Karnata comprises the majority of the Indian Subcontinent. They have been one of Wuyue's closest allies, with the ruling dynasty being propped up by Wuyue, only coming to power and unifying the region thanks to Wuyue's support in previous generations. However, many regions of the empire, especially in the north, express a desire for greater autonomy or separation due to cultural differences.

Keleyite Khanate

Formal Name: Keleyite Khanate

Capital: Dadu

Ruler: K

Languages: Keleyite, Hanguk, Sogdian, others

Description: The largest country by geographic territory in the world, the Keleiyte Khanate stretches from Hanguk in the east all the way to the border of the Volga Roman Tsardom in the west. The Keleyites are traditionally nomadic peoples, and expanded their empire through the conquest of neighbouring lands, incorporating conquered peoples into their nation, such as Hanguk's House of Yi.

Khorasan

Formal Name: Khorasani Empire

Capital: Samarkand

Ruler: Khorasanshah

Languages: Khorasani Persian, Sogdian, others

Description: A large empire at the heart of the Silk Road, much of the overland trade between the Tang Realms and the West passes through Khorasan. In recent years, they have had territorial disputes with many of their neighbours, including Karnata to the southeast, the Volga Roman Tsardom to the northwest, and the Oghuz Rumeli to the west.

Nanyue

Formal Name: Kingdom of Nanyue

Capital: Panyu

Ruler: House of Zhen

Languages: Nanyueyu, others

Description: The smallest of the three kingdoms of the Tang Realms, Nanyue is nevertheless a stable and prosperous nation that has a long history stretching back centuries. They are closely aligned with Wuyue, with Empress Yinfeng being the younger sister of Nanyue's Emperor.

Nippon

Formal Name: Empire of Nippon

Capital: Edo

Ruler: The Ansei Emperor

495

Languages: Nipponese, others

Description: A small archipelago nation in the east, Nippon is nevertheless the most powerful maritime force in the region after Wuyue. The Nipponese were the first from the Old World to sail to the Land of the Heavenly Mountains, setting up colonies across the ocean to extract resources.

Norden

Formal Name: Norden Empire

Capital: Lund

Ruler: King Erlend II

Languages: Norse, Anglish, Frisian, Gaelic, Livonian, Sami, Suomi, Vinlandic, others

Description: One of the most powerful nations in the West, Norden rules over an expansive empire across the Northern Ocean encompassing dozens of cultures and languages. Their maritime fleet is the most powerful in Europe after that of Oghuz Rumelia. Norden's expansion into continental Europe and the islands of the Atlantic Ocean has taken place over the course of centuries. One such territory under Norden's dominion is the mysterious land of Vinland across the Atlantic Ocean, from which Caleb hails.

Oghuz Rumelia

Formal Name: Sultanate of Oghuz Rumelia

Capital: Constantinople

Ruler: Sultan Osman VI

Languages: Oghuzi, Arabic, Armenian, Greek, Latin, Syriac, Venesian, others

Description: The largest and most powerful country in all the West, Oghuz Rumelia rules an empire stretching across three continents and dozens of cultures and languages. Its capital, Constantinople, is known as one of the most magnificent cities in the world. The Oghuz Rumelis are known for their expansionism, which at times has brought them to war with neighbouring states such as Khorasan to the east and Norden and the Volga Romans to the north. Many lands have been acquired by the Oghuz Rumelis over the centuries, including Egypt, Venisia, and Rome. The Oghuz Rumelis claim direct descent from the Roman empire after having conquered Constantinople, a claim which is contested with the Volga Romans.

Tahuantinsuyu

Formal Name: Tahuantinsuyu

Capital: Cusco

Ruler: House of Huancahuari

Languages: Quechua

Description: A mysterious empire across the Taiping Ocean from which Amaru Huancahuari hails. Few from the Old World have seen it with their own eyes. It is known for its mountainous terrain.

Tlaxcala

Formal Name: Tlaxcala

Capital: Unknown

Ruler: Unknown

Languages: Unknown

Description: A mysterious land across the Taiping Ocean north of Tahuantinsuyu. Little is known about it other than the fact that it is fertile and produces countless crops that are unknown to the rest of the world.

Wuyue

Formal Name: Empire of Wuyue

Capital: Qiantang

Ruler: Emperor Jinlong

Languages: Wuyueyu, Malabari, Melayu, Merinan, Persian, Sogdian, Syriac, Tsimshian, Zanzibari, others

Description: The most powerful empire in the world. Wuyue started off as one of many small kingdoms of the Tang Realm after the collapse of the Tang Dynasty over a millennium ago, but has risen to dominance in the region due to maritime trade that has brought them an abundance of wealth. Over the centuries, they have gradually expanded their territory beyond the Tang Realms, setting up colonies and tributary states across the Taiping and Southern Oceans. These include Malabar, a region bordering Karnata along the southern shore of the Indian Subcontinent; Merina, a large island in the Southern Ocean from which the vorompatra birds hail; Melaya, a tropical region to the south home to innumerable islands and natural resources; Tsimshian, a mysterious land along the far eastern shore of the Taiping Ocean from which Kanen hails; and Zanzibar, a trading hub in the Dark Continent to which Olekina traces his ancestry. Many foreigners have come to settle in Wuyue over the centuries, not only from the colonies and tributary states, but from across the world.

Volga Roman Tsardom

Formal Name: Volga Roman Tsardom

Capital: Moskva

Ruler: Tsarina Sofia III

Languages: Volga Slavonic, others

Description: One of the largest countries in the West, the Volga Roman Tsardom claims direct descent from the Roman Empire. After the Fall of Constantinople to the Oghuz Rumelis many centuries prior, the Roman emperor fled to Moskva. The Volga Roman Tsardom borders Norden to the northwest, Oghuz Rumelia to the south, and the Keleyite Khanate to the east. Sandwiched between these three much more powerful states, the Volga Romans have a long history of defending themselves from various invasion attempts by their neighbours. The Tsardom has managed to survive as a state up until the present only due to the fact that it acts as a buffer between the other three empires, playing them against one another and often forming alliances with them for mutual benefit. Currently, the Volga Romans are in close alliance with Norden.

Xin

Formal Name: Xin Empire

Capital: Kaifeng

Ruler: Emperor Hongli

Languages: Xinyu, others

Description: The Xin Empire is the largest nation geographically and in terms of population in the Tang Realms but is also the poorest and least developed. Unlike their neighbours, Wuyue and Nanyue, the Xin have weak naval capabilities and do not partake heavily in maritime trade, instead focusing on overland Silk Road trade. The Xin are the newest state in the Tang Realms, having arisen only a few centuries ago. Ever since the fall of the Tang Dynasty, the southern Tang Realms have remained relatively stable and unified under Wuyue and Nanyue, while the north has seen the repeated rise and fall of several dynasties, as well as invasions and conquests by nomadic peoples of the steppe. With a lack of access to many of the fertile, rice-growing regions of the southern Tang Realms, the Xin have had to rely on imports from Wuyue and Nanyue along the Grand Canal which connects the Chang River to the Xin capital of Kaifeng.

Preview for Book Two

Ten Thousand Lights

Crimson Dawn

I. Sailing West

3/12/18th Year of the Golden Dragon Emperor

Year of the Wooden Goat

The deep azure waters from the west mixed with the ruddy waves of the north as the two tributaries converged to form the Chang River. Far in the distance, mountains rose up from the flat terrain, climbing higher and higher the further west they went as they formed a massive range that consisted of the edge of the Sichuan Basin. The basin itself, a massive, fertile valley, was the southwesternmost territory of the Xin Empire.

For more than a week now, the Second Prince of Yue was aboard a ship full of nobles fleeing the chaos that had unfolded in Wuyue's Imperial Palace. Their ship had been sailing through Xin territory under the banner of a Merinan merchant vessel. It wasn't a disguise— Lady Arivesto Ramanantsoa was captain of the ship, and there was indeed a large shipment of goods from all over the world within the hull. The Merinan noblewoman had already been planning to travel further into the Tang Realms, but that voyage had been delayed after Qiantang had been put under lockdown due to civil unrest.

From the Imperial Palace, it had been a day's journey up the Qiantang River before they crossed into Xin territory, and another day before they reached the Western Grand Canal that connected the Qiantang to the Chang River. The canal took a day's journey itself, and since then, they'd traversed westwards along the winding path carved out by the Chang River between the mountains.

"Why are we going west through Xin territory and not east to the ocean?" Qian Mingyue had asked on the second day of their travels.

The Yue Prince had been badly injured in the attack on the palace, shot by an arrow in the leg by an unknown assailant, and had his head slammed violently against the ground by Chu Kening, the trusted physician who had betrayed them. The Empress's physician, Doctor Peng, who was now treating him aboard the ship, diagnosed him with a mild concussion, advising him to remain in bed for the duration of the journey.

"Aren't the Xin the ones who launched the attack on the palace in the first place?"

"The Empress said that traveling west from Qiantang is too dangerous," said a young man with dazzling, jade-green eyes—Erik, the Crown Prince of Norden. Erik brushed Mingyue's long, dark hair from his face. "Wuyue loyalists and the rebels are fighting one another, and now Xin forces have also been involved. Going east is much safer for a merchant vessel. Besides, she wants to seek refuge in Ailao."

The Ailao Empire, on the western border of the Tang Realms, south of the Tibetan Plateau, was a mountainous nation where the Chang River and many other great rivers flowed through. Princess Xi Yanggui, one of the cousins of Mingyue's late mother, had married the Crown Prince of Ailao and had previously offered asylum to her relatives in Wuyue. This offer had been turned down at the time, in hindsight a regrettable mistake.

Ten days after they had first set out on the Chang River, they reached the city of Yibin, at the fork where the Jinsha and Min Rivers[34] met. The deep azure of the Jinsha intermingled with the ruddy red of the Min to mark the border between Xin and Ailao territory.

"Captain says to head below deck!" The voice of a young woman echoed from the hallway.

The door flung open, revealing the petite Melayu girl named Keiy who was a traveling merchant alongside Arivesto.

"Below deck?" Erik wondered. "The physicians want Mingyue to stay here until we get to Ailao."

"The Xin border patrol is doing inspections," Keiy shook her head.

She glanced at the bed next to Mingyue, where a pale, sickly looking man lay unconscious—Hong Xue, one of the rebel soldiers who'd been assigned to protect the prince. He'd been badly injured

---

[34] Jīnshājiāng (金沙江) and Mínjiāng (岷江): The names of two rivers that comprise of the upper portion of the Yangtze River and its tributary.

during their escape, and the physicians were pessimistic about his recovery.

"I'll get someone to bring him too. There's a hidden compartment down in the cargo bay. Go join the others there."

They did as they were told. By the time the ship came to dock at the port of Yibin, Mingyue and Erik had joined the others in the hull of the ship. With them was Sundar Singh, the tall, handsome, olive-skinned Karnatan prince, and Amaru Huancahuari, a prince with brilliant green eyes from the land of Tahuantinsuyu on the far eastern shore of the Taiping Ocean. There was a woman with fiery-red hair, Agnes, and the brooding brunette young man, Caleb, Erik's two attendants who had accompanied him to Wuyue. Hong Xue, who'd been carried down to the room by the Empress's physicians, was joined by his fellow rebel soldier—he was an angsty young man by the name of Jiang Chu. He would be considered conventionally handsome if it weren't for the perpetual scowl on his face. The Empress herself was quietly seated at the end of the room. Everyone kept a fair distance from her, unwilling to intrude on her personal space.

Last to arrive were Mingyue's attendants. There was his guard, Olekina Lenku, a well-built Kunlun man, by far the tallest person present on the ship. Next to him was Hansini Villarvattom, a Malabari woman who constantly wore a serious expression. Finally, there was Ao Neili, the nervous young eunuch. He was a native of Ailao who had come to serve in Wuyue's court during his youth. Mingyue couldn't help but notice that he seemed to be the most anxious regarding their journey to his homeland.

It took nearly half the day for the border guards to inspect the ship. In the meantime, Arivesto, Keiy and the crew unloaded some of their goods to sell in the port. Mingyue sat down with the others to play some card games, and find whatever other means of entertainment they could to pass the hours. They found the most entertainment in watching the interactions between Dudu and Lasta. Dudu was Mingyue's pet duniao bird that Erik had gifted him a few months prior.

She had grown significantly since then and was far too heavy to be carried around anymore, so she stayed mostly below deck. Lasta was Prince Amaru's pet llama that he had brought with him on his travels from the Land of the Heavenly Mountains. Mingyue had no idea how he had managed to get her aboard the ship when they were fleeing the chaos of the palace siege the other night.

Dudu and Lasta eyed one another with curiosity, with Dudu nudging her head against Lasta's fluffy wool, while Lasta shook her body every so often to scare the bird away. In secret, Dudu plucked tuffs of fur from the llama, creating a small nest out of it over the course of the day.

It was evening by the time they set sail again, and everyone was relieved to get out and stretch their legs. Mingyue typically had his meals delivered to him in his quarters, but today, he insisted on going down to the mess hall to have dinner with the others. The chef had cooked up a spicy noodle dish with ingredients they bought from the port in Yibin.

"What news is there from Qiantang?" Yinfeng asked.

The Empress was seated at a table alongside Mingyue and Erik, and had summoned Arivesto to join them to deliver them details on what had transpired in Wuyue since their departure. After all, information traveled faster than their ship did. It was simply a matter of determining facts from rumors.

"The border guards said that Xin forces have driven the Qinglong rebels from the palace and restored order to the capital," Arivesto said.

"*Tch*," Yinfeng scoffed. "Those are exaggerated claims, I'm sure."

"Most likely."

"And what do they say happened to my grandchildren, the Crown Prince Zukang, and First Princess Sheli?"

"They claim that the entire House of Qian was slaughtered by the rebels before they could secure the palace, including the Second Prince and yourself, your Majesty."

Mingyue's heart sank as he and his grandmother shared a stern gaze. Obviously, the claim that the two of them had been killed was completely false, but the fact that their bodies weren't present to be provided as evidence would likely be attributed to the fires which had burned down much of the palace on that dreadful day. The charred corpse of a servant or soldier could easily be disguised as one of the nobility's bodies, and what objection could anyone hold against that claim if there was no other evidence that they had survived?

"I'm sure the Crown Prince and the First Princess are safe," Erik said hopefully.

Mingyue thought back to when they had fled the palace. He didn't remember much of it, having been carried on a stretcher by the others as he faded in and out of consciousness. According to Erik, Sheli's husband, the Nipponese Prince Ansei Hyousuke, had been cut down by soldiers during their escape, and Sheli had insisted on going back to save him.

We'll see each other again soon, Sheli had promised Mingyue.

That, he remembered. It had been over a week since then, and with the only news of her whereabouts being that she'd been killed in the fire, Mingyue's hope that he would see his elder sister again faded.

"What about A-Shen?" Mingyue whispered.

Xi Shenzhong was his older second cousin, and in love with a Venesian noblewoman by the name of Alaneya Fatima Maria, the girl that Mingyue had been arranged to marry. Neither Mingyue nor Alaneya was enthusiastic about going through with the marriage and had agreed to call it off. His meeting with her, when he had told her she was free to marry Shenzhong, was the last place he had gone before the palace was laid siege to. Since then, he hadn't heard anything of what had become of them.

"Xi Shenzhong?" Arivesto clarified. "They didn't say. He and his father are considered members of the House of Xi, not the House of Qian, correct? Perhaps they may have survived…"

"Who is currently governing Wuyue?" Yinfeng pressed. "There is no emperor. Have they placed a puppet onto the throne?"

Arivesto shook her head. "I apologize, your Majesty. That is all I know."

"Very well," Yinfeng sighed, taking a sip of her tea. "Keep me informed of the situation."

Mingyue hurried to finish his meal, and while the Empress scolded him for this, telling him to slow down, he informed her that he had to be back in the infirmary by sundown. Yinfeng assumed this must've been the physicians' orders, but really, it was Mingyue's own decision.

We should take every chance we get from now on to come out and watch the sunset, Erik had said to him just after they fled from the palace. That was the first time Mingyue had seen the sunset for himself. The Imperial Palace, situated on a mountain slope that faced eastwards, was completely hidden from view of the western horizon. But now, as they journeyed west along the Chang River, the sun could always be seen every evening descending into the waves of the river, casting its golden and crimson glow dancing across the surface of the waves. Since that day, Mingyue hadn't missed an opportunity to watch the sunset together with Erik, insisting that the Norden prince come join him in the infirmary so they could watch the sun go down together. Tonight was no different.

"Every sunset is the same," Erik smiled, his jade-green eyes sparkling in the evening light. "And yet, each one is unique."

Mingyue nodded in agreement. Around them, the scenery was constantly changing, the mountains growing ever higher with each passing day as they made their way upstream toward the Tibetan Plateau. And yet, it was the same sun that followed them day after day across the sky, casting the same warmth down upon them no matter where in the world they went.

"How is your arm?" Mingyue asked.

508

During their escape from the palace, Erik had been stabbed in the arm by a knife while defending Mingyue from his physician. It wasn't a serious wound compared to those sustained by Mingyue or Hong Xue, but Mingyue still felt guilty that the Norden prince had been harmed protecting him.

"Doesn't hurt so much anymore," Erik smiled, giving himself a pat on the arm. "I wonder what my brother will think the next time I see him. I went to Wuyue to help establish an embassy there and came back with nothing but a stab wound."

"Will you go back to Norden?" Mingyue asked, his voice barely more then a whisper.

"One day, I suppose."

"What will you do when we get to Ailao?"

Erik's gaze met Mingyue. "I promised your sister I would protect you. So, for now, that's what I'll do."

"The Empress doesn't want to stay in Ailao for long," Mingyue explained. "Probably for no more than a few days. She's planning on returning to Nanyue. That's her homeland; her elder brother is the king there."

"Will you follow her there?"

Mingyue shook his head. "I don't know. She wants to get their military support to launch a counterattack against the rebels and Xin forces in Wuyue. But we will need support from more than just Nanyue to accomplish that."

"Norden would be happy to offer assistance!" Erik exclaimed. "My brother is the king. I'm sure if you sought his help, he would provide it."

"Norden is on the other side of the world," Mingyue muttered doubtfully.

"But our navy is world-renowned," Erik pointed out. "We dominate the Atlantic and Northern Oceans. In the Southern Ocean, we have the third most powerful maritime fleet after only Wuyue and Oghuz Rumelia."

"Oghuz Rumelia…" Mingyue whispered. "It's my fault that the alliance with them is broken."

"Oh…" Erik said in a gentle tone. "So, you told her? You called off the wedding?"

The Yue prince responded with a simple nod.

"How did she take it?"

"It was what we both wanted. She is in love with A-Shen. I wonder how they are doing now…"

"They're alive," Erik spoke assuredly.

"How can you be sure?"

A warm smile lit up the Norden prince's face. Mingyue's heart fluttered in his chest. In the distance, the sun had almost completely disappeared beneath the horizon, casting the last shimmering rays of light dancing across the surface of the water. In Mingyue's eyes, even such a magnificent natural beauty couldn't compare to Erik's smile.

"You just have to have some faith."

A sudden violent spat of coughing startled both of them, ruining the otherwise tranquil moment of peace between the two as they gazed into one another's eyes. On the bed next to Mingyue, Hong Xue had begun stirring. He had been in a coma ever since his stabbing back in the palace. Erik hastily ran out of the room to summon the physicians. While he was gone, Hong Xue's eyes flew open, frantically taking in his surroundings.

"It's alright," Mingyue said in as calm of a tone as he could. "There's nothing to be afraid of. You're safe here."

"Your Highness!" Hong Xue's voice was hoarse. "Lusine is—"

"I know," Mingyue said. "I know they stabbed you."

"No," he shook his head frantically. "Lusine didn't. It was your physician, Chu Kening."

"Chu Kening did this to you?" Mingyue's heart sank.

"He appeared down the corridor while I was on guard. I knew something was off when he was approaching, but I didn't expect him to attack me. I was taken off guard. He took my key and unlocked the

510

room. He was trying to kill Lusine, but Lusine fought back. Neither of them had the upper hand. They both were injured. Lusine managed to escape. Kanen fled soon after. They both must've thought I was dead. *I* thought I was dead. The next thing I knew, you had arrived."

The man's face paled as he frantically recounted the events of that night to Mingyue. When he had finally finished, he burst into another fit of coughing, spewing blood across the sheets. His face was drenched in sweat, his eyes twitching as he struggled to keep them open.

"Hong Xue?!"

It was Jiang Chu. He and Erik rushed back into the room with Doctor Peng by his side.

"He's lost too much blood…" Doctor Peng cursed. "Quick! Get me fresh bandages!"

Mingyue and Erik tore open the cupboards while Jiang Chu stood paralyzed in the doorway. There was nothing.

"A towel! A bedsheet! Anything will do!" Doctor Peng was at Hong Xue's side, pressing down on the man's abdomen as blood seeped through the old wrappings.

Erik leaped into action, tearing off the blanket from the bed where Mingyue had been laying and tossing them over to Doctor Peng.

"Call in the other physicians," Doctor Peng said.

Erik nodded, taking hold of Mingyue's hand and pulling him down the corridor.

"Jiang Chu?" Mingyue called out.

Jiang Chu remained in the doorway, unmoving as he gazed hopelessly down at his comrade. It was as if he were lost in a trance. His eyes were wide in fear, his lips slightly parted as though he were trying to gasp for air but was unable to. Mingyue gently tugged at his sleeve. Jiang Chu whipped his head in the prince's direction, snapping back to reality in an instant.

"Let's go," Mingyue said calmly. "Let Doctor Peng and the others do their job."

Jiang Chu hesitated momentarily. He managed a shaky nod, taking off after Mingyue and Erik down the corridor.

"Looks like I won't have a place to sleep tonight," Mingyue noted.

"*Hm?*" Erik cocked his head.

"You tossed my sheets to Doctor Peng."

"Ah…yes. Well, you can stay with me then."

"Is there another bed in your quarters?"

"No. I can take the floor."

"No. We can share."

"S-share?" Erik gasped in disbelief. "Y-you won't get into trouble, will you?"

A slight smile lit up Mingyue's face. "No one needs to find out."

The story continues in Book Two

Ten Thousand Lights

Crimson Dawn

Printed in Great Britain
by Amazon

36232276R00290